Health Sciences

Pamela Minett, David Wayne, David Rubenstein

CollinsEducational

An imprint of HarperCollins*Publishers*

Published by Collins Educational
An imprint of HarperCollins*Publishers*
77–85 Fulham Palace Road
London W6 8JB
www.**fire**and**water**.com

© 1999 Pamela Minett, David Wayne, David Rubenstein

First published 1999

ISBN 0 00 327834 4

Pamela Minett, David Wayne, David Rubenstein assert the moral right to be identified as the authors of this work.

British Library Cataloguing in Publication Data
A catalogue record for this book is available from the British Library.

Design by Newton Harris Design Partnership
Cover design by Chi Leung
Illustrations by Barking Dog Art, Russell Birkett, Jerry Fowler, Peter Harper, and Illustrated Arts
Printed and bound by Scotprint, Musselburgh, Scotland

Acknowledgements

Every effort has been made to contact the holders of copyright material, but if any have been inadvertently overlooked, the publishers will be pleased to make the necessary arrangements at the first opportunity.

Figure 5 in Chapter 10: after Peter Kneebone, from drawing in D. R. Lawrence, *Clinical Pharmacology*, Churchill Livingstone.

The publishers would like to thank the following for permission to reproduce photographs (T = Top, B = Bottom, C = Centre, L= Left, R = Right):

Advertising Archives, 14; Allsport/R Casey, 231; T Duffy, 146, 151T; J Gichigi, 248; M Powell, 214L; G Mortimore, 214R; Biophoto Associates, 7T&C, 12, 25R, 35R, 264; Photos from: www.johnbirdsall.co.uk, 1B, 255B, 263, 268; Mary Evans Picture Library, 40TL; Sally & Richard Greenhill Photography, 221, 227; Robert Harding Picture Library, 252; RHPL/Shout, 40TR&BR, 232; Andrew Lambert, 211; D G Lyons, 29L, 71T, 73, 111B, 117, 168C, 219, 258; NASA, 26; Panos Pictures/A le Garsmeur, 191; James Paget Healthcare NHS Trust, 56L; Clive Barda/Performing Arts Library, 63; Gareth Price, 208; Rex Features Ltd, 143; Science Photo Library, 1T, 3, 5CR,CL,BR&BL, 6, 7B, 21, 23, 25L, 29TR, 34T, 35L, 37, 38, 43, 48, 53, 56R&T, 61, 66, 76, 77, 93, 100, 109, 111T, 120, 123, 127, 141, 158T, 161, 170, 179, 183, 200, 210, 255T, 277, 279, 280, 282; Still Pictures/R Giling, 242B; N Dickinson, 242C; Tony Stone Images, 9, 16B, 22, 71C, 74, 86, 151B, 158B, 163T, 218L, 247; Telegraph Colour Library, 16T, 33, 40BL;

Front cover and title page: Tony Stone Images

This book contains references to fictitious characters in fictitious case studies. For educational purposes only, the photographs have been used to accompany these case studies. The juxtaposition of photographs is not intended to identify the individual in the photograph with the character in the case study. The publishers cannot accept any responsibility for any consequences resulting from this use of photographs and case studies, except as expressly provided by law.

Contents

Preface

Health Sciences provides an excellent introduction to the range of skills and knowledge used by people studying human biology or working in the health care field.

The text is clear and direct with each part clearly identified by question headings. Most of your enquiries will be answered directly from the text. However, the diagrams and photographs are integral parts of the book and help to complete the explanation, and often add extra detail. The diagrams provide an overview of processes and structures. The annotations are important and should be read alongside the main text. Where body parts have been drawn, remember that these are shown as part of an explanation of function rather than as a statement on the exact anatomy of the part. Students seeking detailed anatomical information should consult a specialist anatomy text.

The photographs often relate the scientific content to everyday experiences showing how our knowledge of health and medical matters affects the decisions we make about our lives. Read the captions – they will help to make this connection clear.

The questions within the main text are designed to help you to build a set of notes. They can be answered from material within the book. If you are following a taught course, your teacher or tutor may set work for you using these questions. If you are working through this book by yourself, you will find it useful to look at the questions to check that you understand the material you are reading.

The key skills assignments allow you to collect evidence of your competencies in:

- communication
- application of number
- information technology.

Many modern courses require this evidence if you are to achieve a pass.

Our acknowledgements are due to the following helpful people, none of whom has seen the final draft and none of whom therefore can be blamed for any inaccuracies which might have found their way into the book which you now hold in your hands.

From James Paget Hospital, Great Yarmouth:

- Dietician   Patrick Friel
- Medical Illustration   Madeleine Borg
- Librarian   Christine Thompson
- Obstetrician   Andy Pozyczka
- Radiologist   Vinod Kumar
- Paediatrician   Tony Edelsten
- Nurse Educator   Sarah Roberts.

From Morden Hill Surgery, London SE13:

- Family planning   Jill Purkiss.

Pamela Minett, David Wayne and David Rubenstein 1999

The *human* body

Learning objectives

By the end of this chapter you should be able to:

- **describe** the main regions of the human body
- **define** cell, tissue, organ and system
- **list** the major systems of the human body
- **describe** the structure of the skin

- **list** the factors that affect skin colour
- **describe** the effect of sunlight on skin colour
- **describe** acne and its treatment
- **describe** the structure and growth of hair and nails.

The human body is extremely complex. It is made up of billions of different cells organised into tissues and organs and systems. The human brain is vastly more complicated, with millions more connections, than the most advanced computer. How can we ever hope to understand the whole body?

This book uses the approach outlined below to try to explain this complexity. It asks a few straightforward questions about each part of the body so that we can begin to build up a picture of the complete organism from these parts. Although each section follows these ideas, not all the questions are asked in every section.

The human body can be all sorts of different shapes, sizes and colours.

- **How is the body part organised? (Ontogeny)**
  This will show us how the body part we are studying is organised at a level that we can see.
- **How is it put together? (Anatomy)**
  This allows us to look in more detail at parts of the body. Sometimes we use electron micrographs to study the smaller individual parts.
- **How does it work? (Physiology)**
  This lets us look at what the particular part of the body does. We can also ask how it changes over time or works with other body parts.
- **What can go wrong with it? (Pathology and medicine)**
  This lets us look at how illness can prevent parts of the body from working properly.

1.1 Basic structure

How is the human body organised?

The human body consists of three main regions (see Figure 1).

- **Head**
  The brain takes up about half the space within the head. It is protected by the skull, which also protects nearby sense organs – the eyes, ears, nose and tongue.

Figure 1 The main organs of the human body

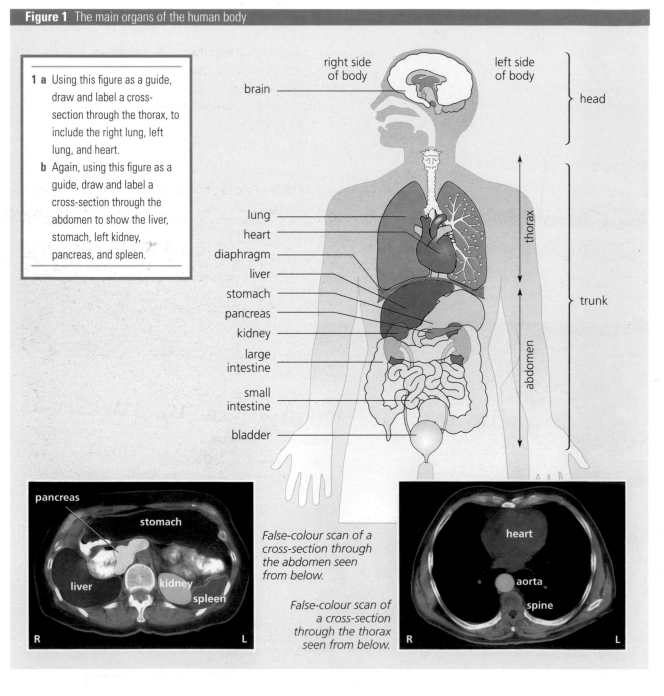

1 a Using this figure as a guide, draw and label a cross-section through the thorax, to include the right lung, left lung, and heart.

b Again, using this figure as a guide, draw and label a cross-section through the abdomen to show the liver, stomach, left kidney, pancreas, and spleen.

right side of body

left side of body

brain

head

lung

heart

diaphragm

liver

stomach

pancreas

kidney

large intestine

small intestine

bladder

thorax

trunk

abdomen

pancreas

stomach

liver

kidney

spleen

R   L

False-colour scan of a cross-section through the abdomen seen from below.

False-colour scan of a cross-section through the thorax seen from below.

heart

aorta

spine

R   L

2 a Name:

  i the two parts of the trunk

  ii the sheet of muscle that separates these two parts.

b Say what the following consist of:

  i tissues

  ii organs

  iii systems.

- **Trunk**

  This forms the main part of the body. The large cavity inside the trunk is separated into two parts by a tough, thin sheet of muscle called the **diaphragm**. The upper part of the trunk is called the **thorax** and contains the heart and lungs. The lower region, called the **abdomen**, contains the main organs of digestion, excretion and reproduction.

- **Limbs**

  These are the arms and legs.

The human body is a complex structure made up of millions and millions of individual cells. These cells need to work together to keep the body healthy:

- cells of the same type are grouped together to form tissues
- tissues are grouped together to form organs
- organs work together to form systems
- systems all link together to form the whole body which enable a person to carry out the functions of life.

What is a cell?

All living things consist of tiny building blocks called **cells** (see Figure 2).

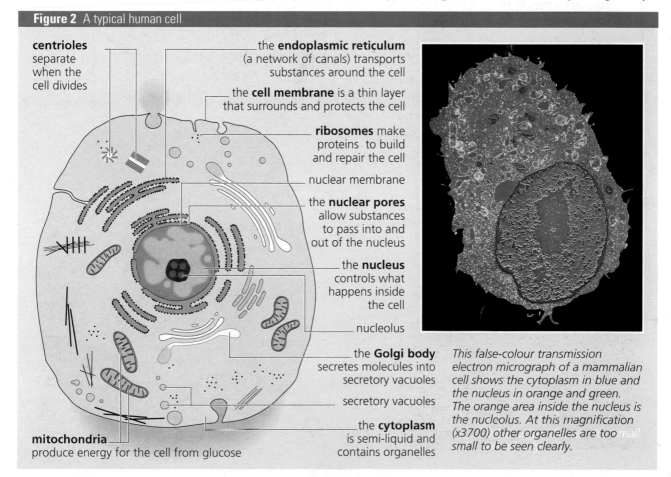

Figure 2 A typical human cell

centrioles separate when the cell divides

the **endoplasmic reticulum** (a network of canals) transports substances around the cell

the **cell membrane** is a thin layer that surrounds and protects the cell

ribosomes make proteins to build and repair the cell

nuclear membrane

the **nuclear pores** allow substances to pass into and out of the nucleus

the **nucleus** controls what happens inside the cell

nucleolus

the **Golgi body** secretes molecules into secretory vacuoles

secretory vacuoles

the **cytoplasm** is semi-liquid and contains organelles

mitochondria produce energy for the cell from glucose

This false-colour transmission electron micrograph of a mammalian cell shows the cytoplasm in blue and the nucleus in orange and green. The orange area inside the nucleus is the nucleolus. At this magnification (x3700) other organelles are too small to be seen clearly.

Cells can only been seen through a microscope. Although they are very small, every cell is highly organised with:

• a **nucleus**, the large spherical body that controls how the cell works
• the semi-liquid **cytoplasm**, the material that contains the nucleus and many other organelles (an **organelle** is a specialised part of the cytoplasm with its own particular function)
• a **cell membrane**, the thin layer around the outside of the cell.

Substances are continually passing into and out of living cells. In general, food and oxygen pass into the cell, and carbon dioxide and other waste substances leave it. The cell membrane helps to control which substances pass into and out of the cell.

3 a List the three parts of a cell, and give the function of each.

b What is an organelle?

c Look back at Figure 2 and identify three organelles.

d What controls the movement of substances into and out of a cell?

e Name two substances that pass into a cell and two substances that pass out of a cell.

Cell types

There are at least 20 different types of cell in the body. They have all have the same basic parts shown in Figure 2, but their size, shape and contents vary according to the particular job which each type of cell has to do (see Figure 3).

Figure 3 Different types of cell

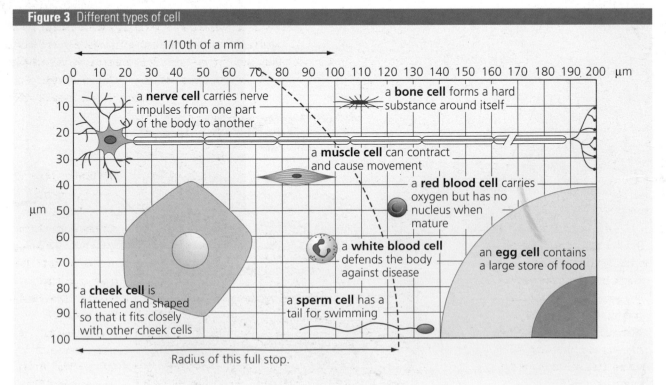

Because cells are so small, they are measured in micrometres. A micrometre (µm) is one thousandth of a millimetre. The diameter (width across) of cells varies from 7.5 µm for red blood cells to up to 300 µm for a fully developed egg cell – the largest type of cell. The egg cell in Figure 3 is smaller than this; it is not yet fully developed. Some nerve cells have very long fibres – for example, those going from the lower back to the toes.

4 a Draw a cheek cell and label the cell membrane, nucleus, and cytoplasm. Give its diameter.

  b Study the cells in Figure 3 then, for each, give at least one way in which its structure differs from all the others.

This false-colour scanning electron micrograph shows a single neurone from the outer grey matter of the brain. The neurone is coloured yellow and has several processes. The magnification of this micrograph is ×3245.

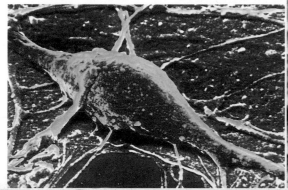

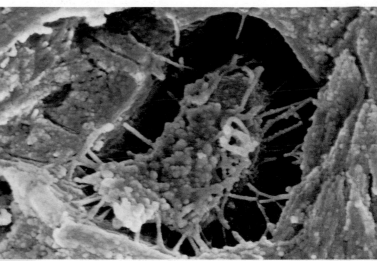

In this coloured scanning electron micrograph, you can see a bone cell (coloured pink) in the centre of a dark cavity called a lacuna. The cell has many processes (coloured pale blue) that link the cell with other bone cells. The processes pass through the bone (coloured brown) in tiny channels. The magnification of this micrograph is ×8575.

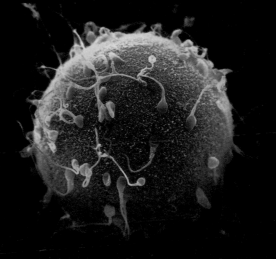

This coloured scanning electron micrograph clearly shows red blood cells as biconcave discs. The red cells are smaller and more numerous than the white cells. White cells are spherical and have many tiny projections over their surface. The magnification of this micrograph is ×5174.

This false-colour scanning electron micrograph shows clearly the very different sizes of human sperm and a human egg cell. The long tail of the sperm is used for swimming. Only one of all these sperm will penetrate the surface of the egg and fertilise it. The magnification of this micrograph is ×1210.

What is a tissue?

A **tissue** is a group of cells with a particular function (see Figure 4). There is usually one main type of cell, and a matrix is often present. The **matrix** is the substance between the cells of a tissue. It can be hard, soft, or liquid, depending on the type of tissue. Generally, the matrix allows movement of food, gases, and hormones throughout the tissue.

Figure 4 Different types of tissue

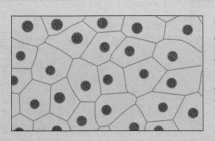

Epithelial tissue
An epithelium is a single layer of flattened cells that forms a smooth lining to internal surfaces such as the inside of the cheek.

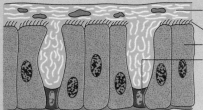

direction of mucus movement → mucus with trapped dust particles — cilia — ciliated cell — goblet cell

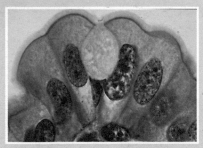

This light micrograph shows cells with cilia (pink) and goblet cell (blue).

Mucous membrane
This is a single layer of tall cells that lines the gut and the air passages in the lungs. The tissue is kept moist by **mucus**, a thick, sticky substance produced by the goblet cells. In some places – for example, in the air tubes in the lungs – the cells have **cilia**. These are tiny hair-like structures that beat regularly, and in the same direction, to move the mucus along.

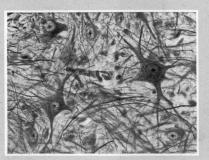

Nerve tissue
This tissue forms a network throughout the body to conduct and coordinate nerve impulses.

These are nerves cells from the brain. They have many projections and form a dense network.

Glandular tissue
This lines the spaces of glands and secretes substances into these spaces.

gland cell
substance being secreted
space

Muscle tissue
This consists of bundles of cells or fibres which contract or relax in order to bring about movement. It is the most abundant tissue in the body:
- **striped muscle**, also called striated muscle or skeletal muscle, consists of bundles of parallel muscle fibres; its function is to move the skeleton

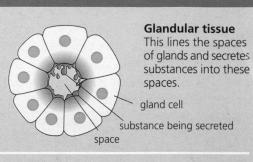

striped muscle fibres

nucleus

- **smooth muscle** consists of long, pointed cells that interlock; it is found in the walls of blood vessels, intestines and other tubes in the body, and its function is to move substances along them

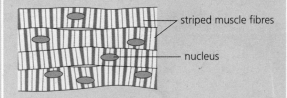

smooth muscle cell

nucleus

- **cardiac muscle** consists of cells that branch and join together to form a network; these cells contract and relax rhythmically throughout life.

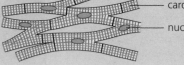

cardiac muscle cell

nucleus

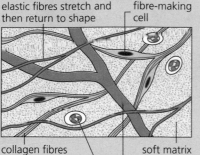

elastic fibres stretch and then return to shape

fibre-making cell

collagen fibres are tougher and stronger than elastic fibres but do not stretch

soft matrix

blood vessel

white blood cell

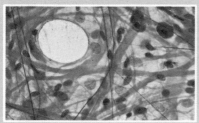

This is areolar connective tissue. It is found beneath the skin and between organs that are next to each other.

Cartilage

This is a tough, flexible tissue found in those parts of the body that require firm support, for example, the lobe of the ear, tip of the nose, the cartilage joints, and the discs between the vertebrae of the backbone. The matrix is a firm gel in which a network of dense fibres is embedded.

cartilage cell   fibres   matrix

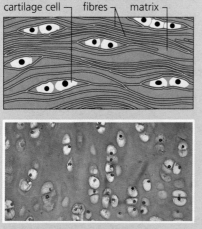

The cartilage in this light micrograph is stained pink. The dark dots are the nuclei of the cartilage-making cells.

Connective tissue

This contains cells and fibres set in a soft matrix:

- **fibrous tissue** contains large numbers of collagen fibres and occurs where strength is required, for example, in tendons and ligaments
- **elastic tissue** contains large numbers of elastic fibres and occurs in the walls of blood vessels, allowing them to stretch and spring back
- **fatty tissue** contains cells that store fat as oil droplets; acting as an insulation and energy store, it is found under the skin and in the abdomen.

nucleus

cytoplasm

oil droplet

blood vessel

connective tissue

Blood

This tissue has a variety of cells in a liquid matrix called plasma.

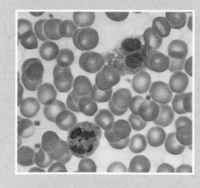

This light micrograph shows many red cells (pink), two white cells (each mauve with a purple nucleus) and some platelets (tiny purple spots).

Bone

This hard tissue forms the skeleton; it is hard due to calcium deposited in the matrix. Bone cells are in holes called **lacunae** in cylindrical layers around a central channel called a **Haversian canal**, which contains a blood vessel. Tiny channels called **canaliculi** connect the cells with each other and with the central channel. Fluid moves through the canaliculi, bringing food, oxygen and hormones to the bone cells. This keeps them alive and allows bone growth and repair to take place.

lacunae   hard matrix   Haversian canal

canaliculi   blood vessel

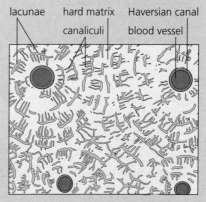

5 a Draw and label a:
  i gland cell
  ii fatty tissue cell
  iii goblet cell
  iv ciliated cell
  v fibre-making cell
  vi cartilage-making cell.
b Say which of the tissues in Figure 4:
  i gives firm support
  ii stores fat
  iii lines the inside of the cheeks
  iv produces mucus
  v is found between organs
  vi forms the skeleton
  vii moves the skeleton
  viii secretes substances.
c What is the matrix of a tissue?
d Name a tissue with:
  i a hard matrix
  ii a soft matrix
  iii a liquid matrix.

What is an organ?

An **organ** is a part of the body with a special function or functions. Here are some examples of organs and their functions:

- the heart pumps blood round the body
- the lungs exchange gases
- the stomach holds food for the early stages of digestion
- the bladder stores urine.

What is a system?

A **system** is a group of organs working together to carry out one or more functions (see Figure 5).

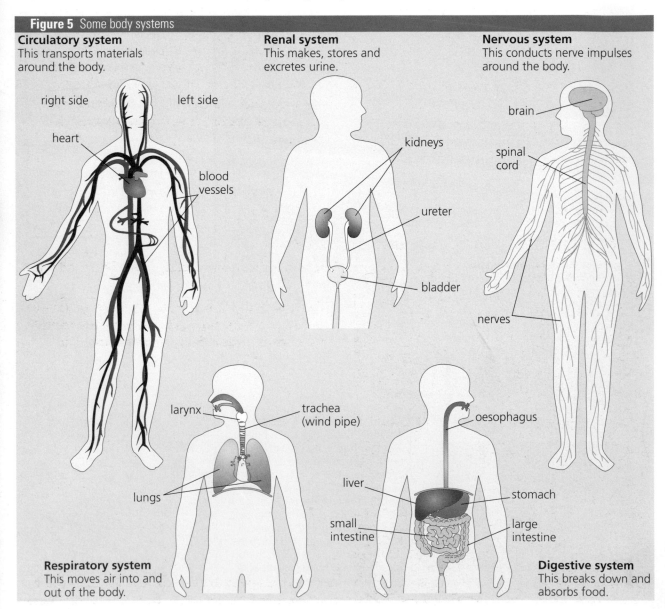

Figure 5 Some body systems

Circulatory system
This transports materials around the body.

right side   left side

heart

blood vessels

Renal system
This makes, stores and excretes urine.

kidneys

ureter

bladder

Nervous system
This conducts nerve impulses around the body.

brain

spinal cord

nerves

Respiratory system
This moves air into and out of the body.

larynx   trachea (wind pipe)

lungs

Digestive system
This breaks down and absorbs food.

oesophagus

liver   stomach

small intestine   large intestine

6 a Explain the difference between an organ and a system.

b Name nine different organs shown in Figure 5.

c Copy and complete Table 1 using the information in Figure 5.

Table 1 Function and organs of the five systems in Figure 5

Name of system	Main function	Main organs
nervous system		
respiratory system		
digestive system		
renal system		
circulatory system		

Summary of the human body

- The human body has three main regions: head, trunk and limbs.
- The diaphragm divides the trunk into the thorax above and the abdomen below.
- Different cells are adapted to do different jobs in the body.
- A tissue usually contains cells of only one type. An organ contains more than one type of tissue.
- A system consists of a group of organs working together to carry out one of the main living processes.
- The main tissue types in the body are: connective tissue, epithelial tissue, glandular tissue, muscle tissue, nerve tissue, bone tissue and blood.
- The main body systems are the circulatory, renal, nervous, respiratory, digestive and reproductive systems.

1.2 Skin

What tissues does the skin contain?

The skin is the outer covering of the body and it has two main layers:

- the **epidermis** is the tough, outer layer of the skin that protects the more delicate tissues underneath
- the **dermis** is the soft inner layer of the skin.

Tattoos are permanent because the ink is placed deep in the dermis. It stays there as, unlike the epidermis, the dermis is not constantly replaced.

7 a What is the difference between the epidermis and the dermis?

b Which part of the skin grows continuously, and why?

c What happens to the new cells?

The epidermis (epi = outer, dermis = skin) is thickest on those parts of the body that have the hardest wear – the palms of the hands and soles of the feet – and thinnest on the lips. The innermost layer of epidermal cells grows and divides continuously to replace the dead cells that are constantly being lost from the outer surface of the skin. When new cells are produced, they move outwards and become filled with a tough substance called **keratin**. They die and become part of the tough, protective outer layer before flaking off or being rubbed away. In this way, the epidermis is completely replaced every few weeks.

The dermis is thicker than the epidermis and contains blood vessels, nerves, glands, and hair roots (see Figure 6). These are held in place by connective tissue, which also contains elastic fibres that pull the skin back into place after it has been stretched.

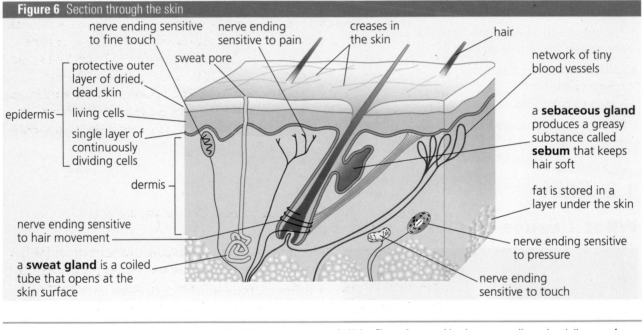

Figure 6 Section through the skin

8 a Say whether the epidermis or the dermis does the following:

   i forms a protective outer layer

   ii contains blood vessels

   iii contains nerves

   iv grows continuously.

b Using Figure 6 as a guide, draw a two-dimensional diagram of a section through skin showing the epidermis, dermis, fat layer, a hair and its sebaceous gland, a sweat gland, and a nerve ending.

c What are the nerve endings in Figure 6 sensitive to?

d Name the two types of gland in the skin.

What does skin do?

The skin has many functions; it:

- covers the body and protects it from damage
- is a barrier against the entry of microorganisms
- prevents unregulated water loss from the body
- regulates body temperature
- makes vitamin D and melanin
- makes a person aware of the surrounding conditions because it is sensitive to touch, temperature and pain.

9 List six functions of skin.

What influences skin colour?

Skin colour is largely due to the amount of pigment present, but the colour of paler skins is also affected by other factors.

Melanin is a dark brown pigment that is produced in the innermost layer of the epidermis. Everybody has about the same number of melanin-producing cells in the skin, but these cells are more active in people with darker-coloured skins.

Some people are unable to produce melanin; they have white hair, pink eyes and pink skin. This condition is called **albinism**.

In people whose skin is pale enough to allow the blood colour to show through, skin colour is affected by both the thickness of the epidermis and the amount of blood in the skin. So, the lips of people with light-coloured skin look red because the epidermis on the lips is thin. When the many small blood vessels in the skin are open, a large amount of bright red oxygenated blood flows near the surface, making light-coloured skin look red or 'flushed'. When the small blood vessels are closed due to cold or fear, there is less blood near the surface, so light-coloured skin looks pale or even slightly blue. The blue colour is due to the presence of large amounts of dark red deoxygenated blood. The thickness of the epidermis and the amount of blood near the skin surface is the same whatever the colour of the skin, but the effect of redness is only seen if the skin is light in colour.

10 a Name three factors that affect the colour of skin.

b What is meant by 'albinism'?

Effects of the sun

Some effects of the sun on skin are beneficial, some are not.

- **Darkening**
  Skin is stimulated to produce melanin in response to ultraviolet (UV) rays in sunlight. All skin darkens when more melanin is produced, but this effect is most obvious in pale skins. Melanin helps to protect skin cells from the harmful effects of UV radiation in sunlight.
- **Freckles**
  These brown pigment spots on pale skins become more obvious when they darken because the sun activates the melanin-producing cells.
- **Ageing**
  Long-term exposure of skin to the sun quickens the ageing process and wrinkling.
- **Vitamin D**
  This vitamin is made in the dermis when the skin is exposed to the sun. Lack of vitamin D causes the bones in the legs of children to bend outwards. This is called rickets.
- **Cancer**
  Long-term exposure of skin to the sun increases the likelihood of skin cancer, which is more common in sunny climates.
- **Sunburn**
  This is damage to the skin by over-exposure to the sun's rays. Pale skin turns red, and over the next few hours becomes painful and blistered.

11 a When skin is exposed to sunlight, name two substances that are produced, and give one advantage of each to the body.

b Give two effects of long-term exposure or over-exposure of the skin to the sun.

What is acne?

Acne is the name given to the skin condition in which spots develop on the face and shoulders. It is a normal part of adolescence, often occurring between the ages of 16 and 17 in girls, and 17 and 19 in boys. Even a quite mild case of acne can seem very serious to teenagers. A lot of money is spent on creams and lotions to clear up this common skin condition.

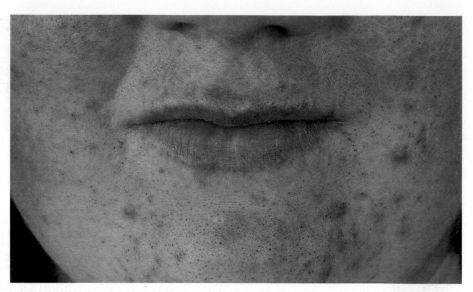

The sebaceous glands (grease glands) in the skin become very active at puberty and the openings of the glands may become blocked and form blackheads – the first sign of acne. A **blackhead** is a plug of greasy material that blocks the pore and turns black at the skin surface where it is in contact with the air. If the blockage persists, greasy material builds up under the skin and becomes infected with bacteria, and small **abscesses** form (pimples with pus). When the infection spreads, the infected skin becomes inflamed. Squeezing pimples can scar the skin.

There is no treatment for acne that is guaranteed to work and acne normally disappears after a few years. However, the following may help:

- keep the skin clean
- avoid make-up
- expose the skin to a moderate amount of sunlight
- try some of the special anti-acne lotions and creams sold by pharmacists.

You may need to consult your doctor if the acne is persistent or keeps returning. Small doses of antibiotic such as tetracycline are sometimes given in a course lasting several months. This is often very effective but, as with all potent drugs, can only be obtained from your doctor.

12 a What is acne?

  b In which age groups is acne most common?

  c How do blackheads form?

  d What causes pimples with pus?

1.3 Hair and nails

What is hair?

A hair consists mainly of keratin, the same substance found in the dead outer layer of the skin. Hairs are found on nearly every part of the body. The hair on the head can be very long, curly or straight, and of various colours. The eyelashes, beard, and pubic hairs are very thick. On many parts of the body the hairs are very small – this gives the appearance of hairlessness. Pigment-producing cells in the cortex give hair a brown or red colour (see Figure 7). In white hair, cortex cells contain only air.

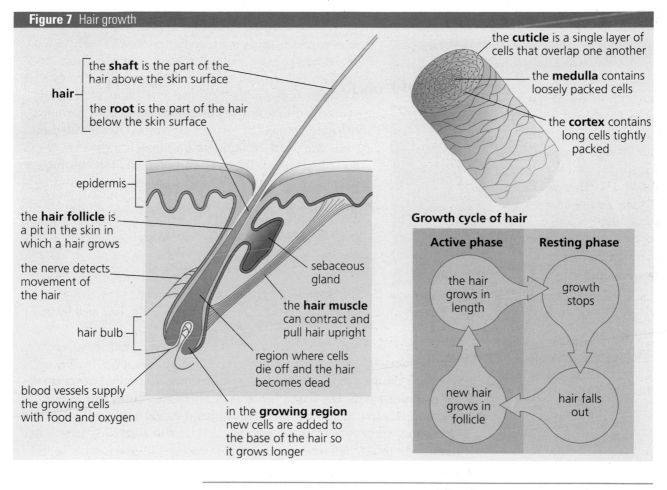

Figure 7 Hair growth

the **shaft** is the part of the hair above the skin surface

hair

the **root** is the part of the hair below the skin surface

the **cuticle** is a single layer of cells that overlap one another

the **medulla** contains loosely packed cells

the **cortex** contains long cells tightly packed

epidermis

the **hair follicle** is a pit in the skin in which a hair grows

the nerve detects movement of the hair

hair bulb

blood vessels supply the growing cells with food and oxygen

sebaceous gland

the **hair muscle** can contract and pull hair upright

region where cells die off and the hair becomes dead

in the **growing region** new cells are added to the base of the hair so it grows longer

Growth cycle of hair

Active phase	Resting phase
the hair grows in length	growth stops
new hair grows in follicle	hair falls out

13 a Draw a diagram of a hair labelling the hair, hair follicle, hair muscle, sebaceous gland, nerve, blood vessels, and the growing region.

   b What happens when the hair muscle contracts?

   c Does the nerve enter the hair itself?

   d Why is no pain felt when hair is cut?

   e Why is pain felt when hair is pulled?

   f What gives hair its colour?

How does hair grow?

14 a Draw a diagram to show where a hair lengthens.

   b Why do new cells die as they move away from the growing region?

   c Describe the growth cycle of a hair as shown in Figure 7.

A hair grows from its root. A layer of cells constantly produces new cells at the base of the hair, making it grow. As the cells move away from the growing region at the base they fill with keratin and die.

Hair growth follows the cycle shown in Figure 7. A single follicle has alternate active and resting phases, so it produces many hairs during its lifetime. In humans, hair growth is not synchronised, so the hairs do not all fall out at the same time. This does happen in some animals and is called moulting.

What causes baldness?

Baldness affects most men, sometimes quite early in life. Normal hair recedes and is replaced with very short, fine, pale hairs. Baldness may affect women as they grow older, but usually only causes thinning of the hair. A receding hair-line is the common pattern of baldness in men, but some men go bald by losing hair in the region called the crown. The medical name for baldness is **alopecia**.

The causes of baldness are complex and not completely understood. A number of factors are involved including:

- family history of baldness
- some illnesses.

Despite many claims, there is no simple way to cure baldness. However, a great deal of money is spent in trying to diguise hair loss.

What causes dandruff?

15 a What is lost when a person goes bald?

b What is lost when a person has dandruff?

Dandruff is a common condition in which the scalp is covered by small flakes of dead skin. The flakes come away when the hair is brushed or combed. It is harmless but may be considered unsightly. Dandruff can be kept under control by washing hair frequently with a specially medicated shampoo.

What are nails?

Like hair, nails are keratin – but in a different form. Nails are outgrowths of the epidermis that strengthen and protect the ends of the fingers and toes. Cells in the root of the nail divide and grow and become filled with a hard form of keratin. The nail is continuously pushed forward as more cells form (see Figure 8).

On average, finger nails grow about a millimetre a week, which is about three times faster than toe nails. Fingernails enable the hands to pick up small objects more easily.

How can nails be damaged?

There are lots of ways in which nails get damaged. For instance, disease and deficiencies in the diet can cause abnormal nails (see Figure 9). If the root of a nail is severely damaged, perhaps by being hit, the nail will come away within a week or two. The new nail that then grows may be misshapen. The fungus that causes athlete's foot can also infect toenails, making them thicken, discolour and crumble. This is not harmful, and is easy to treat. There are a number of different factors that can cause nails to split and become painful.

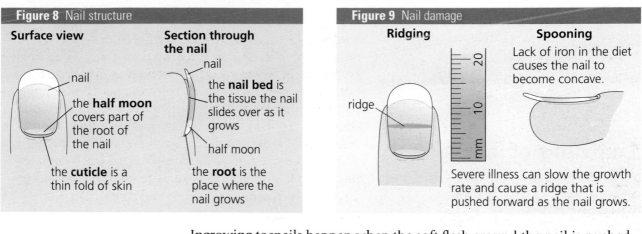

Figure 8 Nail structure

Surface view

nail

the **half moon** covers part of the root of the nail

the **cuticle** is a thin fold of skin

Section through the nail

nail

the **nail bed** is the tissue the nail slides over as it grows

half moon

the **root** is the place where the nail grows

Figure 9 Nail damage

Ridging

ridge

Spooning

Lack of iron in the diet causes the nail to become concave.

Severe illness can slow the growth rate and cause a ridge that is pushed forward as the nail grows.

Ingrowing toenails happen when the soft flesh around the nail is pushed against the rough edge of the nail. Expert advice is needed for this problem and it might be necessary to remove part or all of the nail.

16 **a** Name two places besides nails where keratin is found.

b Draw a diagram of a nail to show where growth takes place.

c What happens when the root is damaged?

d Say how nails might be affected by:

  i severe illness

  ii lack of iron in the diet.

e On average, nails grow about 1 mm per week. About how long ago was the person whose ridged nail is shown in Figure 9 seriously ill?

Summary of skin, hair and nails

- The skin has two layers: the outer epidermis and the inner dermis.
- Skin protects the body against microorganisms, UV radiation and excessive water loss, regulates body temperature, makes vitamin D and contains nerves to detect touch, pain and temperature.
- Skin colour depends mainly on the amount of melanin in the skin. In light-coloured skin, the amount of blood and the thickness of the epidermis also affect skin colour. An increase in the amount of melanin in the skin protects against the UV radiation in sunlight.

- Acne is caused by glands in the skin becoming blocked with grease. It is best treated by regular washing, moderate exposure to the sun and, in extreme conditions, medication.
- Hair is a protein called keratin. It grows from structures in the dermis all over the body. Hair has different thicknesses, lengths and possibly colour in different parts of the body.
- Dandruff is small flakes of dead skin. It is easily controlled by suitable shampoos.
- Nails are also made of a type of keratin and grow from the epidermis.

Learning objectives

By the end of this chapter you should be able to:

- **list** the main regions of the human skeleton
- **describe** the main structures in the human skeleton
- **list** the functions of the skeleton
- **explain** the function of the disks in the backbone
- **list** the main types of joints
- **describe** the functioning of a named synovial joint
- **describe** the two main diseases affecting joints
- **describe** the structure and functioning of skeletal muscle
- **explain** the term antagonistic system.

2.1 The skeleton

How is the skeleton arranged?

The human skeleton contains 206 bones. They fit together to form a framework for the soft tissues of the body and are held in place by muscles and ligaments. The skull and backbone form the central axis of the body. The rib cage, the shoulder girdle, the pelvis, and the limbs are attached to this main axis (see Figure 1).

1 a How many bones are there in the human skeleton?

  b How many bones are you able to count in Figure 1?

  c Suggest reasons why the number of bones in (a) differs from that in (b).

  d What holds the bones in place in the skeleton?

  e Using Figure 1, give the scientific name for:

    i lower jaw

    ii wrist bones

    iv hip bone

    v thigh bone

    vi knee cap.

Both of these people have the same number of bones and muscles. Training has ensured that the muscles of one are much more developed than the other.

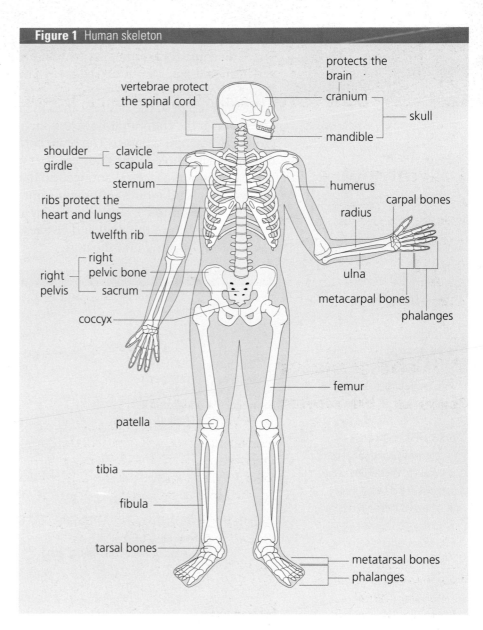

Figure 1 Human skeleton

protects the brain

vertebrae protect the spinal cord

cranium

skull

mandible

shoulder girdle

clavicle

scapula

sternum

humerus

ribs protect the heart and lungs

carpal bones

radius

twelfth rib

right pelvic bone

right pelvis

ulna

sacrum

metacarpal bones

phalanges

coccyx

femur

patella

tibia

fibula

tarsal bones

metatarsal bones

phalanges

What are the functions of the skeleton?

The skeleton has four functions:

- supporting the body
- protecting the internal organs
- making blood cells – the bone marrow makes all the red cells and some of the white cells
- storing calcium so that there is always a supply readily available.

2 a From Figure 1, list three ways in which the skeleton protects the internal organs.

  b What are made inside bones?

  c What is stored in bones?

Skull

The skull consists of more than 20 bones that are interlocked to form a very firm and rigid structure. The lower jaw is the only movable part (see Figure 2).

The largest part of the skull is called the **cranium**. It encloses the brain. The shape of the cranium follows the shape of the brain, and as the brain grows the cranium enlarges. The brain connects with the spinal cord through a large hole in the floor of the cranium.

The bones of the face are arranged so that they surround the openings of the eyes, nose and mouth. Although some of these bones seem to be very thick, they are hollow inside; the cavities are called **sinuses**. Sinuses reduce the weight of the skull and give resonance to the voice. Each sinus has a narrow opening into the nose.

3 a Say which part of the skull:
- **i** is able to move
- **ii** protects the brain
- **iii** contains the middle and inner parts of the ear.

b Where does the brain connect with the spinal cord?

c What are the cavities in the bones of the face called?

d Where do these cavities open into?

e Give two effects of having sinuses in the skull.

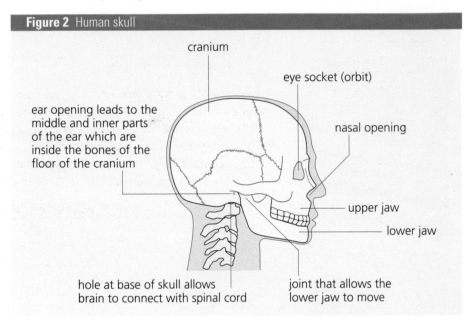

Figure 2 Human skull

cranium

eye socket (orbit)

ear opening leads to the middle and inner parts of the ear which are inside the bones of the floor of the cranium

nasal opening

upper jaw

lower jaw

hole at base of skull allows brain to connect with spinal cord

joint that allows the lower jaw to move

Rib cage

The sternum, ribs, and part of the backbone form a cage around the thorax (see Figure 3). Each of the 12 pairs of ribs are joined to one of the 12 thoracic vertebrae of the backbone, and the 10 upper pairs are also joined to the sternum. Although the other two pairs are firmly held in place by the muscles of the back, they are sometimes called 'floating ribs' because they are not fixed to the sternum.

Shoulder girdle

The shoulder girdle is composed of four bones – two clavicles (collar bones) and two scapulae (shoulder blades, each one is called a scapula). It is connected to the rest of the skeleton at the sternum and held there by muscles (see Figure 4).

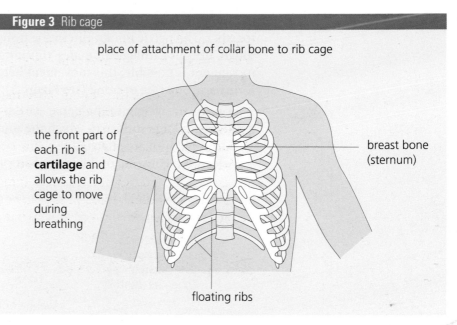

Figure 3 Rib cage

place of attachment of collar bone to rib cage

the front part of each rib is **cartilage** and allows the rib cage to move during breathing

breast bone (sternum)

floating ribs

4 a How many pairs of ribs are there?

b Why are the two lower pairs of ribs called 'floating ribs'?

c Which bone in the rib cage is attached to the collar bones?

The scapulae help to form a shoulder joint with the arms; they also provide large areas of bone to which the muscles of the arm, back and chest are attached. Each scapula is able to slide over the ribs. When it does this, it takes the arm with it, so increasing the range of arm movement.

The clavicles help to steady the shoulder joints and keep the shoulders in position. Sports injuries often involve a broken clavicle.

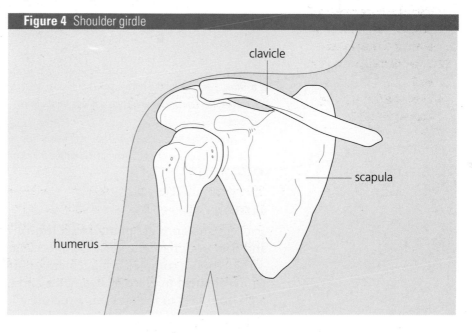

Figure 4 Shoulder girdle

clavicle

scapula

humerus

5 a Give two functions of the scapulae (shoulder blades).

b Name the two bones to which a clavicle or collar bone is joined.

Pelvis

The pelvis consists of the right and left pelvic bones and the lower part of the backbone to which they are joined. This part of the backbone is called the **sacrum**. It is a triangular bone formed from five vertebrae fused together. The pelvic bones join in the front and are held together by tough, fibrous cartilage. In males, this joint is rigid; in females, slight movement is possible; this movement helps during childbirth. The pelvis forms a strong ring of bone (see Figure 5). The strength of the pelvis:

- supports the weight of the upper part of the body
- provides a large surface to which the muscles of the legs, back and abdominal wall are attached
- protects the contents of the lower part of the abdomen.

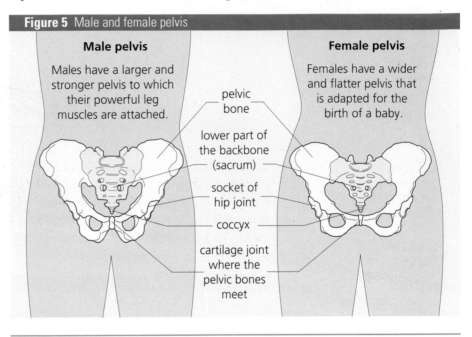

Figure 5 Male and female pelvis

Male pelvis

Males have a larger and stronger pelvis to which their powerful leg muscles are attached.

Female pelvis

Females have a wider and flatter pelvis that is adapted for the birth of a baby.

pelvic bone

lower part of the backbone (sacrum)

socket of hip joint

coccyx

cartilage joint where the pelvic bones meet

6 a Draw a diagram of the female pelvis and label pelvic bone, backbone, socket of hip joint, cartilage.

 b Give three reasons why the pelvis needs to be strong.

 c Explain:

   i why males have a larger and stronger pelvis than females

   ii how the shape of the female pelvis differs from that of the male.

Limbs

The legs and arms are **pentadactyl limbs** (penta = five, dactyl = fingered) and they both have the same plan (see Figure 6).

The foot is a complex arrangement of interlocking bones (see Figure 6), which are held in place by ligaments and muscles. The bones make an arch from heel to toe and this structure allows the foot to carry out its two main functions:

- supporting the weight of the body in a standing position
- acting as a lever to propel the body along when walking or running – to do this, the foot must be strong, springy, and able to bend.

Feet grow throughout the first 18 years of life. They grow fastest in early childhood and during puberty. The bones in the feet of young children are rather soft and can be bent by shoes or socks that are not big enough. This is not painful, so the child is not likely to complain. If tight shoes are worn regularly, the bones harden into an imperfect shape, and the muscles cannot then work properly.

Figure 6 The pentadactyl limb

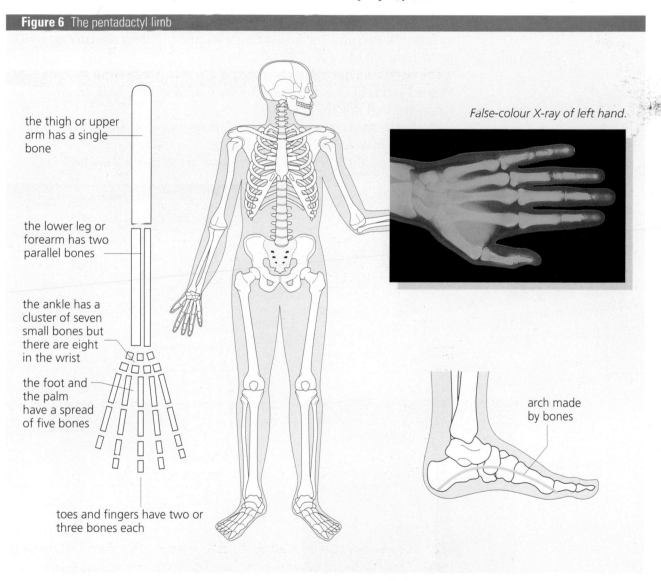

the thigh or upper arm has a single bone

the lower leg or forearm has two parallel bones

the ankle has a cluster of seven small bones but there are eight in the wrist

the foot and the palm have a spread of five bones

toes and fingers have two or three bones each

False-colour X-ray of left hand.

arch made by bones

7 a Using the scientific names, list the bones in Figure 6 in:

  i an arm

  ii a leg.

b Describe what you can see in the X-ray in Figure 6.

c Give two functions of feet.

d When do feet grow fast?

e What happens when children often wear shoes that are tight?

2.2 The backbone

How is the backbone organised?

The backbone is also called the **vertebral column**, the spinal column or the spine. It consists of thirty-three small bones each of which is called a **vertebra** (plural: vertebrae) arranged on top of one another. The top twenty-four vertebrae are separate bones, the next five are joined together to form the **sacrum**. The lowest four are joined to form the **coccyx**, which is the remnant of a tail.

The backbone has a natural curved shape when seen from the side (see Figure 7). It is held in this shape by the muscles of the back and by ligaments that link the vertebrae.

The backbone is protected against damage in two ways:
- its shape makes it behave like a spring
- the cartilage discs between the vertebrae act as shock absorbers.

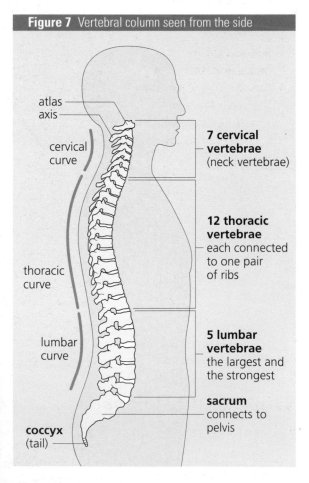

Figure 7 Vertebral column seen from the side

atlas
axis

cervical curve

thoracic curve

lumbar curve

coccyx (tail)

7 cervical vertebrae (neck vertebrae)

12 thoracic vertebrae each connected to one pair of ribs

5 lumbar vertebrae the largest and the strongest

sacrum connects to pelvis

Even though a giraffe has a much longer neck than a human, it still has the same number of neck vertebrae as you do.

What are the functions of the backbone?

8 a Name the vertebra:
  i that forms a joint with the skull
  ii that moves when you turn your head from side to side.

  b Give a reason why the backbone is curved and not straight.

  c What is the function of the cartilage discs between the vertebrae?

  d What is the advantage of having a backbone composed of many small bones and not just one bone?

  e How many vertebrae are there in Figure 7?

  f Some vertebrae connect with other bones. Say which vertebrae:
  i connect with the ribs
  ii connect with the pelvis.

The backbone has four functions:

- providing points of attachment for the ribs, and for the muscles of the back
- enclosing and protecting the spinal cord
- supporting the upper part of the body
- allowing movement of the head and the trunk.

The top vertebra is called the **atlas** and the next one down is called the **axis**. Movement of the head is possible because:

- the joint between the skull and the atlas allows the head to move backwards and forwards
- the joint between the atlas and axis allows the atlas to turn from side to side; as the atlas turns, it carries the head with it.

The joints between the other vertebrae each allow a small amount of movement, and the combined movement of all the separate joints allows the trunk to bend and turn.

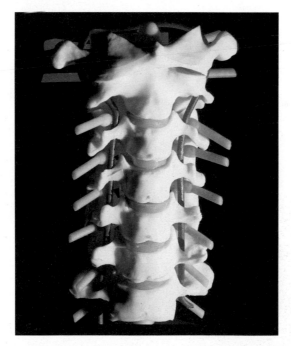

This is a model of the seven cervical vertebrae of the neck. Between each pair of vertebrae is a cartilage disk (grey-green). Twin rows of spinal nerves (yellow and orange) emerge through gaps between the vertebrae. The vertebral arteries are coloured red.

Why are the discs important?

In a young person, about a quarter of the total length of the backbone is made up by the discs and about three-quarters by the vertebrae. The discs join the individual bones of the backbone together, making the whole structure flexible and strong.

Each disc has a tough outer layer of strong fibrous cartilage and a soft jelly-like centre. With every movement of the back, some or all of the discs are squeezed or stretched in different places. They return to their normal shape when the back is straightened.

9 a Describe the structure of a disc.

  b How is the shape of the disc affected by movement of the back?

What is a 'slipped disc'?

10 a What causes a 'slipped disc'?

b Draw a diagram to show how a 'slipped disc' can touch a nerve.

c Explain why a 'slipped disc' can cause:

  i lumbago

  ii sciatica

  iii pain in the arms.

When strain is put on the back, a disc may crack, allowing jelly from the centre of the disc to bulge out. This is sometimes called a 'slipped disc'. The bulging disc can cause pressure on nerves leaving the spinal cord (see Figure 8).

If the pressure affects nerves in the lumbar region, pain is felt in the lower back. This pain is called **lumbago**. If the sciatic nerve is affected, pain is felt in the leg because the sciatic nerve runs down the leg. This pain is called **sciatica**. When the nerves in the neck region are affected, pain may be felt in the arms, and 'pins and needles' in the fingers.

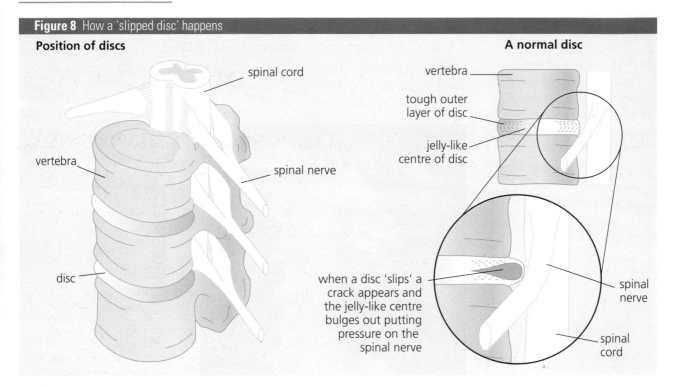

Figure 8 How a 'slipped disc' happens

Position of discs

spinal cord

vertebra

spinal nerve

disc

when a disc 'slips' a crack appears and the jelly-like centre bulges out putting pressure on the spinal nerve

A normal disc

vertebra

tough outer layer of disc

jelly-like centre of disc

spinal nerve

spinal cord

Summary of the skeleton and backbone

- The human skeleton contains 206 bones. Some of these are fused together (for example, the cranium of the skull) so may appear as a single bone.
- The skeleton can be divided into two main regions: the skull and backbone, and the girdles and limbs.
- The skeleton has four main functions: supporting the body, protecting the internal organs, making blood cells, and storing the mineral calcium.
- Arms and legs follow the same basic, pentadactyl pattern.

- The backbone or vertebral column is a stack of thirty-three vertebrae. The top twenty-four are separated from each other by disks. The bottom five are fused to form the coccyx. The next five up are joined to form the sacrum.
- The backbone provides: a site to attach the ribs, protection for the spinal cord, support for the upper body, and movement for the head and trunk.
- The disks between the vertebrae act as shock absorbers to prevent damage to the vertebrae. A slipped disk can result from the back being stressed too far.

2.3 Bones

Are bones alive?

11 a Several holes can be seen in the bone in Figure 9. Why are these necessary?

b Draw and label a diagram showing the regions where a bone grows:

 i in length

 ii in width.

c Name four things that bones need for growth.

d Draw a diagram of the inside of a bone and label five different parts.

Bones are living structures that are built and maintained by cells. If bones are damaged, they are painful; if broken, they can mend. A bone only looks clean and white when all the living tissue has been removed.

Throughout life, cells within bones are constantly rebuilding and remodelling the bone (see Figure 9). This is why young bones are able to enlarge and change shape as the body grows, and why repairs can be made to damaged bones. These cells are more active in children than in adults.

In order to grow, bones require an adequate supply of:

- protein, which forms the framework of the bone
- calcium, which makes the bone hard
- vitamin D and parathyroid hormone, which together enable calcium to be absorbed from the intestine and deposited on the framework of the bone.

Figure 9 Bone

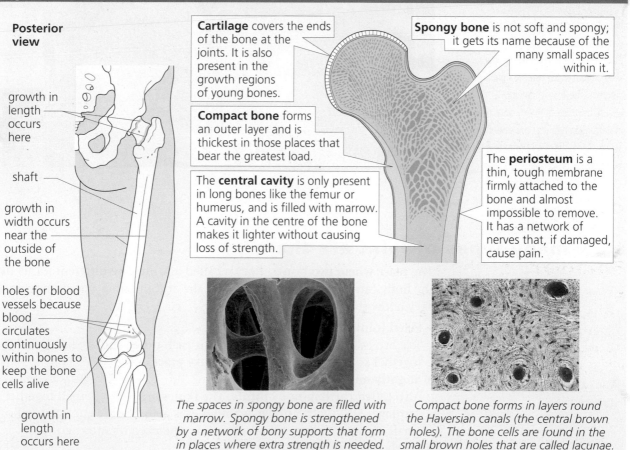

The spaces in spongy bone are filled with marrow. Spongy bone is strengthened by a network of bony supports that form in places where extra strength is needed.

Compact bone forms in layers round the Haversian canals (the central brown holes). The bone cells are found in the small brown holes that are called lacunae.

What happens inside bones?

12 a Name:

   i two places where bone marrow is found

   ii three things made in bone marrow.

  b Study the photograph and its caption, then name two things that bones need to maintain their strength, and say why.

Manufacture of blood cells

Red cells, white cells and platelets are made in the red marrow in bones. At birth, red marrow occurs throughout the skeleton in the many small spaces in spongy bone and in the central cavity of long bones. In adults, the red marrow of the long bone central cavities has been replaced by yellow marrow. Yellow marrow consists largely of fat and does not make blood cells.

Movement of calcium

There is continuous interchange between the large store of calcium in bones and the calcium in the blood. This allows the blood calcium level to stay constant, which is important for the healthy functioning of cells.

Astronauts rapidly lose calcium from bones in conditions of zero-gravity or weightlessness. When people are paralysed, the limbs they cannot move tend to lose calcium. The loss of calcium occurs because the body only maintains bones that are under stress. Movement and gravity both put a stress on bones.

2.4 Joints

How many types of joint are there?

The place where two bones meet is called a **joint**. The different joints in the body can be grouped according to the amount and type of movement they allow (Figure 10).

- **Fixed joints**
  The bones interlock where they touch each other and are firmly fixed together so that no movement can take place.
- **Slightly movable joints**
  Also called **cartilaginous joints**. The bones are firmly joined together by cartilage. Although cartilage is tough, it is also flexible enough to allow a small amount of movement when it is squeezed or stretched.
- **Freely movable joints**
  Also called **synovial joints**. These joints allow considerable movement between two bones. They include the following types of joint.

Ball and socket joints where the end of one bone is rounded and fits into the socket of another bone, so movement in nearly all directions is possible.

Hinge joints which act like door hinges and allow movement in one plane only.

Gliding joints in which the bones slide over each other.

Pivot joints where one bone rotates alongside another.

13 a Using the text and Figure 10, describe and give two examples of:

  i a slightly movable joint

  ii a ball and socket joint

  iii a gliding joint.

b Describe a hinge joint, and give five examples.

c Describe a pivot joint, and give one example.

d Draw a section through a synovial joint labelling the bones, cartilage, capsule, synovial membrane, and synovial fluid.

e Say what you think would be the effect on a synovial joint if:

  i the cartilage was worn away

  ii no synovial fluid was produced

  iii the capsule was torn.

f Say how smooth movement at the joint is helped by:

  i cartilage

  ii synovial fluid.

g Draw a diagram to show ligaments at the elbow joint.

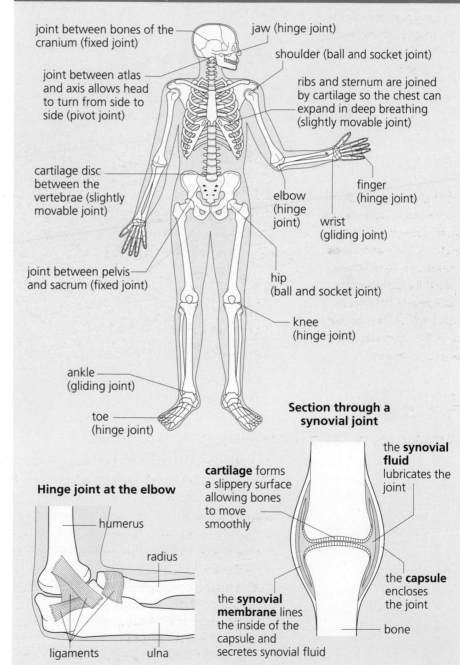

Figure 10 Joints in the body

joint between bones of the cranium (fixed joint)

jaw (hinge joint)

shoulder (ball and socket joint)

joint between atlas and axis allows head to turn from side to side (pivot joint)

ribs and sternum are joined by cartilage so the chest can expand in deep breathing (slightly movable joint)

cartilage disc between the vertebrae (slightly movable joint)

finger (hinge joint)

elbow (hinge joint)

wrist (gliding joint)

joint between pelvis and sacrum (fixed joint)

hip (ball and socket joint)

knee (hinge joint)

ankle (gliding joint)

toe (hinge joint)

Section through a synovial joint

Hinge joint at the elbow

humerus

radius

ligaments

ulna

cartilage forms a slippery surface allowing bones to move smoothly

the **synovial fluid** lubricates the joint

the **synovial membrane** lines the inside of the capsule and secretes synovial fluid

the **capsule** encloses the joint

bone

14 a What mainly holds the
   bones in place at a joint?

b What do ligaments do?

Ligaments are bands of tough tissue linking bones at a joint. The bones are mainly held in place by muscles, but the ligaments also help to keep them in position. Ligaments bend but do not stretch. They limit the range of movement and so prevent the joint from being dislocated.

A **sprain** is a torn ligament. This happens when a joint is forced beyond its normal range of movement. Sprains mostly occur in ankles and wrists.

What is a synovial joint?

15 List three ways in which a
   synovial joint is kept stable.

Synovial joints are the most common in the body. The bones move smoothly due to the presence of cartilage and synovial fluid. The cartilage also acts as a shock-absorber. The joint is held in place and kept stable by the muscles surrounding the joint, ligaments linking the bones, and a tough capsule that encloses and seals the joint.

What is arthritis?

Arthritis is inflammation of a joint. Inflamed joints are painful, may be hot and swollen, and movement is limited. Two common types of arthritis are:

- osteoarthritis
- rheumatoid arthritis.

Osteoarthritis ('wear and tear' arthritis)

Osteoarthritis tends to affect joints that have a lot of wear, for example, the weight-bearing joints of the back, hips and knees, and the joints at the base of the thumbs. It occurs chiefly in the elderly and in those who are overweight. It may also develop in intensively used joints of athletes, in injured joints, and in badly set fractures.

The cartilage at the ends of the bones becomes worn. This causes pain and stiffness when the bones are moved. Once developed, this condition tends to get worse. Treatment is usually with pain relievers and anti-inflammatory drugs.

Rheumatoid arthritis

This condition is most obvious in the joints, but it affects all the tissues of the body. The small joints of the fingers and toes are usually affected first. The disease can start suddenly in an otherwise fit young person, often under 40 years old, and occurs more often in females than males.

The joints become inflamed, painful and stiff. The condition is usually worst first thing in the morning. At the beginning, the sufferer can also feel generally ill with exhaustion, weight loss and fever. The condition follows an 'up and down' course over weeks or months. Some people recover completely; others have permanent changes such as gnarled old hands that remain even after the inflammation has gone.

Treatment for rheumatoid arthritis is similar to that for osteoarthritis. It is possible to replace badly affected joints with artificial ones.

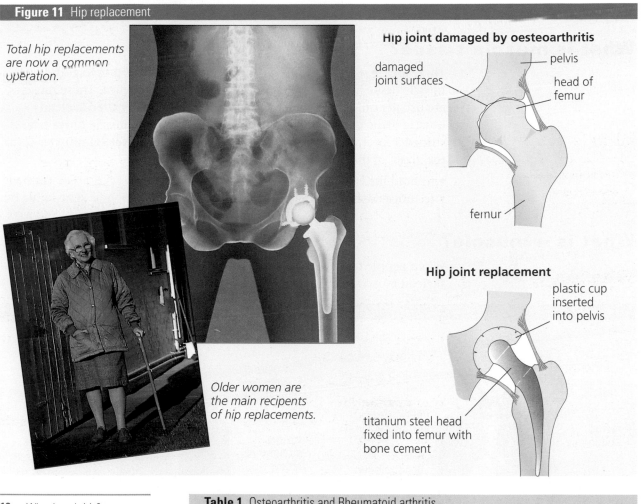

Figure 11 Hip replacement

Total hip replacements are now a common operation.

Older women are the main recipients of hip replacements.

Hip joint damaged by oesteoarthritis

damaged joint surfaces

pelvis

head of femur

femur

Hip joint replacement

plastic cup inserted into pelvis

titanium steel head fixed into femur with bone cement

16 a What is arthritis?
b Copy and complete Table 1.

Table 1 Osteoarthritis and Rheumatoid arthritis

Question	Osteoarthritis	Rheumatoid arthritis
What parts of the body are affected?		
Which age group is mainly affected?		
What are the symptoms?		
Do people recover from this condition?		
What treatment can be given?		

Summary of bones and joints

- Bones are living structures that can grow and repair themselves. They require a supply of protein and calcium to grow as well as small amounts of vitamin D and parathyroid hormone.

- The connection between two bones is called a joint. There are three main types of joint: fixed, slightly movable and freely movable.

- Synovial joints have a cartilage layer and synovial fluid to reduce friction between the bones. They are the commonest, most movable joints in the body.

- Ligaments join bone to bone. They do not stretch, but they are flexible.

- Osteoarthritis and rheumatoid arthritis are the commonest types of disease associated with joints.

29

2.5 Skeletal muscles

What is muscle tissue?

There are three types of muscle tissue. Here, you are going to consider the muscle tissue in muscles that are attached to the skeleton. These muscles are usually called **skeletal muscles** and their tissue is called skeletal muscle tissue or **striped muscle**. This is because the muscle fibres have a striped appearance when seen under a microscope. Skeletal muscles form the 'flesh' of the body and they have two functions:

- to hold the bones in position
- to move the bones when required.

What is a muscle?

When people talk about 'a muscle' they usually mean an individual skeletal muscle, for instance, the biceps muscle that bends the arm. The

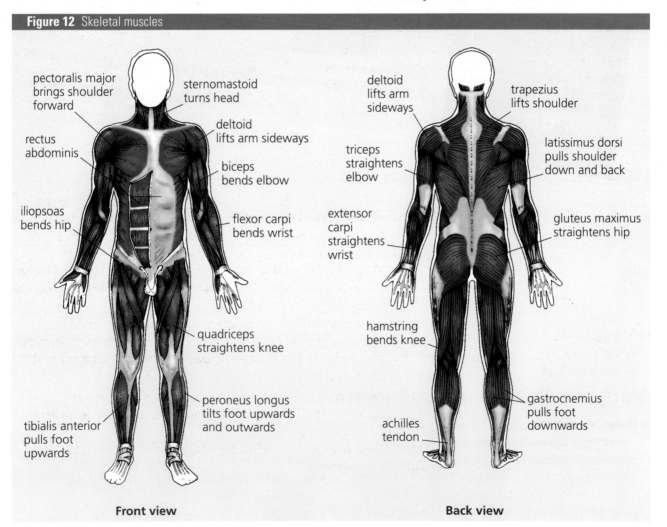

Figure 12 Skeletal muscles

pectoralis major brings shoulder forward

sternomastoid turns head

rectus abdominis

deltoid lifts arm sideways

biceps bends elbow

iliopsoas bends hip

flexor carpi bends wrist

quadriceps straightens knee

peroneus longus tilts foot upwards and outwards

tibialis anterior pulls foot upwards

Front view

deltoid lifts arm sideways

trapezius lifts shoulder

triceps straightens elbow

latissimus dorsi pulls shoulder down and back

extensor carpi straightens wrist

gluteus maximus straightens hip

hamstring bends knee

gastrocnemius pulls foot downwards

achilles tendon

Back view

biceps, like all skeletal muscles, is composed of many long, thin muscle fibres arranged in bundles. Muscles are thicker in the centre because there are more fibres in this part. Skeletal muscles are also known as **voluntary muscles** because you can use them when you want to, for example, to chew, to lift a bag, to climb stairs, or to do sports. There are about 600 individual muscles in the human body (see Figure 12).

Tendons

A **tendon** is a tough cord that attaches a muscle to a bone. It is an off-white colour and is often known as 'gristle'. Tendons are very strong and flexible, but do not stretch. Usually, there is a tendon at each end of a muscle, although in some cases muscles are attached directly to the bone (see Figure 13).

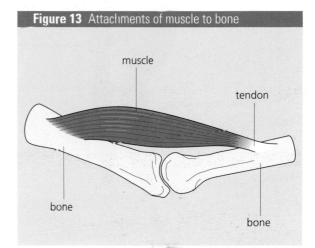

Figure 13 Attachments of muscle to bone

muscle

tendon

bone

bone

17 a Say why the muscles that move bones can be called:
  i skeletal
  ii voluntary
  iii striped.
b What is a muscle composed of?
c Why is a muscle thicker at the centre?

18 a Draw diagrams to show two ways muscles can be attached to bones.
b Describe a tendon.

How do skeletal muscles work?

Muscles can pull bones but not push them, so they always work in groups of two or more. One muscle pulls the bone to make it move in one direction, then another muscle pulls it back to its original position.

Even when they are at rest, muscles are always in a slight state of contraction. This is called **muscle tone**. Movement only takes place when the muscle on one side of a joint contracts more and pulls harder than the muscle on the other side. The muscle that is not contracting, relaxes gradually and this keeps the movement smooth and under control.

Muscles that work together to produce movement in opposite directions are called **antagonistic**, and form an **antagonistic system**. Examples of antagonistic systems are:

- the biceps (bends the arm) and the triceps (straightens the arm)
- the hamstring muscles (bend the knee) and the quadriceps muscles (straighten the knee)
- the shin muscle (bends the ankle upwards) and the calf muscles (straighten the ankle).

19 a Why do muscles always work in groups?
b What is muscle tone?
c What is an antagonistic system?
d Give an example of an antagonistic system, and say what each muscle does.

Flexors and extensors

Muscles are called 'flexor' or 'extensor' according to whether they cause a joint to bend (flex) or straighten (extend). A **flexor muscle** bends a joint, and an **extensor muscle** straightens a joint.

Figure 14 Antagonistic systems

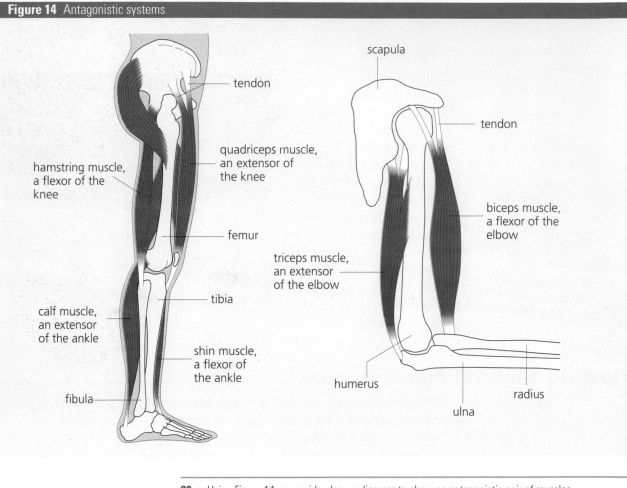

hamstring muscle, a flexor of the knee

tendon

quadriceps muscle, an extensor of the knee

femur

calf muscle, an extensor of the ankle

tibia

shin muscle, a flexor of the ankle

fibula

scapula

tendon

biceps muscle, a flexor of the elbow

triceps muscle, an extensor of the elbow

humerus

ulna

radius

20 a Using Figure 14 as a guide, draw a diagram to show an antagonistic pair of muscles.

  b From Figure 14, name the antagonistic pair of muscles that:
  i bend and straighten the knee
  ii bend and straighten the elbow.

What controls muscle movement?

Movement of muscles is controlled by nerves. The muscles are supplied with nerves from the spinal cord; the spinal cord and the nerves relay impulses from the brain (Figure 15). The nerves branch many times so that each muscle fibre has its own nerve endings called neuro-muscular junctions (Figure 15). When the muscle fibres receive impulses from the brain, they contract and make the muscle shorter. When the impulses cease, the muscle relaxes and returns to its former shape.

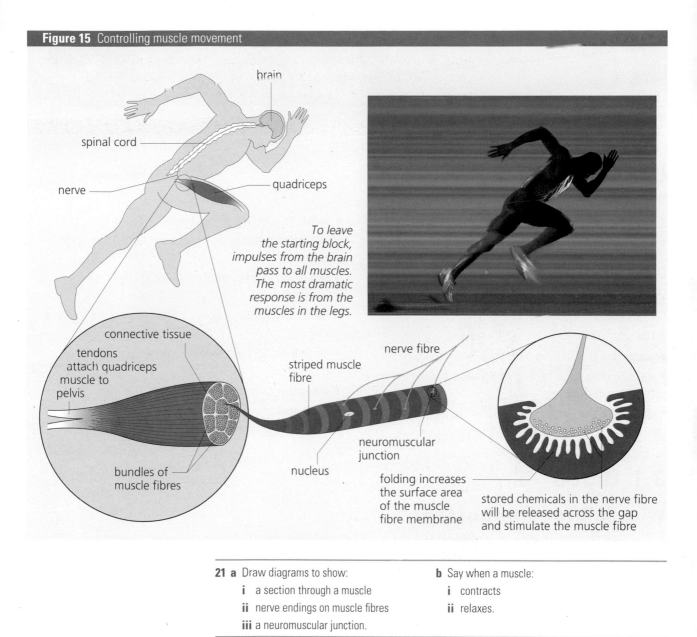

Figure 15 Controlling muscle movement

brain

spinal cord

nerve

quadriceps

To leave
the starting block,
impulses from the brain
pass to all muscles.
The most dramatic
response is from the
muscles in the legs.

connective tissue

tendons
attach quadriceps
muscle to
pelvis

striped muscle
fibre

nerve fibre

bundles of
muscle fibres

nucleus

neuromuscular
junction

folding increases
the surface area
of the muscle
fibre membrane

stored chemicals in the nerve fibre
will be released across the gap
and stimulate the muscle fibre

21 a Draw diagrams to show:
  i a section through a muscle
  ii nerve endings on muscle fibres
  iii a neuromuscular junction.

b Say when a muscle:
  i contracts
  ii relaxes.

Summary of skeletal muscles

- Most of the muscle in the body is skeletal muscle. Skeletal muscle is called skeletal because it is attached to the skeleton. It is also called striped or voluntary muscle.

- Tendons attach muscles to bones. Tendons are flexible but do not stretch.

- Muscles can contract or relax. They can pull on a bone but cannot push it.

- Muscles are arranged in antagonistic pairs so that they can move a bone and then move it back.

- Muscles that bend limbs are called flexors, muscles that straighten the limb again are called extensors.

- Movement in muscles is controlled by nerve endings embedded in individual muscle fibres.

Circulation 3

Learning objectives

By the end of this chapter you should be able to:

- **list** the functions and components of the blood
- **explain** how blood carries oxygen and carbon dioxide
- **explain** how blood clots
- **explain** how white blood cells protect the body against disease
- **list** common disorders of the blood
- **describe** the ABO and rhesus blood groups
- **explain** the factors that must be considered in blood transfusions
- **describe** the position and function of the heart
- **explain** how the heart maintains the circulation
- **describe** the use of an ECG in detecting heart disease
- **list** the common heart disorders, their causes and symptoms
- **describe** the structure of arteries, capillaries and veins
- **define** blood pressure and describe how it is measured
- **describe** common disorders of the circulation
- **describe** the structure and function of the lymphatic system.

3.1 Blood

Why is blood important?

Blood is a thick, red liquid that circulates continuously around the body in the blood vessels. As it circulates, some items are added and others are removed. Blood has many functions:

- nutrients from food are absorbed from the gut and carried via the liver to the cells for use or storage
- oxygen is collected in the lungs and carried to the cells
- carbon dioxide is collected from the cells and carried to the lungs to be excreted
- urea is collected from the liver and carried to the kidneys to be excreted
- medicines, drugs and alcohol enter the bloodstream through the gut, lungs or skin and are distributed around the body; they are eventually excreted by the kidneys
- the number of white cells and antibodies in the blood increases in response to infection; this helps to protect the body against disease
- clotting prevents loss of blood from wounds
- heat is carried from the central parts of the body to the outer parts, such as the hands, feet and tip of nose to warm them up if they are cold; if the body is too hot, heat is lost through the skin and by sweating.

1 a List eight things blood carries.

 b Give two other functions of blood.

What does blood contain?

2 What are the four parts of the blood?

Blood has four main parts: plasma, red cells, white cells, and platelets. When blood is centrifuged or allowed to stand, with a chemical added to prevent clotting, it separates into the layers (see Figure 1).

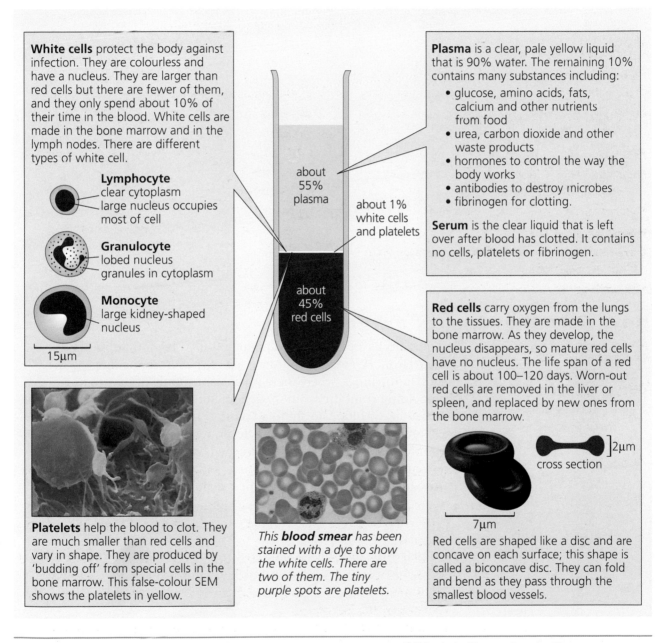

White cells protect the body against infection. They are colourless and have a nucleus. They are larger than red cells but there are fewer of them, and they only spend about 10% of their time in the blood. White cells are made in the bone marrow and in the lymph nodes. There are different types of white cell.

Lymphocyte
clear cytoplasm
large nucleus occupies most of cell

Granulocyte
lobed nucleus
granules in cytoplasm

Monocyte
large kidney-shaped nucleus

15μm

about 55% plasma

about 1% white cells and platelets

about 45% red cells

Plasma is a clear, pale yellow liquid that is 90% water. The remaining 10% contains many substances including:

- glucose, amino acids, fats, calcium and other nutrients from food
- urea, carbon dioxide and other waste products
- hormones to control the way the body works
- antibodies to destroy microbes
- fibrinogen for clotting.

Serum is the clear liquid that is left over after blood has clotted. It contains no cells, platelets or fibrinogen.

Red cells carry oxygen from the lungs to the tissues. They are made in the bone marrow. As they develop, the nucleus disappears, so mature red cells have no nucleus. The life span of a red cell is about 100–120 days. Worn-out red cells are removed in the liver or spleen, and replaced by new ones from the bone marrow.

]2μm

cross section

7μm

Red cells are shaped like a disc and are concave on each surface; this shape is called a biconcave disc. They can fold and bend as they pass through the smallest blood vessels.

Platelets help the blood to clot. They are much smaller than red cells and vary in shape. They are produced by 'budding off' from special cells in the bone marrow. This false-colour SEM shows the platelets in yellow.

This **blood smear** has been stained with a dye to show the white cells. There are two of them. The tiny purple spots are platelets.

3 a What forms the largest percentage of blood?

b List some of the substances this liquid contains.

c How does serum differ from plasma?

d Name three parts of the blood made in bone marrow.

e Draw labelled diagrams of a red cell and a white cell. Give the function of each.

f What is the lifespan of a red cell?

g What happens to red cells when they are worn out?

h Describe what you can see in the blood smear.

What does blood carry?

Many substances are transported round the body in the blood (see Table 1).

4 a Name four items carried to all the tissues, and say where each came from.

b Write down where carbon dioxide is:

  i carried from

  ii carried to.

c Say where urea is:

  i carried from

  ii carried to

  iii removed from the body.

Table 1 Substances carried by the blood

Substance carried	Carried from	Carried to	Notes
oxygen	lungs	all tissues	all living cells need oxygen
carbon dioxide	all tissues	lungs	all living cells produce carbon dioxide
nutrients from food	gut	all tissues via the liver	cells need nutrients for energy and growth
urea	liver	kidneys	urea is removed from the body in urine
antibodies	lymph nodes	all tissues	antibodies help to protect the body against disease
hormones	endocrine glands	all tissues	hormones control various processes
heat	warmer parts of body	colder parts	helps to keep all parts of the body at an even temperature

How does blood carry oxygen?

5 a Name:

  i the red pigment that carries oxygen

  ii the substance formed by combining oxygen and the red pigment.

b Where is oxygen released from oxyhaemoglobin?

c Explain why blood is:

  i bright red when it leaves the lungs

  ii dark red when it returns to the lungs.

Red blood cells are full of a red pigment called **haemoglobin** that contains iron. Haemoglobin transports oxygen from the lungs to the tissues. In the lungs, where there is constant supply of oxygen, the haemoglobin combines with oxygen and to form **oxyhaemoglobin**. This is carried in the bloodstream to all parts of the body. In places where there is a shortage of oxygen, oxyhaemoglobin releases its oxygen to the cells. This forms haemoglobin, which is carried back to the lungs in the bloodstream to collect more oxygen.

The equation below shows that the reaction can go both ways.

$$\text{haemoglobin} + \text{oxygen} \rightleftharpoons \text{oxyhaemoglobin}$$
$$\text{dark red} \qquad\qquad\qquad \text{bright red}$$

Blood leaving the lungs is saturated with oxygen and is bright red. As the blood loses oxygen, it turns dark red – this is the colour of blood returning to the lungs.

How does blood carry carbon dioxide?

Carbon dioxide is a waste product formed by all living cells and is carried to the lungs by the blood. Some is dissolved in the plasma but most is carried in the red blood cells.

6 a Give two ways in which carbon dioxide is carried in the blood.

b In your own words, explain what is happening in Figure 2, starting at point X.

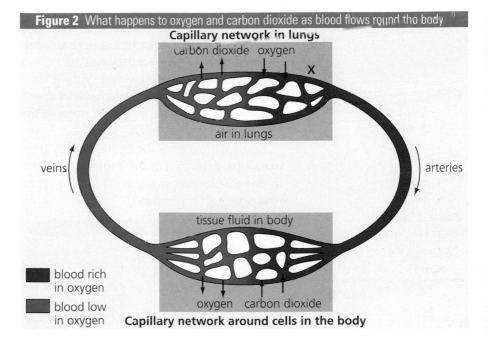

Figure 2 What happens to oxygen and carbon dioxide as blood flows round the body

Capillary network in lungs

carbon dioxide   oxygen

X

air in lungs

veins

arteries

tissue fluid in body

■ blood rich in oxygen

■ blood low in oxygen

oxygen   carbon dioxide

Capillary network around cells in the body

How does blood clot?

Bleeding from small cuts, grazes and pinpricks soon stops because the surrounding blood vessels get narrower and cut off or reduce the blood supply. We say the blood vessels **constrict**. A blood clot forms over a wound (see Figure 3).

If a large blood vessel is cut, particularly an artery, the pressure of blood flowing from the wound may be too great to allow a clot to form. A serious loss of blood is called a **haemorrhage**.

7 a Describe the process of clotting by sorting these statements into the correct order:
  * jelly-like blood clot forms
  * fibrin in plasma forms sticky threads
  * tissue underneath is repaired
  * hard scab forms
  * scab drops off leaving a scar
  * blood vessel is damaged
  * blood cells and platelets are trapped.

b What is a haemorrhage and why is it dangerous?

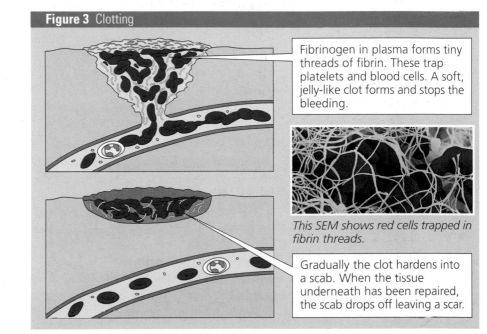

Figure 3 Clotting

Fibrinogen in plasma forms tiny threads of fibrin. These trap platelets and blood cells. A soft, jelly-like clot forms and stops the bleeding.

This SEM shows red cells trapped in fibrin threads.

Gradually the clot hardens into a scab. When the tissue underneath has been repaired, the scab drops off leaving a scar.

How do white cells protect against infection?

White cells are more or less spherical when they are floating in the bloodstream. However, they can also crawl along the inside of blood vessel walls and they can change their shape as they do so. This enables them to squeeze between the cells of the thin walls of the tiniest blood vessels and so leave the bloodstream to move around between the cells of the tissues.

Some white cells called **phagocytes** are able to engulf bacteria and other small particles and destroy them (see Figure 4). **Lymphocytes**, another type of white cell, make **antibodies** that can destroy microorganisms or the poisons they make.

8 Give two ways in which white cells protect the body against infection.

Figure 4 Phagocytes

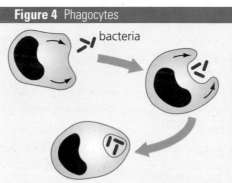

bacteria

→ movement of the cytoplasm as it surrounds and encloses the bacteria

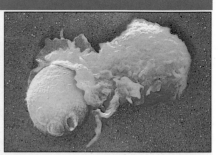

This false-colour scanning electron micrograph shows a lymphocyte (blue) engulfing a yeast cell (yellow).

What can go wrong with the blood cells?

Leukaemia and anaemia are problems associated with white and red blood cells, respectively.

Leukaemia

There are several types of leukaemia. They are all forms of cancer, and all involve the production of enormous numbers of abnormal white cells. Some leukaemias respond well to treatment by drugs, radiation or bone marrow transplant. For example, some childhood leukaemias have a 75% disease-free survival rate.

Anaemia

A lack of functional haemoglobin is called **anaemia**. Haemoglobin carries oxygen, so an anaemic person often feels tired, weak and breathless. There are various causes of anaemia:
- iron-deficiency anaemia
- pernicious anaemia
- hereditary anaemia
- anaemia due to malaria.

Iron-deficiency anaemia This occurs when there is not enough iron to make haemoglobin. This is the most common reason for anaemia and it can result from:

- excess blood loss caused by
  - heavy periods
  - piles
  - peptic ulcers
  - hookworm disease
- increased need for iron during
  - rapid growth at puberty
  - pregnancy, because of the baby's need to make blood
- poor absorption of iron
  - coeliac disease
  - gastritis
- insufficient intake of iron
  - due to a low-iron diet without meat, eggs, or vegetables
  - in babies who are fed entirely on milk for more than 9 months.

Iron taken as tablets or liquid quickly enables the bone marrow to increase its output of red blood cells. However, the reason for the iron deficiency must also be identified and treated.

Pernicious anaemia A shortage of vitamin B_{12} prevents bone marrow from making enough red cells. This type of anaemia develops when the stomach fails to make a substance called **intrinsic factor**. Intrinsic factor helps the body to absorb vitamin B_{12} in the small intestine. This anaemia is treated with vitamin B_{12} injections every 1 to 2 months.

Hereditary anaemia There are a number of inherited diseases with abnormal types of haemoglobin. For example:

- **sickle-cell anaemia** is found mainly in people from West Africa; the red cells contain an abnormal type of haemoglobin called haemoglobin S, which causes the red blood cells to be short lived and to change to a sickle shape when there is a shortage of oxygen
- **thalassaemia** is found mainly in people from countries bordering the eastern Mediterranean, the Middle East, India and Asia.

Anaemia due to malaria This anaemia is due to an infection in which the malaria parasite destroys red blood cells.

9 a What is leukaemia?

b What is anaemia?

c Give four causes of anaemia.

d Why may iron-deficiency anaemia occur:

   i in babies who are fed entirely on milk for over 9 months

   ii in someone who does not eat meat, eggs or vegetables

   iii at puberty

   iv during pregnancy

   v due to heavy periods

   vi due to piles or peptic ulcers?

e When might a patient be treated with vitamin B_{12}?

f Name two types of hereditary anaemia.

What is a blood transfusion?

A **blood transfusion** is the transfer of blood from a healthy person to a sick person. The person who gives the blood is called the **donor**. The donated blood is mixed with a chemical to prevent clotting and can then be stored for a short time. The person who receives the transfusion is called the **recipient**. However, not all transfusions consist of whole blood.

Most of the blood given by donors is split up into its individual parts. This means that each patient can be given only the part they need.

Figure 5 Different types of transfusion

Factor VIII is given to people with haemophilia, an inherited bleeding disorder. Queen Victoria passed haemophilia on to her descendants.

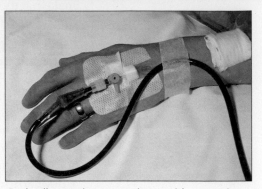

Red cells are given to patients with anaemia.

Whole blood is given to patients who have just lost a great deal of blood, for example in an accident or during surgery.

Hospitals in the UK use about 10 000 bags of blood every day.

Fibrinogen transfusions are very rare. They are given if, as occasionally happens, a woman has heavy bleeding after giving birth.

Plasma is given in cases of severe burns to replace the liquid from the blood that has been lost through the skin.

10 a Using Figure 5, what type of transfusion is likely to be given during surgery?

   b Why do doctors recommend transfusion of red cells for severe anaemia?

   c Why are patients with severe burns given plasma?

   d What may be given to stop haemorrhage?

   e What disorder is treated with Factor VIII?

How many blood groups are there?

Every person has an individual blood group that is inherited and does not change throughout life. The group depends on:

- one of the four groups in the ABO system
- whether the rhesus factor is present or not
- a range of other blood factors that are not usually important in blood transfusions.

The ABO system

Every person's blood belongs to one of the four blood groups in this system: A, B, AB and 0 (see Figure 6). These groups depend on the presence or absence of:

- two proteins, called A and B, on red cells
- two antibodies, called anti-A and anti-B, in plasma.

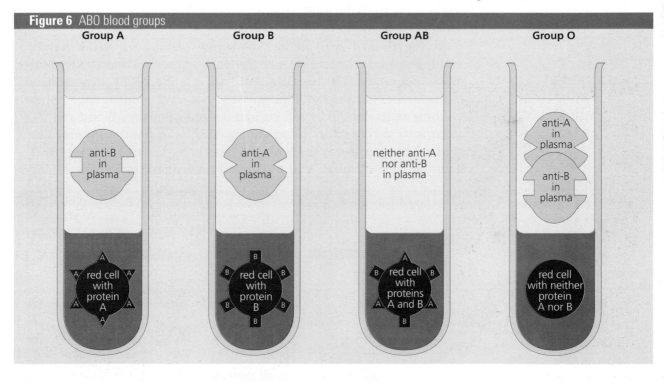

Figure 6 ABO blood groups

Group A · Group B · Group AB · Group O

11 **a** In the ABO system, what does a person's blood group depend on?
   b Use Figure 6 to say which items each of the four blood groups contain.
   c Describe what happens when anti-B mixes with protein B.

You can see in Figure 6 that none of the blood groups contain both protein A and anti-A, or protein B and anti-B. If plasma containing anti-A mixes with red cells carrying protein A, the anti-A can bind to protein A. Each anti-A links to more than one red cell, so the red cells are held together. This is called **clumping**. The same problem arises if anti-B mixes with cells carrying protein B.

A patient with blood group A has anti-B in their plasma. If such a patient were given a transfusion of group B blood, the patient's anti-B would cause the transfused red cells to stick together. This could lead to collapse, kidney failure and death.

Rhesus system

Blood is also grouped according to the presence or absence of the rhesus factor. A person who has the rhesus factor is rhesus positive, this is usually written Rh positive. Someone without, is Rh negative. So, a person whose blood is group AB and has the rhesus factor would be AB Rh positive. A person with group B blood and no rhesus factor would be B Rh negative.

Why is the rhesus factor important?

If Rh negative people receive Rh positive blood in transfusion they will form antibodies against the rhesus factor. Any future transfusion of Rh positive blood will cause a huge increase in these antibodies which will then react with the transfused blood.

The rhesus factor is important during pregnancy if the mother is Rh negative and the father Rh positive. The rhesus factor can be inherited and, if the baby is Rh negative like its mother, there will be no problem. However, if the baby is Rh positive like its father, then a dangerous situation can arise.

During labour a small amount of the baby's blood can mix with the mother's blood. The mother then develops antibodies against Rh positive blood but, as the baby has been born, it is not affected by them. However, if the mother has *another* Rh positive baby she will produce large numbers of these antibodies. They will get into her unborn baby's blood and destroy its red cells. This causes damage such as anaemia and jaundice, and might even lead to the birth of a dead baby. Giving birth to a dead baby is called **stillbirth**. This situation is preventable (see Figure 7).

12 a Say what it means when a person is:

   i Rh positive

   ii Rh negative

 b When and why is the rhesus factor important in pregnancy?

 c What develops in a Rh negative mother's blood when she has a Rh positive baby?

 d What will be produced in the same mother's blood if she has another Rh positive baby, and what effect can this have on the child?

 e Describe how this situation can be prevented.

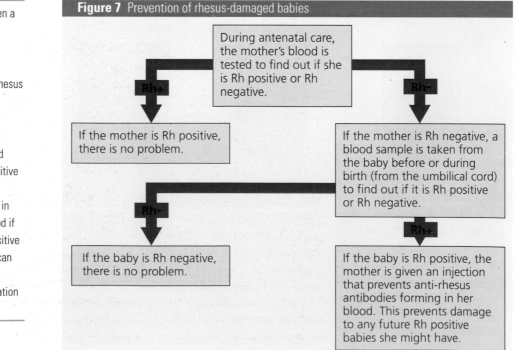

Figure 7 Prevention of rhesus-damaged babies

During antenatal care, the mother's blood is tested to find out if she is Rh positive or Rh negative.

Rh+ → If the mother is Rh positive, there is no problem.

Rh– → If the mother is Rh negative, a blood sample is taken from the baby before or during birth (from the umbilical cord) to find out if it is Rh positive or Rh negative.

Rh– → If the baby is Rh negative, there is no problem.

Rh+ → If the baby is Rh positive, the mother is given an injection that prevents anti-rhesus antibodies forming in her blood. This prevents damage to any future Rh positive babies she might have.

Must blood groups match for safe transfusions?

13 a What is compatible blood?
  b In what ways must transfused blood be compatible with the patient's blood?

Before a transfusion is given, a drop of the patient's blood is tested with the blood to be transfused. The test ensures that the patient receives **compatible blood**, that is, blood that can safely mix with the patient's own. The transfused blood must be compatible in both ABO type and rhesus type. It is important to understand that 'compatible' does not mean 'the same as' (see Table 2).

Table 2 ABO compatibility

Donor blood group	Recipient blood group			
	A	B	AB	O
A	✓	✗	✓	✗
B	✗	✓	✓	✗
AB	✗	✗	✓	✗
O	✓	✓	✓	✓

✓ = the blood is compatible and the recipient can accept it safely

✗ = the blood is not compatible and must not be transfused

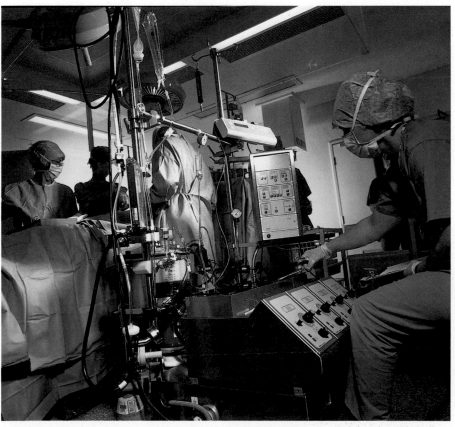

Even during a heart operation blood must circulate around the body to supply the cells with nutrients and oxygen, and to remove their waste products. Oxygen is supplied by a heart–lung machine like the one being monitored by the technician on the right of this photograph. Extra transfused blood is also required.

Rh negative blood can be given to either Rh positive or Rh negative people. Rh positive blood should only be given to Rh positive people. So:

- group 0 Rh negative blood *can be given to any other group*; people with this group are called **universal donors**.
- group AB Rh positive *can receive blood of any group*; people with this group are called **universal recipients**.

Rare factors

There are many minor blood groups that are not routinely checked, but a patient who has had many blood transfusions, will have acquired a number of different antibodies to these minor groups. Such a person needs blood that will not react with any of these antibodies, so a suitable donor may be hard to find.

14 a Say which people can safely receive a transfusion of:
   i Rh negative blood
   ii Rh positive blood
   iii group 0 Rh negative blood
   iv group AB Rh positive blood.

Summary of blood

- The blood is a thick, red liquid containing red cells, white cells and platelets suspended in a liquid called plasma. Plasma is 55% of the blood and is a complex solution of sugars, salts, fat droplets, proteins and hormones in water.

- Red blood cells make up roughly 45% of the blood and are packed with haemoglobin. Haemoglobin is able to react reversibly with oxygen and is used to transport oxygen from the lungs to the tissues. Red blood cells are made in the bone marrow, have no nucleus, cannot divide and last roughly 100 days before they are destroyed by the spleen and liver.

- White blood cells make up less than 1% of the blood and are made in the bone marrow or lymph glands. There are three main types, all of which have a nucleus. They are mainly concerned with protecting the body against disease.

- Blood clotting depends on a series of reactions between air and fibrinogen and other chemicals in the plasma. Clotting is a defence mechanism that helps to stop the flow of blood from damaged blood vessels and prevents entry of foreign substances into the bloodstream.

- Anaemias are due to a lack of haemoglobin in the blood. They have a range of causes but usually result in tiredness, weakness, and shortage of breath due to the blood being unable to carry oxygen efficiently.

- Leukaemias are all forms of cancer that affect the bone marrow making it produce large numbers of ineffective white blood cells. Some childhood leukaemias respond well to treatment.

- The main blood groups are A, B, AB and O. Blood groups are defined by the proteins found on the surface of red blood cells. Group A has protein A on the red cells and an antibody in the plasma called anti-B. Anti-B reacts with protein B on the red cells of blood group B. Group B has the antibody anti A in the plasma; this reacts with Protein A on the red cells of Group A.

- Compatible blood groups can be safely transfused. compatible blood groups are not always the same group. Blood for tranfusion must be compatible in both ABO group and rhesus type.

- The rhesus blood group depends on the presence or absence of the rhesus factor.

- People with O Rh negative blood are called universal donors. People with AB Rh positive blood are called universal recipients.

3.2 The heart

Where is the heart and what does it do?

The heart is situated in the thorax between and in front of the lungs (see Figure 8). It is centrally placed, but tilted so that most of the heart muscle is to the left of centre. This is why the heartbeat can be felt on the left side of the chest. The **pericardium** is a thin tough membrane that surrounds and encloses the heart and holds it in position. The size of a person's heart is about the size of the fist, and the heart walls are composed almost entirely of a special type of muscle called cardiac muscle.

The function of the heart is to pump blood. It is a double pump: the right side pumps blood to the lungs to collect oxygen, and the left side pumps the oxygenated blood from the lungs to the rest of the body. Both sides of the heart work together and at the same time.

15 a Draw and label a diagram to show the position of the heart in the body.

b Explain why the heartbeat is felt on the left side.

c Why can the heart be regarded as a double pump?

How is the heart organised?

The heart is composed of four chambers (see Figure 9):

- right atrium
- left atrium
- right ventricle
- left ventricle.

The right side of the heart is completely separate from the left side. Blood flowing through one side does not mix with the blood flowing through the other side.

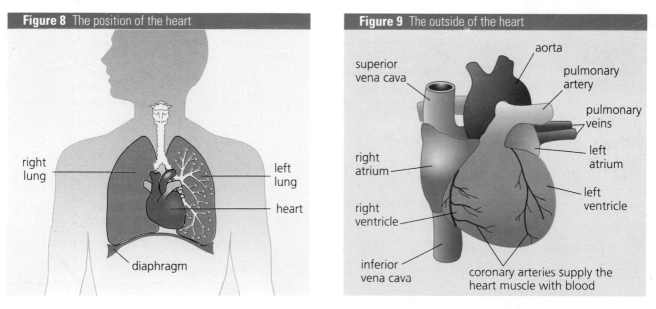

Figure 8 The position of the heart

right lung

left lung

heart

diaphragm

Figure 9 The outside of the heart

superior vena cava

aorta

pulmonary artery

pulmonary veins

right atrium

left atrium

right ventricle

left ventricle

inferior vena cava

coronary arteries supply the heart muscle with blood

16 a Name the two chambers on:

   i the right side of the heart

   ii the left side of the heart.

b Why is there no mixing of the blood on the left and right side of the heart?

Figure 10 shows that the atria have thin walls and the ventricles have thick walls. The left ventricle has a thicker wall than the right one because it needs more muscle power to pump blood to all parts of the body. The right ventricle pumps blood only to the lungs.

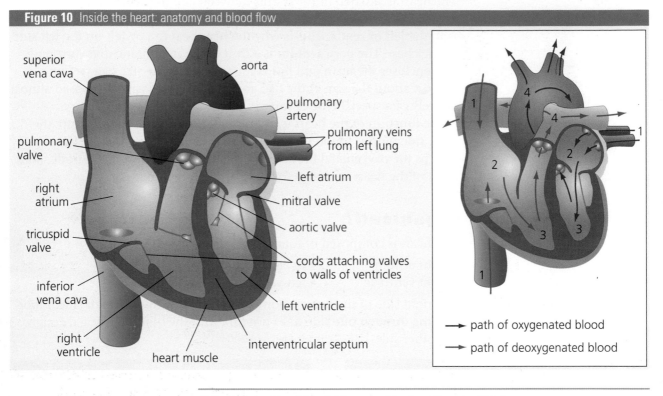

Figure 10 Inside the heart: anatomy and blood flow

superior vena cava
aorta
pulmonary artery
pulmonary veins from left lung
pulmonary valve
left atrium
right atrium
mitral valve
aortic valve
tricuspid valve
cords attaching valves to walls of ventricles
inferior vena cava
left ventricle
right ventricle
interventricular septum
heart muscle

→ path of oxygenated blood
→ path of deoxygenated blood

17 Study Figure 10 and then list the parts of the heart through which flows:
  i deoxygenated blood
  ii oxygenated blood.

What are the valves for?

There are four valves in the heart. Each consists of two or three small flaps of tissue that surround an opening. The valves ensure a one-way flow of blood through the heart. They are pushed open by blood flowing forwards; blood trying to flow backwards pushes them closed.

18 a Name the four heart valves shown in Figure 10.
  b Explain why blood can only flow in one direction through the heart.

What is the heartbeat?

Heartbeat is the alternate contraction and relaxation of the muscular walls of the ventricles (see Figure 11). There are two phases to each heartbeat:
• systole (pronounced siss-toe-ly)
• diastole (pronounced die-ass-toe-ly).

19 a What is the heartbeat?
  b Using Figure 11, describe in words what happens in:
    i systole
    ii diastole.

Figure 11 Heartbeat

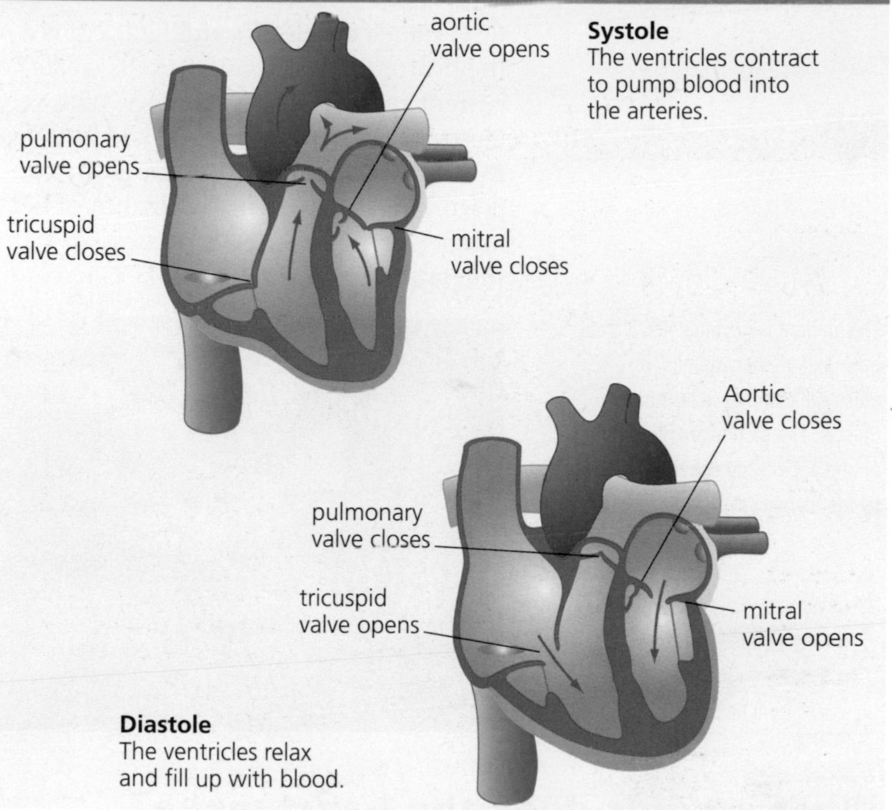

aortic valve opens

Systole
The ventricles contract to pump blood into the arteries.

pulmonary valve opens

tricuspid valve closes

mitral valve closes

Aortic valve closes

pulmonary valve closes

tricuspid valve opens

mitral valve opens

Diastole
The ventricles relax and fill up with blood.

The heart beats regularly because it has a natural pacemaker in the wall of the right atrium. The pacemaker is a small mass of tissue that sends frequent, regular electrical impulses to the heart muscle. Each impulse makes the heart muscle contract. The rate at which the natural pacemaker works is partly controlled by the brain, but it is also affected by hormones such as adrenaline, and by some drugs.

If the heart's own pacemaker fails to make the heart beat satisfactorily, an artificial pacemaker can be fitted. The artificial pacemaker is implanted under the skin of the chest and connected to the heart muscle by a thin wire passing down a vein. It is powered by batteries.

20 a Where is the heart's natural pacemaker?
  b What affects the rate at which the natural pacemaker works?
  c Why might an artificial pacemaker be fitted?

How fast does the heart beat?

21 a What is the average heart rate of an adult when resting?
  b Give four causes for an increase in heart rate.
  c Is a child's heart rate faster or slower than an adult's?
  d Explain why an athlete's heart rate is slower than an average person's.

The **heart rate** is the number of times the heart beats in a minute. In an adult, it is about 70 beats a minute when resting. During exercise, the rate can increase up to 200 beats a minute in order to supply the muscles with more blood carrying extra oxygen and glucose. Heart rate is also increased by excitement, fear, and by some diseases. It is faster in a child and slower in an athlete.

The heartbeat is slower in an athlete because the heart is more muscular and efficient and so pumps out more blood per beat. An athlete's heart rate increases during exercise, but not by as much as that of an untrained person.

What is an ECG?

ECG stands for electrocardiogram. It is a record of the electrical changes in the heart muscle. All muscle cells create very small amounts of electrical current every time they contract. With very sensitive machines, the electrical changes in the atria and in the ventricles can be recorded. An ECG provides information about the condition of the heart and the way it is working. Changes in the rhythm of beating can be analysed and heart attacks can be detected and assessed. Damage caused by heart attacks in the past can also show up in ECG traces of an otherwise healthy person.

This patient is having an ECG. The ECG equipment responds to electrical changes in his heart muscle. The results are displayed on the paper strip being examined by the technician.

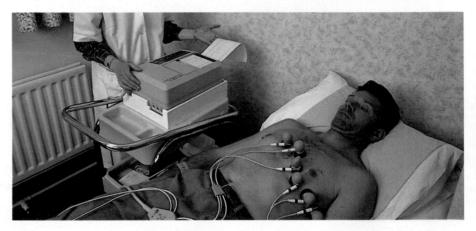

22 a What does ECG stand for?
  b What does an ECG record?
  c What information can you get from an ECG?

What sounds does the heart make?

As the heart beats, it makes rhythmical sounds described as LUB–DUP. LUB is a soft sound made when the tricuspid and mitral valves close. DUP is a shorter, sharper sound made when the pulmonary and aortic valves close. The rhythm of sound is:

$$\xrightarrow{\text{pause}} \text{LUB–DUP} \xrightarrow{\text{pause}} \text{LUB–DUP} \xrightarrow{\text{pause}} \text{LUB–DUP}$$

Heart murmurs are other sounds made by the heart. They happen, for example, when a valve inside the heart is damaged and the blood flow becomes irregular, or if a patient has a 'hole in the heart'.

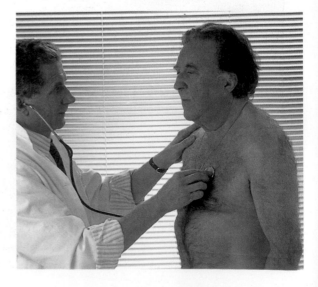

23 a What sound would the doctor in the photograph expect to hear?
  b What can cause heart murmurs?

This doctor is checking the heart sounds of a patient with a healthy heart.

What is a 'hole in the heart'?

The right and left sides of the heart are normally completely separated by a wall of muscle. A gap in this wall is called a 'hole in the heart' (see Figure 12). This condition usually occurs when a baby did not form properly in the uterus. Sometimes, but rarely, it can occur in adults when the heart is weakened by a heart attack.

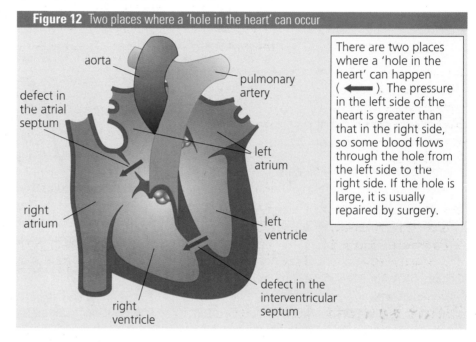

Figure 12 Two places where a 'hole in the heart' can occur

aorta

pulmonary artery

defect in the atrial septum

left atrium

right atrium

left ventricle

right ventricle

defect in the interventricular septum

There are two places where a 'hole in the heart' can happen (⟵). The pressure in the left side of the heart is greater than that in the right side, so some blood flows through the hole from the left side to the right side. If the hole is large, it is usually repaired by surgery.

24 a What is a 'hole in the heart' and where can it occur?

b Give two causes for a 'hole in the heart'.

What is coronary artery disease?

Even though blood flows through the heart, the muscle of the heart walls needs its own supply of blood with oxygen and nutrients from food. The **coronary arteries** carry blood to the muscle of the heart (see Figure 9 on page 45).

When the coronary arteries are narrowed by disease, less blood is able to get through them to supply the heart muscle with oxygen. This causes a cramp-like pain in the centre of the chest, which often spreads to the shoulders, neck and arms. This pain can be angina or due to a heart attack.

Angina is cramp caused by a temporary oxygen shortage in the heart muscle. It is brought on by factors that increase the heart's workload, such as exercise, extreme emotion, heavy meals, and cold weather. The pain disappears with rest.

A **heart attack** is heart muscle cell death due to severe oxygen shortage. Other signs of a heart attack include a cold sweat, nausea, shortness of breath and a feeling of weakness. Whether a heart attack is mild or severe depends on where the blockage takes place and how much of the heart muscle is damaged. Usually, only a small part is affected and the rest of the heart continues to beat normally, but if much muscle is damaged, the heart is unable to work and the person often dies.

25 a Draw a diagram to show a coronary artery (see Figure 9).

b What is the function of coronary arteries?

c What happens when coronary arteries become narrowed?

d Compare angina with a heart attack by saying:
  i what is each due to
  ii whether or not the heart muscle damaged in each case.

If there is a strong family history of heart attack or angina, it is sensible to reduce the risk of suffering from these conditions. The following is particularly important to people at risk, but is good advice for everybody who wishes to reduce the chance of having angina or a heart attack:

• do not smoke
• keep physically fit and slim with sensible, regular exercise
• eat sensibly with no excess of fat or cholesterol
• have the blood pressure and urine glucose checked regularly.

---

26 What advice is given to people who wish to reduce the chance of having angina or a heart attack?

Summary of the heart

• The heart is a muscular organ about the size of your fist and found in the chest. It is centrally placed but tilted so that most of the heart muscle is to the left of centre. It consists of four muscular chambers forming two separate but joined pumps.

• The top two chambers of the heart are called the atria. They squeeze blood into the lower, more muscular ventricles. The right ventricle pumps blood to the lungs. The left ventricle pumps blood around the body. Both sides work together and at the same time.

• Valves in the heart ensure that blood can only flow one way. The heart sounds listened for by a doctor are the sounds of these valves closing.

• The heart beat is controlled by a pacemaker region in the wall of the right atrium. The heart beats at about 70 beats per minute in a resting adult but this can rise to 200 beats per minute during strenuous exercise.

• An ECG or electrocardiogram records the electrical activity of the heart. The changes in electrical signal correspond to activity in the muscles of the heart. ECGs can show permanent damage caused by heart attacks.

• The blood in the left and right sides of the heart is normally kept separate. A hole in the heart allows the blood to mix, either through the ventricles or the atria. This condition usually occurs in babies but occasionally it can occur in an adult after a heart attack.

• The coronary artery supplies blood to the muscles of the heart to provide oxygen and glucose and to remove carbon dioxide. Coronary artery disease narrows this artery and starves the heart, or parts of it, of oxygen and nutrients. Coronary artery disease has a number of causes and people who are overweight, take very little exercise, eat fatty foods, smoke and who have a family history of heart disease are more likely to suffer.

3.3 Blood vessels and circulation

How are blood vessels organised?

Blood vessels are tubes through which the blood flows as it circulates around the body. There are three different types:

- **arteries** carry blood from the heart
- **veins** return blood to the heart
- **capillaries** link arteries to veins.

The largest blood vessel is the aorta, an artery with a diameter of about 2.5 cm; the smallest are the capillaries with a diameter of about 8 μm.

Arteries carry blood to all parts of the body from the heart. They divide into smaller and smaller branches and, finally, into the tiny blood vessels called capillaries. Blood from the capillaries enters small veins. These link up to form larger and larger veins and eventually return the blood to the heart (see Figure 13).

27 **a** What are the different functions of an artery, a vein, and a capillary?

b Name the largest blood vessel in the body and say whether it is an artery or a vein.

Figure 13 Some of the main arteries and veins in the body

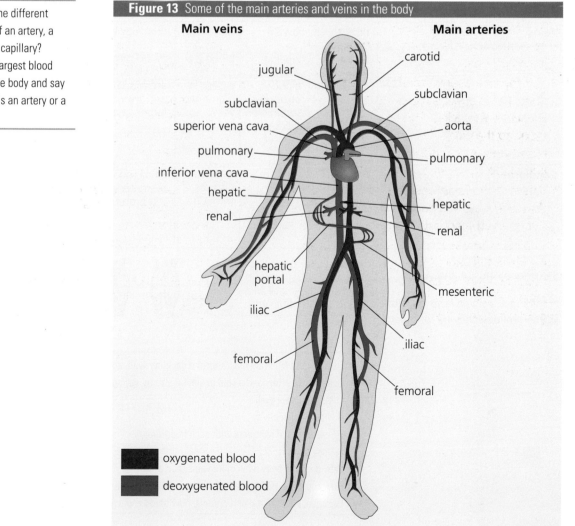

Main veins

Main arteries

jugular

carotid

subclavian

subclavian

superior vena cava

aorta

pulmonary

pulmonary

inferior vena cava

hepatic

hepatic

renal

renal

hepatic portal

mesenteric

iliac

iliac

femoral

femoral

oxygenated blood

deoxygenated blood

What are the walls of blood vessels like?

The walls of all blood vessels have a thin lining of a single layer of cells (see Figure 14). Capillary walls consist only of this layer, but arteries and veins have walls with two extra layers:

- a middle layer of elastic fibres and muscle
- a tough outer layer of connective tissue.

Figure 14 Blood vessels compared

Vessel	Cross section	Direction of flow	Pressure	Oxygen content	Size of passageway	Presence of valves	Properties of wall
Arteries		away from heart	high when an artery is cut, blood spurts out with each heartbeat	high blood is bright red except in pulmonary artery	relatively small blood flows rapidly and at high pressure	no	thick elastic tissue and muscle layer allows the wall to expand and then return to its original size with each heartbeat
Veins	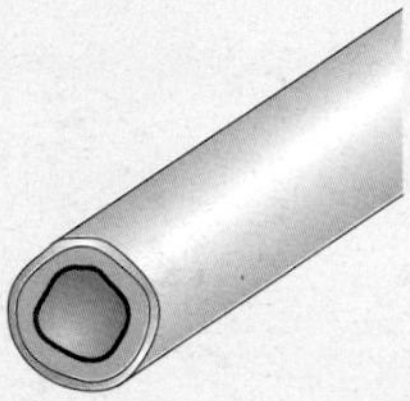	back to heart except in hepatic portal vein	low when a vein is cut, blood oozes out, sometimes quickly, but it never spurts	low blood is dark red except in pulmonary vein	relatively large blood moves slowly so there are more veins and they have larger cavities	yes	thin, expands easily
Capillaries	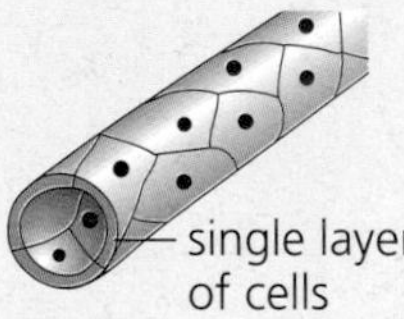 single layer of cells	through organs and tissues	medium	oxygen diffuses through wall	small, about the diameter of one red blood cell	no	one cell thick

- ☐ connective tissue
- ▨ smooth muscle and elastic fibres
- — lining is a single layer of cells
- ▨ central passageway for blood

The pressure of blood pushes the valve open and allows the blood to flow through.

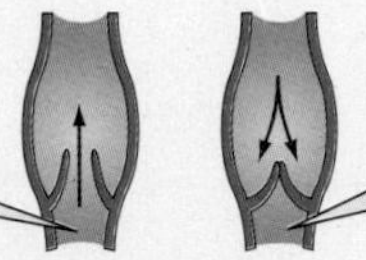

When the pressure is relaxed the valve closes and stops blood flowing back.

28 a Using Figure 14, draw diagrams of a capillary wall, an artery wall and a vein wall.

b Compare an artery and a vein of similar size by saying which:

  i has a thicker wall

  ii has a larger cavity

  iii expands and contracts with each heartbeat

  iv may have valves.

c Why does the body need more veins than arteries?

d How could you tell whether bleeding is from an artery or a vein?

e Describe, with the aid of diagrams, how blood is prevented from flowing backwards in the veins.

What is blood pressure?

Blood pressure is the pressure measured in a major artery. It is usually measured using a machine called a sphygmomanometer (pronounced sfig-mo-man-ometer), which includes a column of mercury against a scale in millimetres. The blood pressure is read from this scale, so it is recorded in 'millimetres of mercury' (mmHg). Hg is the chemical symbol for mercury.

The heart pumps blood into the arteries in sharp bursts at every beat. The blood pressure rises and falls with each beat. The pressure is highest when the ventricles are contracting (systole), and lowest when they are relaxing (diastole). A resting young adult usually has a systolic blood pressure of about 120 mmHg, and a diastolic pressure of 80 mmHg. These are recorded as a blood pressure of 120/80.

Blood pressure varies considerably between individuals. It also changes from minute to minute in any one person according to activity and feelings. Strenuous activity, anger or anxiety raise the blood pressure; rest and contentment lower it. Blood pressure also tends to increase with increasing body weight and with age.

29 a What is blood pressure?
  b Give the usual blood pressure of a young adult.
  c Say what effect the following have on blood pressure:
   i age
   ii strenuous activity
   iii rest
   iv anger
   v anxiety.
  d Explain what the figures mean in a blood pressure of 120/80.

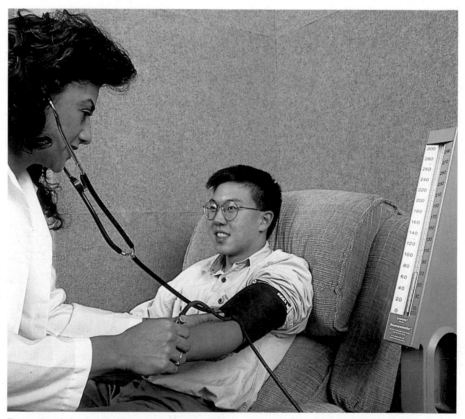

This patient is having his blood pressure taken using a sphygmomanometer. An inflatable cuff is placed round the upper arm and inflated until blood flow into the lower arm stops. No sound can be heard through the stethoscope. Air is let out from the cuff until blood is heard spurting through the artery. The reading on the scale at this point is the systolic pressure. More air is let out until the noise stops; the reading at this point is the diastolic pressure.

What is the circulation?

Blood continuously circulates from the heart to the lungs, back to the heart, and then on to all the other parts of the body (see Figure 15). It takes about half a minute to complete the full circuit each time.

The continuous pumping action of the heart drives blood through the arteries. Every time the heart beats, a pressure wave of blood moves rapidly through the arteries. It can be felt as the pulse, wherever a main artery lies near to the surface of the body. The **pulse** is the rhythmic expansion of the artery wall as it stretched by the wave of blood that is pumped through with each heartbeat.

When the blood reaches the capillaries, the pressure from behind keeps it moving steadily through them and into the veins.

Blood is kept moving through veins by the squeezing action of the surrounding muscles. This squeezing tends to push the blood in both directions but valves in the veins of arms and legs prevent a backward flow (see Figure 14 on page 52).

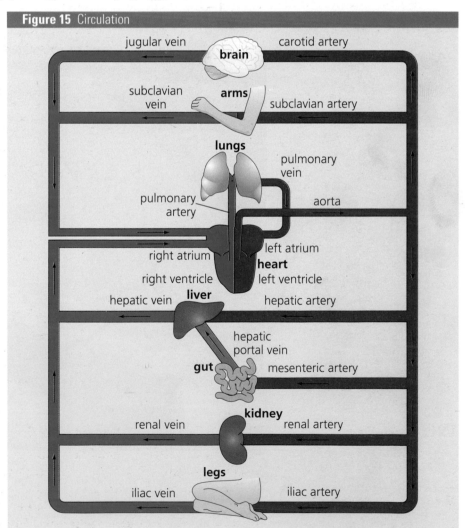

Figure 15 Circulation

30 a Use Figure 15 to draw a flow chart of the route taken by the blood as it flows from:
  i left atrium to legs
  ii right ventricle to the brain
  iii liver to gut.
b What drives blood through the arteries?
c What is the pulse?
d How does blood move through the veins?

What happens in the capillaries?

These tiny blood vessels interconnect to form a network of fine tubes (see Figure 16). This network penetrates all the tissues so that most cells are no more than two or three cells away from a capillary.

Not all the capillaries are open at the same time. There would not be enough blood to fill them if they were. When a tissue is active, its capillaries are open; when the tissue is resting, many capillaries are closed. For example, the capillaries in the stomach wall are open when food is being digested, but most of them are closed when the stomach is empty. The capillaries are opened and closed by rings of muscle fibres called **pre-capillary sphincters**.

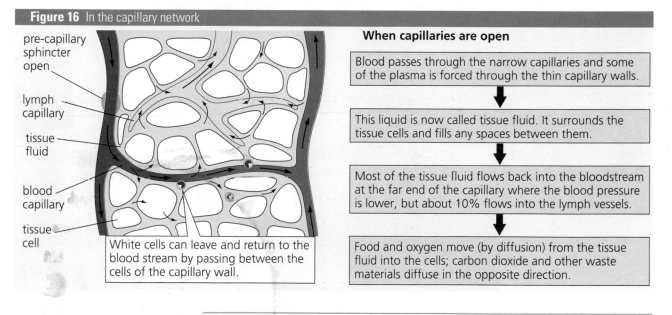

Figure 16 In the capillary network

pre-capillary sphincter open

lymph capillary

tissue fluid

blood capillary

tissue cell

White cells can leave and return to the blood stream by passing between the cells of the capillary wall.

When capillaries are open

Blood passes through the narrow capillaries and some of the plasma is forced through the thin capillary walls.

This liquid is now called tissue fluid. It surrounds the tissue cells and fills any spaces between them.

Most of the tissue fluid flows back into the bloodstream at the far end of the capillary where the blood pressure is lower, but about 10% flows into the lymph vessels.

Food and oxygen move (by diffusion) from the tissue fluid into the cells; carbon dioxide and other waste materials diffuse in the opposite direction.

31 a Why are the capillaries not all open at the same time?
  b Give an example of when capillaries in the stomach might be:
  i open
  ii closed.
  c Use Figure 16 to describe what tissue fluid is, where it comes from and where it goes to.
  d Say what moves from:
  i tissue fluid to cells
  ii cells to tissue fluid.
  e Where and how do white blood cells leave and return to the bloodstream?

What can go wrong with the circulation?

32 a Describe two conditions that affect arteries.

Atheroma and arteriosclerosis are conditions that affect the arteries. **Atheroma** is narrowing of the arteries: rough patches containing cholesterol form inside the artery wall. **Arteriosclerosis** is hardening of the arteries: artery walls become thicker and less elastic. This occurs in everyone as they get older, but it only causes disease if it is severe. The

33 a Describe in your own words the difference between a normal artery and an artery with atheroma, as shown in the micrographs.

b What is a varicose vein?

c What encourages the development of varicose veins?

term arteriosclerosis is often used to include both atheroma and arteriosclerosis because they usually occur together. Both conditions worsen with age.

A **varicose vein** is the name for a vein, near the surface of the leg, that bulges because the valves have failed and blood has stretched the vein. This causes aching and swelling around the ankles, and ulcers may form near the ankle. A tendency to varicose veins often runs in families, and the condition is encouraged by standing for long periods, lack of exercise, and being overweight. Varicose veins also often occur during pregnancy.

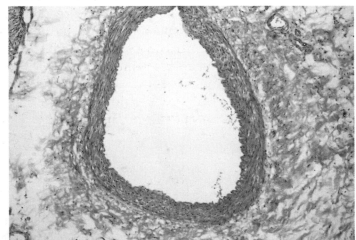

This is a section through a normal human coronary artery. In this light micrograph, the artery wall is stained pink and surrounds a clear passageway.

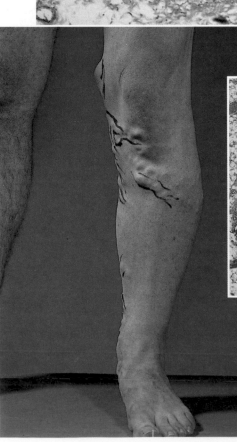

Painful or unsightly varicose veins like these can be removed by surgery or closed up by injections. The blood then returns to the heart through other veins in the legs.

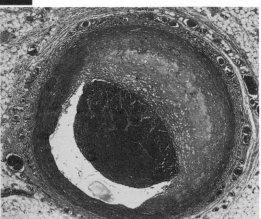

In arteries with atheroma, the central passageway becomes narrower and narrower. Less and less blood can flow through and eventually, the flow might be blocked completely. In this light micrograph, the coronary artery is partly blocked by atheroma (pale pink) and further blocked by a blood clot (dark pink).

What happens when a blood vessel is blocked?

Thrombosis is the formation of a blood clot inside a blood vessel. It can happen when the lining of the blood vessel has been damaged or when the blood flow is very slow. The clot blocks circulation in that area partly or completely. **Deep vein thrombosis (DVT)** is thrombosis in the deep veins of the calf and thigh.

Embolism is caused by a blood clot becoming trapped after it has broken away from where it was formed and travelled round the body in the bloodstream. **Pulmonary embolism** occurs when a blood clot formed elsewhere in the body is trapped in the lungs.

A **stroke** is the sudden interference with the circulation of blood in the brain. Brain cells depend on a continuous supply of oxygen, and if it is cut off for more than 4 minutes they die. The break in the blood supply can be due to a blood clot in an artery to the brain. This is called a **cerebral thrombosis**. Bleeding into the brain from a damaged artery is called a **cerebral haemorrhage**. The area of the brain affected is destroyed and the functions controlled by that part of the brain cease.

34 Explain what is meant by:
  i thrombosis
  ii DVT
  iii embolism
  iv pulmonary embolism
  v stroke
  vi cerebral haemorrhage.

Summary of blood vessels and the circulation

- Arteries are the large vessels that carry blood from the heart, veins are the large vessels that carry blood towards the heart, and capillaries are tiny vessels that join arteries to veins.

- Arteries and veins have three layers in their walls. The layers are different thicknesses. Capillary walls are a single layer of cells.

- Blood pressure is a measure of the pressure of blood in the arteries, for example, 120/80 in a healthy adult. The higher figure is the pressure when the ventricles contract, and the other is the figure when they relax.

- Blood is kept moving by the pumping action of the heart and movement of the body. Muscles press against veins and squeeze blood along. One-way valves in the veins prevent the blood from flowing backwards.

- Plasma can leak out of the capillaries to bathe the cells of the body. This fluid is called tissue fluid. Tissue fluid does not contain the proteins normally found in plasma.

- Capillaries control the flow of blood by narrowing to reduce blood flow to a tissue or expanding to increase the flow. In this way the active tissues that need blood receive the greatest supply.

- Any blockage or restriction in a blood vessel can be dangerous. The level of danger depends on the amount of blockage and where the vessel is blocked. A deep vein thrombosis is a blockage in the deep veins of the calf and thigh. An embolism occurs when a blood clot breaks away from where it was formed and becomes trapped somewhere else. A pulmonary embolism is a blockage in the arteries of lungs. A stroke is a blockage in the vessels that supply the brain.

3.4 The lymphatic system

What is the lymphatic system?

35 a Describe:
  i the lymphatic system
  ii lymph.
  b What are the functions of the lymphatic system?
  c What is the differences between lymph capillaries and blood capillaries?
  d Describe the pathway taken by lymph, by sorting this list into the correct order:
  • large lymph vessel
  • blood vessel
  • small lymph vessel
  • lymph capillaries
  • lymph node.

The **lymphatic system** consists of lymph nodes (also called lymph glands) linked together by a system of tubes called **lymph vessels**. These vessels penetrate all tissues of the body and contain a clear fluid called lymph. **Lymph** is tissue fluid that, instead of flowing back into the blood capillaries, has entered the lymph capillaries (see Figure 17). **Lymph capillaries**, like blood capillaries, have walls one cell thick. However, the walls of lymph capillaries allow much larger particles to pass through them. So, when tissue fluid flows into the lymph capillaries, any bacteria, viruses, protein molecules and other particles from the tissue spaces go with it.

The functions of the lymphatic system are to:

• filter lymph to remove unwanted matter such as microorganisms and other small particles
• produce proteins called antibodies and white cells called lymphocytes to protect the body against illness
• remove some tissue fluid from the tissues
• absorb digested fat from the small intestine.

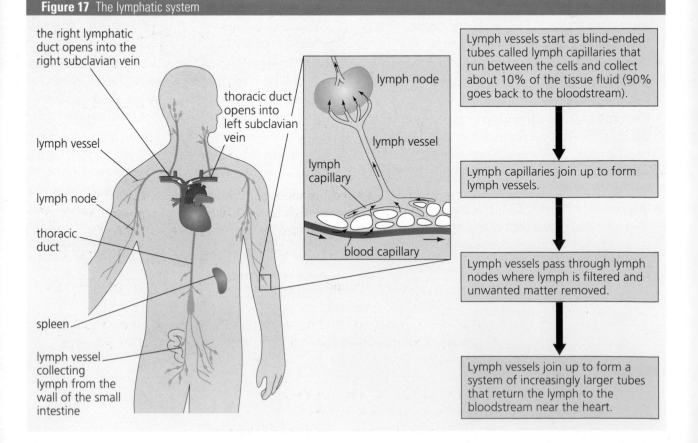

Figure 17 The lymphatic system

the right lymphatic duct opens into the right subclavian vein

thoracic duct opens into left subclavian vein

lymph vessel

lymph node

thoracic duct

spleen

lymph vessel collecting lymph from the wall of the small intestine

lymph node

lymph vessel

lymph capillary

blood capillary

Lymph vessels start as blind-ended tubes called lymph capillaries that run between the cells and collect about 10% of the tissue fluid (90% goes back to the bloodstream).

Lymph capillaries join up to form lymph vessels.

Lymph vessels pass through lymph nodes where lymph is filtered and unwanted matter removed.

Lymph vessels join up to form a system of increasingly larger tubes that return the lymph to the bloodstream near the heart.

Why are lymph nodes important?

Lymph nodes (lymph glands) are sometimes just called glands. They are small bean-shaped bodies situated along the lymph vessels, rather like beads on a string. They contain **lymphoid tissue**, which makes lymphocytes and antibodies (see Figure 18). Lymph nodes vary in size from 1 to 20 mm in diameter. Their functions are to:

- filter lymph; white cells called phagocytes engulf bacteria, viruses and other small particles as they pass through the gland
- make lymphocytes
- make antibodies.

Lymphoid tissue also occurs in the tonsils, adenoids, thymus, spleen, digestive tract and lungs.

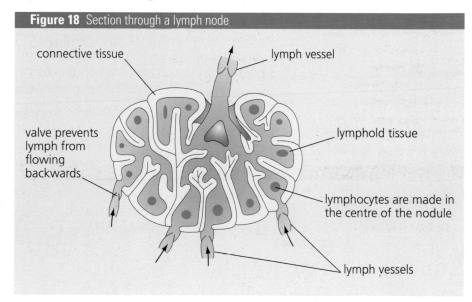

Figure 18 Section through a lymph node

connective tissue

lymph vessel

valve prevents lymph from flowing backwards

lymphold tissue

lymphocytes are made in the centre of the nodule

lymph vessels

36 a Give two other names for lymph nodes.
b Draw a section through a lymph node to show the lymph vessels and lymphoid tissue. Add arrows to show where lymph enters and leaves the node.
c Give the functions of:
i lymph nodes
ii lymphoid tissue.
d Where is lymphoid tissue found apart from lymph nodes?

What is the spleen?

The **spleen** is a dark red-brown organ, slightly smaller than your hand (see Figure 17). It is found high up against the diaphragm on the left side of the abdomen and is protected by the ribs. Its functions are to:

- destroy worn-out red blood cells, which are replaced by new cells from the bone marrow
- make lymphocytes and antibodies to help to protect the body against infection.

The spleen is not essential to adults as its functions are shared with other organs, but people who have had their spleens removed are prone to infection.

37 a Where in the body is the spleen situated?
b Give two functions of the spleen.
c Is it essential for an adult to have a spleen? Explain why.

What can go wrong in the lymphatic system?

Swollen glands

When the body has an infection, the lymph nodes become very active and often swell. The infection may be in the lymph node itself, or some distance away. For example, when a hand is infected, microorganisms from the infection are carried along the lymph vessels and become trapped in the nodes at the elbow or armpit, causing them to swell.

Tonsils and adenoids

The tonsils in the throat and the adenoids at the back of the nose are patches of lymphoid tissue. When microbes from inhaled air fall onto this tissue, it produces antibodies to help protect the body from infection. The tonsils and adenoids are very active in childhood. They usually enlarge when a child is about 5 or 6 years old, and shrink after the age of 10. If the tonsils or adenoids become permanently infected, they might be removed because they have become a source of infection, not a protection against it.

38 a When a hand is infected, why might lymph nodes in the armpit swell?

b Where are tonsils and adenoids found?

c How do tonsils and adenoids help to protect the body and why might they be removed?

d What causes glandular fever and how is it spread?

Glandular fever

Glandular fever is an infectious disease caused by a virus. It is spread by droplets of saliva. Glandular fever starts with a sore throat and tiredness, and the lymph nodes usually swell.

Summary of the lymphatic system

- The lymphatic system of lymph nodes and lymph vessels drains some of the tissue fluid from the tissues. The fluid inside lymph vessels is called lymph. The system filters lymph, produces antibodies and some types of white blood cells, and helps with absorption of fat in the gut.
- Lymph nodes are collections of lymphoid tissue found around the body. They help to protect the body against disease and often swell during times of infection.
- The spleen is a dark red-brown organ that destroys worn-out red cells, and makes lymphocytes and antibodies. Without a spleen, people are prone to infection.
- Tonsils and adenoids might become so badly infected that they can no longer function correctly.
- Glandular fever is an infection of lymph nodes and is caused by a virus. It is spread by droplets of saliva.

Breathing and respiration

4

Learning objectives

By the end of this chapter you should be able to:

- **describe** the gas exchange system in humans
- **describe** how the airways are kept open
- **describe** how the lungs are protected from infection
- **list** common disorders of the respiratory tract
- **explain** how muscles bring about breathing
- **recall** the volume of air in a healthy adult's lungs
- **describe** the differences between inhaled and exhaled air

- **distinguish** between breathing and respiration
- **describe** the process of diffusion
- **explain** how oxygen reaches the body cells
- **recall** the equation for aerobic respiration
- **describe** the role of ATP in energy transfer within cells
- **describe** how carbon dioxide is removed from the body.

4.1 The gas exchange system

How is the gas exchange system organised?

The **gas exchange system** enables the body to take in oxygen and excrete carbon dioxide through the lungs. It is also called the **respiratory system** and consists of air tubes in the head, throat and lungs together with the diaphragm and rib cage. The two lungs occupy most of the thorax with the

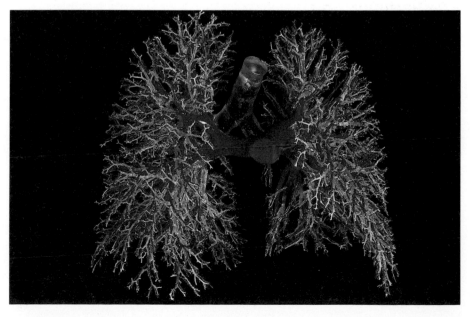

This is a resin cast of the inside of human lungs, seen from the front. The clear, yellowish resin shows the bottom of the trachea dividing into the two bronchi, and all the branching airways that eventually end in air sacs. The red-coloured resin shows the pulmonary arteries and capillaries.

heart situated between them. Each lung consists of air tubes, blood vessels, and millions of tiny air sacs (see Figure 1). The air sacs have pouches called alveoli (singular: alveolus).

Figure 1 The gas exchange system

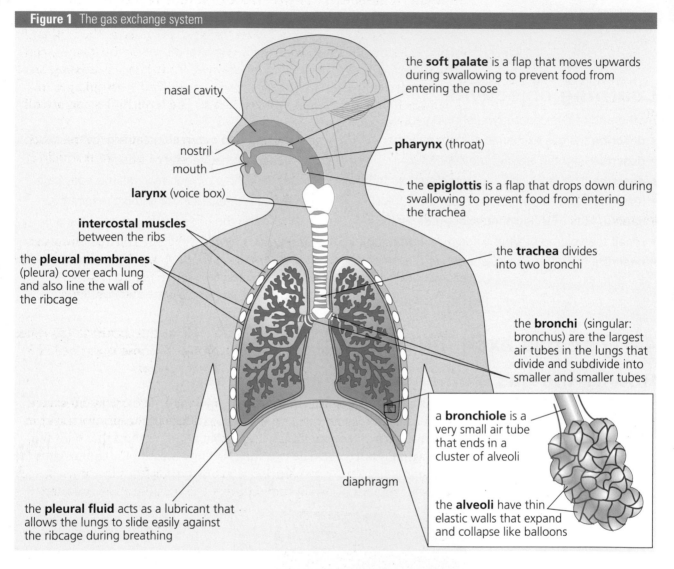

nasal cavity

nostril

mouth

larynx (voice box)

intercostal muscles between the ribs

the **pleural membranes** (pleura) cover each lung and also line the wall of the ribcage

the soft palate is a flap that moves upwards during swallowing to prevent food from entering the nose

pharynx (throat)

the **epiglottis** is a flap that drops down during swallowing to prevent food from entering the trachea

the **trachea** divides into two bronchi

the **bronchi** (singular: bronchus) are the largest air tubes in the lungs that divide and subdivide into smaller and smaller tubes

a **bronchiole** is a very small air tube that ends in a cluster of alveoli

the **alveoli** have thin elastic walls that expand and collapse like balloons

diaphragm

the **pleural fluid** acts as a lubricant that allows the lungs to slide easily against the ribcage during breathing

1 a Sort the parts below in to the order in which air flows from nose to air sac:
  - bronchiole
  - larynx
  - trachea
  - bronchus
  - throat.

b When air is breathed in, the lungs expand. Where in the lungs does this expansion occur?

c Describe how food is prevented from going into:

  i the back of the nose

  ii the trachea.

How are the airways kept open?

2 a Describe the shape of the cartilage in the trachea and in the bronchi.

  b Why are the rings of cartilage in the trachea C-shaped?

  c How can the size of the air tubes be altered?

The **respiratory tract** is the passage along which air flows during breathing. It includes the larynx, trachea, bronchi, bronchioles and alveoli. The walls of the larynx, trachea and bronchi are strengthened by cartilage to keep them open and to let the air to flow freely. The cartilage forms plates in the larynx, incomplete C-shaped rings in the trachea, and complete rings in the bronchi. In the trachea, the cartilage is missing on the side adjacent to the oesophagus, and this allows the oesophagus to expand as food passes down to the stomach. The bronchioles and alveoli do not contain cartilage.

Muscle fibres in the walls of the air tubes can alter the size of the tubes. When they contract, the tubes become narrower and the rate at which air is breathed in and out is reduced.

How are the lungs protected?

The lungs are exposed to dust and to infection by bacteria and viruses in the air. The warm, moist environment inside the lungs is ideal for the growth of bacteria and viruses. The lungs are protected from these microorganisms by the nose, the mucous membrane and coughing.

3 a Describe two ways in which the nose helps to protect the lungs.

  b Give two functions of mucus in the airways.

  c What is the purpose of coughing?

- **The nose**
  Hairs in the nostrils filter out dust containing microorganisms and other particles from inhaled air. Air passing through the nose is warmed and moistened so that it does not dry out the air passages.
- **The mucous membrane**
  This lines the air passages and secretes **mucus**, a clear, sticky substance. Mucus traps dust and dirt and keeps the surface of the airways moist so that it does not dry out, shrink and crack.
- **Coughing**
  Coughing removes large particles or excess mucus from the lungs. It is a reflex action that occurs automatically when the airways are irritated.

Like athletes, Pavarotti and other opera singers, train to control their breathing (see page 66). A singer needs air to control the voice, but during the performance he or she also needs plenty of oxygen to release energy from glucose (see page 69).

What can go wrong with the gas exchange system?

There are many diseases that affect the gas exchange system, some of them are shown in Figure 2.

Figure 2 Some diseases of the gas exchange system

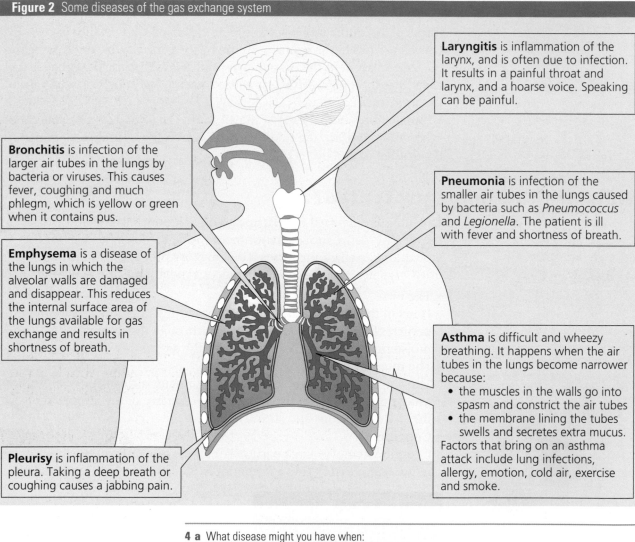

Laryngitis is inflammation of the larynx, and is often due to infection. It results in a painful throat and larynx, and a hoarse voice. Speaking can be painful.

Bronchitis is infection of the larger air tubes in the lungs by bacteria or viruses. This causes fever, coughing and much phlegm, which is yellow or green when it contains pus.

Pneumonia is infection of the smaller air tubes in the lungs caused by bacteria such as *Pneumococcus* and *Legionella*. The patient is ill with fever and shortness of breath.

Emphysema is a disease of the lungs in which the alveolar walls are damaged and disappear. This reduces the internal surface area of the lungs available for gas exchange and results in shortness of breath.

Asthma is difficult and wheezy breathing. It happens when the air tubes in the lungs become narrower because:

* the muscles in the walls go into spasm and constrict the air tubes
* the membrane lining the tubes swells and secretes extra mucus.

Factors that bring on an asthma attack include lung infections, allergy, emotion, cold air, exercise and smoke.

Pleurisy is inflammation of the pleura. Taking a deep breath or coughing causes a jabbing pain.

4 a What disease might you have when:

   i the air tubes in the lungs become narrower   **iv** the larynx is inflamed

   ii the large air tubes become infected   **v** the pleura are inflamed

   iii the smaller air tubes become infected   **vi** the alveolar walls are destroyed.

  b Give a brief description of each disease you have listed.

4.2   Breathing

Breathing happens because of the combined movements of the thorax wall and the diaphragm. These movements are brought about by the intercostal muscles and the diaphragm muscle. As we breathe in, the lungs expand; as we breathe out, they shrink back (see Figure 3).

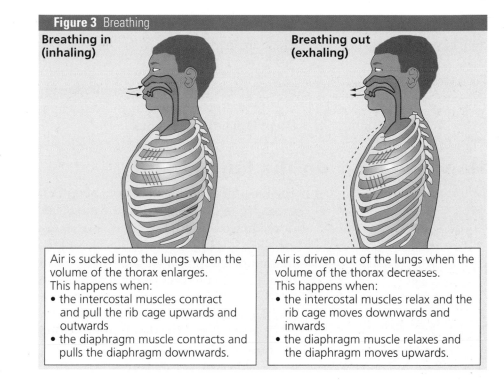

Figure 3 Breathing

Breathing in (inhaling)

Breathing out (exhaling)

Air is sucked into the lungs when the volume of the thorax enlarges.
This happens when:
• the intercostal muscles contract and pull the rib cage upwards and outwards
• the diaphragm muscle contracts and pulls the diaphragm downwards.

Air is driven out of the lungs when the volume of the thorax decreases.
This happens when:
• the intercostal muscles relax and the rib cage moves downwards and inwards
• the diaphragm muscle relaxes and the diaphragm moves upwards.

5 a Name the two parts of the body that move together to achieve breathing.
b Describe what happens to the lungs with each breath.
c Name the muscles involved in breathing.
d Describe what happens to the intercostal muscles and diaphragm:
   i when you breathe in
   ii when you breathe out.

How is breathing controlled?

Breathing is a regular and mainly automatic process under the control of the nervous system (see Figure 4). The amount of carbon dioxide in the blood flowing through the brain is an important factor in the control of this process.

6 a Which system controls breathing?
b What happens when an increased amount of carbon dioxide flows through the brain?

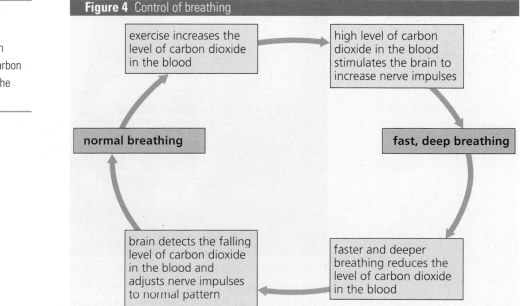

Figure 4 Control of breathing

exercise increases the level of carbon dioxide in the blood

high level of carbon dioxide in the blood stimulates the brain to increase nerve impulses

normal breathing

fast, deep breathing

brain detects the falling level of carbon dioxide in the blood and adjusts nerve impulses to normal pattern

faster and deeper breathing reduces the level of carbon dioxide in the blood

7 Name the muscles mainly used and describe what can be seen in:

i thoracic breathing

ii abdominal breathing.

Although breathing usually involves both the diaphragm and the intercostal muscles, the amount each is used varies with individuals, with training, and with the demands made on the lungs at any particular time. **Thoracic breathing** uses mainly the intercostal muscles, and the chest can be seen to rise and fall. **Abdominal breathing** uses mainly the diaphragm, and the abdomen moves in and out. Quiet breathing (for example, during sleep) is mainly abdominal.

How much air do the lungs hold?

The lungs of a resting adult hold about 3 litres (3 dm^3) of air. When fully expanded in deep breathing, the lungs can hold up to 7 litres (7 dm^3) depending on body size. But no matter how much effort is put into exhaling, it is impossible to squeeze all the air out of the lungs. The maximum amount of air that can be breathed out after taking one deep breath is about 6 litres (6 dm^3) in most healthy young adults.

How much air is inhaled and exhaled per minute depends on the rate and depth of breathing. The **rate of breathing** is the number of breaths taken in a minute. The **depth of breathing** is the amount of air inhaled per breath. The rate and depth of breathing depend on age, level of fitness, and whether the person is resting or active.

8 a Write down how much air the lungs hold when:

i resting

ii breathing deeply.

b Is it possible to squeeze all the air out of the lungs?

c What is the difference between the rate of breathing and depth of breathing?

d What do the rate and depth of breathing depend on?

e Using the information in the photograph caption, calculate:

i how much air the girl breathed in one minute before starting to exercise

ii the maximum amount of air she might breathe when exercising hard.

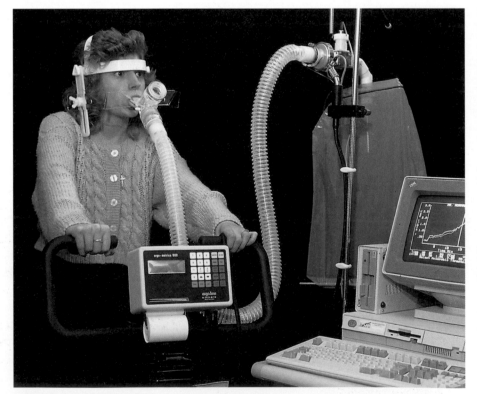

This young woman's respiration is being monitored by computer as she pedals an exercise bike. At rest, a person takes about 16 breaths a minute and inhales about 0.5 dm^3 of air with each breath. Hard exercise can increase breathing rate by up to 50 times a minute, and the amount of air taken in each time can increase to 2.5 dm^3.

What does air contain?

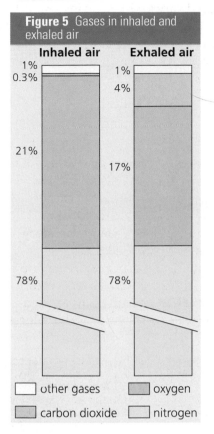

Figure 5 Gases in inhaled and exhaled air

Inhaled air — Exhaled air

1% — 1%
0.3% — 4%
21% — 17%
78% — 78%

☐ other gases   ▨ oxygen
▨ carbon dioxide   ☐ nitrogen

Air that is breathed into the lungs is called inhaled air. It contains oxygen, nitrogen, carbon dioxide and a range of other gases. The proportion of these gases is remarkably constant. The air also contains water vapour but the amount is variable; dry air contains little and damp air a great deal, especially if warm. Dust, pollen, and smoke can also be present.

Air that is breathed out from the lungs is called exhaled air. It contains the same gases as inhaled air, but in different amounts (see Figure 5). Exhaled air is always saturated with water vapour that has come from the layer of moisture lining the air sacs. While in the lungs, the air was warmed to body temperature, 37 °C, so exhaled air is warmer that inhaled air – unless the outside air is exceedingly hot.

9 Copy and complete Table 1.

Table 1 Substances carried by the blood

Gas	Inhaled air / %	Exhaled air / %
nitrogen		
oxygen		
carbon dioxide		

4.3   Respiration

Is respiration the same as breathing?

People often use the words 'breathing' and 'respiration' as though they mean the same thing, but they do not. **Breathing** is moving air into and out of the lungs. This process is carried out by the gas exchange system of the body; confusingly, this system of air tubes in the head, throat and lungs plus the diaphragm and rib cage is sometimes called the respiratory system.

Respiration is the process of releasing energy from an energy source such as glucose. It takes place in all living cells. In order for respiration to occur, the cells must also have a constant supply of oxygen. Supplying cells with oxygen involves:

- breathing
- exchange of gases in the lungs between air and blood
- transport of gases in the bloodstream
- diffusion of gases between blood and cells.

9 a What is the difference between respiration and breathing?
  b Where does each of these processes take place?
  c In addition to breathing, name three other processes that are necessary for respiration to occur.

How are gases exchanged in the lungs?

Diffusion is the natural movement of molecules from an area of high concentration to one of low concentration. This process enables oxygen and carbon dioxide to move between air and blood in the lungs. The gases diffuse in opposite directions because each moves down its own concentration gradient (see Figure 6).

The structure of the lungs enables gases to move rapidly between air and blood because:

• there is an excellent blood supply
• there is a large surface area
• air and blood come very close together.

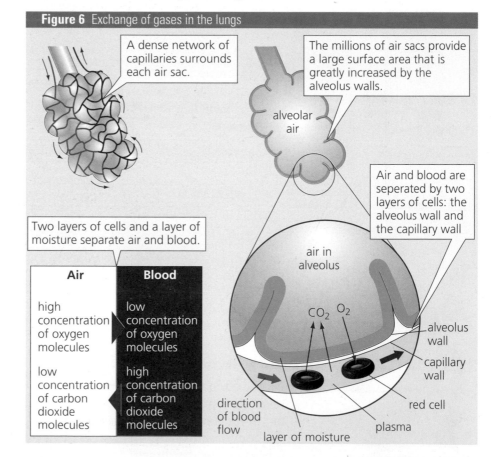

Figure 6 Exchange of gases in the lungs

A dense network of capillaries surrounds each air sac.

The millions of air sacs provide a large surface area that is greatly increased by the alveolus walls.

alveolar air

Air and blood are seperated by two layers of cells: the alveolus wall and the capillary wall

Two layers of cells and a layer of moisture separate air and blood.

air in alveolus

Air	Blood
high concentration of oxygen molecules	low concentration of oxygen molecules
low concentration of carbon dioxide molecules	high concentration of carbon dioxide molecules

CO_2 O_2

alveolus wall

capillary wall

red cell

direction of blood flow

layer of moisture

plasma

11 a What is diffusion?

b Draw a diagram to show the diffusion of oxygen and carbon dioxide in the lungs.

c Explain why the lungs have:
  i a very good blood supply
  ii a large surface area.

d What separates air from blood in the lungs?

How does oxygen move from air to blood and reach all the body's cells?

There is more oxygen in the air in the lungs than there is in the blood in the lung capillaries, so oxygen moves from air to blood by diffusion. Blood that has taken up oxygen quickly leaves the lungs and is replaced by blood with a low oxygen level, so rapid diffusion of oxygen into the blood continues.

Oxygenated blood collects into the pulmonary vein and returns to the heart. It is then pumped through the arteries, which sub-divide many times to form capillaries between cells in all tissues. Where there is an oxygen shortage in the tissue, oxygen moves from the blood into the cells. As long as the cells rapidly use up the oxygen and keep the level low, more oxygen continues to diffuse from the blood to the cells (see Figure 7).

11 a What process causes oxygen in the lungs to move from air to blood?

b Write a paragraph to describe the pathway taken by oxygen as it moves from air to combine with haemoglobin in the red cells

c Write a paragraph to describe the pathway taken by oxygen as it moves from the red cells to the tissue cells.

Figure 7 Getting oxygen from the lungs to the tissues

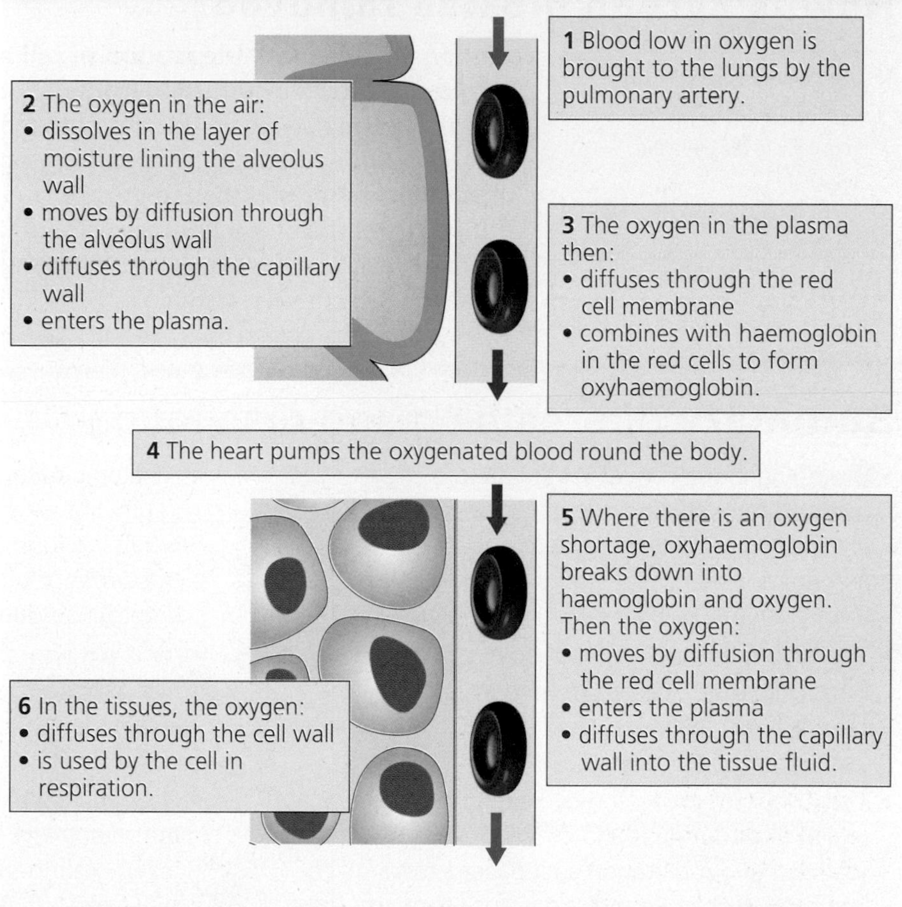

1 Blood low in oxygen is brought to the lungs by the pulmonary artery.

2 The oxygen in the air:
- dissolves in the layer of moisture lining the alveolus wall
- moves by diffusion through the alveolus wall
- diffuses through the capillary wall
- enters the plasma.

3 The oxygen in the plasma then:
- diffuses through the red cell membrane
- combines with haemoglobin in the red cells to form oxyhaemoglobin.

4 The heart pumps the oxygenated blood round the body.

5 Where there is an oxygen shortage, oxyhaemoglobin breaks down into haemoglobin and oxygen. Then the oxygen:
- moves by diffusion through the red cell membrane
- enters the plasma
- diffuses through the capillary wall into the tissue fluid.

6 In the tissues, the oxygen:
- diffuses through the cell wall
- is used by the cell in respiration.

How is energy released from glucose?

12 a What is the chemical equation for respiration?

b What controls cell respiration and where does it take place?

c Write out the full name of:
  i ATP
  ii ADP.

d Describe how ATP is formed.

Respiration releases energy inside a cell when glucose and oxygen are converted to carbon dioxide and water. The chemical equation is:

$$C_6H_{12}O_6 \; + \; 6O_2 \longrightarrow 6CO_2 \; + \; 6H_2O \; + \; \text{energy}$$

glucose containing stored energy — oxygen — carbon dioxide — water

Respiration is controlled by enzymes and takes place in the mitochondria. As the energy is released, it is used to build molecules of **ATP** (adenosine triphosphate) from **ADP** (adenosine diphosphate) and phosphate:

$$\text{ADP} + \text{phosphate} + \text{energy} \longrightarrow \text{ATP}$$

14 How is ADP formed?

The ATP molecule contains energy that can be used by any part of the cell that requires it. The energy in ATP can remain stored until it is needed.

After releasing its energy, ATP changes back to ADP and phosphate, which are then ready to be used to make more ATP:

$$ATP \rightleftharpoons ADP + phosphate + energy$$

How is carbon dioxide removed?

15 Describe the route taken by carbon dioxide as it moves from cells to the air in the lungs.

Carbon dioxide is a waste product of cell respiration and must be excreted. It moves by diffusion from the cell through the capillary wall into the plasma. Most diffuses into the red cells. When blood carrying carbon dioxide reaches the lungs, the concentration of the carbon dioxide in the blood is greater than in the air. Therefore, the carbon dioxide diffuses from the blood, through the capillary wall, through the alveolus wall and its layer of moisture, and into the air in the alveolus. It is then excreted when the air is exhaled.

Summary of breathing and respiration

- Breathing is the movement of air into and out of the lungs. Gas exchange occurs at the surface of the alveoli where oxygen diffuses into the blood and carbon dioxide diffuses out of the blood into the air in the lungs.

- The respiratory tract is kept open by cartilage in rings or plates. The lungs themselves are more flexible and can expand and contract as air moves in and out.

- The lungs are protected by hairs in the nostrils which filter out dust and other particles. Air is also warmed and moistened as it passes towards the lungs. Mucus lining the respiratory tract surfaces traps dust and dirt.

- Asthma is a disease of the lungs in which sufferers find it difficult to breathe. An asthma attack can be a reaction to dust or chemicals in the environment or to stress.

- Breathing depends on the intercostal muscles and the diaphragm. It is controlled by a part of the brain that is sensitive to carbon dioxide levels in the blood.

- A healthy resting adult can hold about 3 litres (3 dm³) of air in their lungs. Both the rate of breathing (number of breaths per minute) and the depth of breathing (volume of air moved per breath) rise during strenuous exercise.

- Air is a mixture of gases. The composition of this mixture is changed by breathing. Oxygen levels are lower and carbon dioxide levels are higher in exhaled air than in inhaled air.

- Gaseous exchange in the lungs takes place at the alveoli and depends on diffusion. Gases are taken around the body by the bloodstream.

- Respiration is the release of energy from an energy source such as glucose in the body cells. It occurs in every living body cell. It needs oxygen and glucose and produces carbon dioxide and water as waste products.

- ATP (adenosine triphosphate) is a chemical used to transfer energy into reactions that need energy. ATP forms ADP (adenosine diphosphate) during the reaction. ADP can then be used to make more ATP using energy from respiration.

Food, digestion *and* excretion 5

Learning objectives

By the end of this chapter you should be able to:

- **list** the main food types and give examples of each
- **describe** the chemical structure of carbohydrates, fats and proteins
- **list** the most important vitamins and minerals and their associated deficiency diseases
- **define** metabolism, catabolism and anabolism
- **describe** the chemical structure of enzymes and explain their importance in living organisms
- **describe** the growth and structure of teeth and list the causes of tooth decay

- **describe** the gross anatomy of the digestive system
- **relate** the structure of each part of the digestive system to its function
- **list** the functions of liver and pancreas
- **describe** common disorders of the digestive system, liver, pancreas and kidneys
- **describe** appropriate treatments for these disorders.

5.1 Food

What is food?

Food is any solid or liquid that can supply the body with substances for growth, repair or replacement of tissues, and energy.

1 a List the seven substances in food.

b Why do we need food?

Most foods are mixtures containing one or more of the following nutrients:

- carbohydrates
- fats
- proteins
- minerals
- vitamins
- fibre
- water.

Diet is the combination of food that a person eats. **Nutrients** are substances derived from food that are essential to life.

71

What are carbohydrates?

Carbohydrates include sugars, starches and fibre. They always contain the chemical elements carbon, hydrogen and oxygen. The hydrogen to oxygen ratio is always 2:1 All types of carbohydrate are called saccharides because they consist of sugar units (see Figure 1).

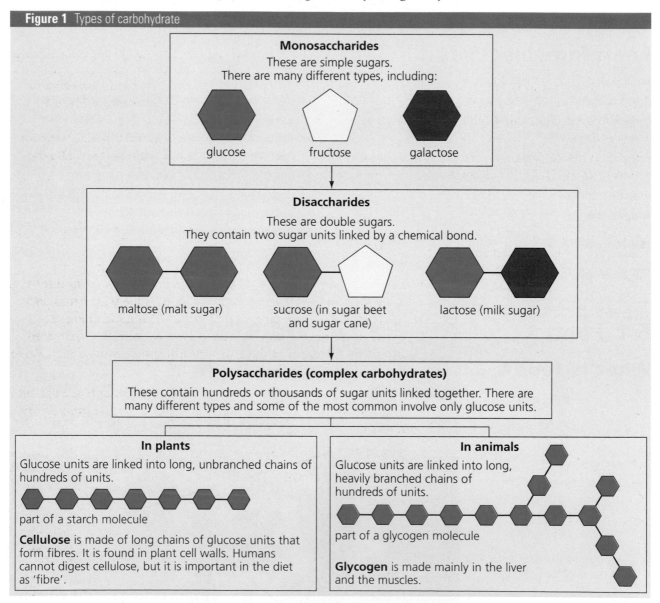

Figure 1 Types of carbohydrate

Monosaccharides
These are simple sugars.
There are many different types, including:

glucose   fructose   galactose

Disaccharides
These are double sugars.
They contain two sugar units linked by a chemical bond.

maltose (malt sugar)   sucrose (in sugar beet and sugar cane)   lactose (milk sugar)

Polysaccharides (complex carbohydrates)
These contain hundreds or thousands of sugar units linked together. There are many different types and some of the most common involve only glucose units.

In plants
Glucose units are linked into long, unbranched chains of hundreds of units.

part of a starch molecule

Cellulose is made of long chains of glucose units that form fibres. It is found in plant cell walls. Humans cannot digest cellulose, but it is important in the diet as 'fibre'.

In animals
Glucose units are linked into long, heavily branched chains of hundreds of units.

part of a glycogen molecule

Glycogen is made mainly in the liver and the muscles.

Sugar and starch are important in our food (see Table 1). Starchy foods form the largest part of the diet of most humans. If we eat more starch and sugar than we need for energy, the liver converts the excess into either fat or glycogen for storage. Fat is stored in the fatty tissue under the skin and in the abdomen. Glycogen is stored in the liver and muscles.

Saccharin, aspartame and acesulfame K taste sweet but do not contain sugar, so they are often used to sweeten reduced-calorie drinks and food.

Table 1 Foods containing sugar and starch

These foods contain sugar	These foods contain starch
honey	potatoes
sweets and chocolates	peas and beans
jam and marmalade	flour (in pasta, bread, chapatis, biscuits, cakes)
non-diet fizzy drinks	rice
biscuits and cakes	cereals

2 a Which group of substances do sugar and starch belong to?

b List the three elements in a carbohydrate.

c List the differences between a simple sugar, double sugar and a complex carbohydrate.

d Draw and label diagrams of four carbohydrates that consist only of glucose.

e Name two carbohydrates made in animals.

f How does sucrose differ from maltose?

g Which sugar unit is cellulose made from, and where is cellulose found?

3 a If you eat more carbohydrate than your body requires, what happens to the excess?

b List three artificial sweeteners and say why they are used in reduced-calorie drinks.

Why is fibre useful in the diet?

Fibre in the diet is a mixture of cellulose and other complex carbohydrates. When eaten, fibre absorbs water and swells. It cannot be digested, so it passes along the gut to the large intestine where it makes the waste matter bulkier and softer. The increased bulk stimulates the muscles in the intestine wall to move the contents along. The increased softness means the contents of the large intestine move more easily. There are two types of fibre in food:

- **insoluble fibre**, such as wheat bran, which absorbs water like a sponge
- **soluble fibre**, such as oat bran, which is not really soluble but it forms a gel with water.

4 a What is dietary fibre?

b What happens to fibre when it is eaten?

c What is the difference between insoluble fibre and soluble fibre?

d Study the photograph and then list some foods containing fibre.

These foods all contain fibre.

What are fats and oils?

Fats and oils belong to a group of substances called **lipids**, which also includes cholesterol. Lipids contain carbon, hydrogen and oxygen, but in different proportions to carbohydrates. Lipids that are solid at 20 °C are usually called fats. Lipids that are liquid at this temperature are usually called oils. Animals tend to store fats, while plants tend to use oils. Human fat is liquid at body temperature (37 °C); so it is stored in liquid form in fat cells.

Both fats and oils are necessary in the diet, for example, to form cell membranes. They are also a source of energy, containing more than twice as much energy as carbohydrates per unit mass. If more fats and oils are eaten than the body requires, the excess is stored as fat under the skin, around the heart, and in the abdomen.

Fats in food are mainly triglycerides. Each triglyceride molecule consists of three fatty acid units joined to one glycerol unit (see Figure 2).

There are dozens of different fatty acids but they fall into two groups called saturated and unsaturated fatty acids. Fats in food contain both types of fatty acid, but in differing proportions:

- **saturated fatty acids** are mainly found in animal fats
  - cream
  - butter
  - cheese
  - fat meat
  - egg yolk
  - lard

- **unsaturated fatty acids** occur mainly in plant oils
  - olive oil
  - sunflower oil
  - palm oil
  - rape seed oil
  - coconut oil.

The body can convert most fatty acids from one to another as needed. But a few, called **essential fatty acids**, cannot be produced by the body. As they are essential for life, they must be obtained from food.

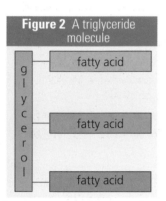

Figure 2 A triglyceride molecule

glycerol — fatty acid
glycerol — fatty acid
glycerol — fatty acid

5 a What is the difference between a fat and an oil?

b Why is fat essential in the diet?

c Where is excess fat in the body stored?

d List some foods containing animal fats and say what type of fatty acid they mainly contain.

e List some oils from plants and say what type of fatty acid they mainly contain.

Sumo wrestlers deliberately build up body fat for their sport.

What is cholesterol?

Cholesterol is a waxy fat-soluble substance that is mainly made in the body. The rest comes from various foods, particularly those containing animal fats. Cholesterol is used to maintain cell membranes and to make steroid hormones. There are two kinds of cholesterol.

- **HDL cholesterol (HDL = high density lipoprotein)**
  This sometimes called 'good' cholesterol. It is removed from the blood in the liver and is excreted from the body in bile.
- **LDL cholesterol (LDL = low density lipoprotein)**
  This is sometimes called 'bad' cholesterol. It tends to be deposited in blood vessels and can block the arteries. A high level of LDL in the blood increases the risk of a heart attack, angina or stroke.

Only some fat-containing foods, usually those with saturated animal fat, tend to increase LDL (see Table 2). The level of LDL is more sensitive to fat intake, than to cholesterol intake.

6 a Name two ways in which the body obtains cholesterol.

b What is cholesterol used for in the body?

c What is the name given to 'bad' cholesterol and why is it regarded as bad?

d What happens to the 'good' cholesterol in the body?

e List three foods that can help to:

  i raise the level of LDL in the blood

  ii lower the level of LDL.

Table 2 Effects of certain fats on LDL level

Food	Raise LDL level	Lower LDL or raise HDL
cheese	✔	
butter	✔	
fatty meat	✔	
lard	✔	
oily fish		✔
sunflower oil		✔
polyunsaturated margarines		✔

What is protein?

7 a List some parts of the body that contain large amounts of protein.

b What is the name for the units which link together to form proteins?

c How is it possible to have a vast number of different proteins?

d What is the difference between essential and non-essential amino acids?

Protein is found in all living things. It contains carbon, hydrogen, oxygen, nitrogen, and sometimes sulphur and phosphorus. Protein makes up about 12% of the weight of a healthy human body. It is found in muscles, hair, enzymes, hormones, antibodies, and a range of other substances. There are a vast number of different types of protein because:

- they are made from 20 different **amino acids** and the number of ways in which these can link together to form different proteins is enormous
- the chains of amino acids are folded, coiled and cross-linked in ways that are specific to each protein.

Amino acids can be divided into two groups.

- **Essential amino acids**
  These cannot be made in the body, so it is essential that they are present in food. A mixed diet normally supplies sufficient essential amino acids.
- **Non-essential amino acids**
  These can be made in the body if they are not present in the food. They are made from other amino acids.

Each protein molecule is built up from hundreds or thousands of small units called amino acids (see Figure 3).

8 Use Figure 3 to describe in your own words how amino acids link together to form proteins.

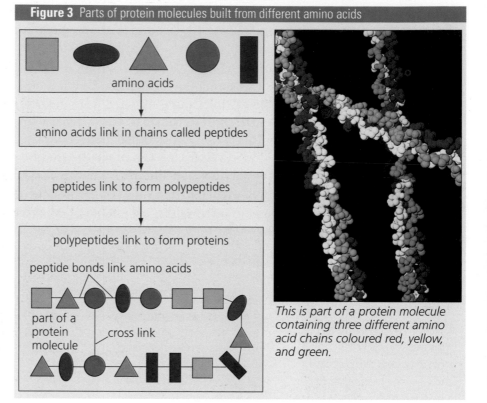

Figure 3 Parts of protein molecules built from different amino acids

amino acids

amino acids link in chains called peptides

peptides link to form polypeptides

polypeptides link to form proteins

peptide bonds link amino acids

part of a protein molecule

cross link

This is part of a protein molecule containing three different amino acid chains coloured red, yellow, and green.

How much protein do we need?

A healthy person needs about 50 grams of protein per day, but it must contain the right amount of essential amino acids. It is an advantage to eat a mixture of protein-containing food at each meal because a complete assortment of amino acids is likely to be present (see Table 3). Amino acids are not stored in the body and those that are not immediately required are broken down in the liver (see Figure 4).

9 a What is the advantage of eating a mixture of foods containing protein at each meal?

b What happens when more protein is eaten than the body needs?

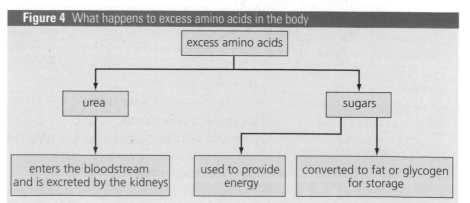

Figure 4 What happens to excess amino acids in the body

excess amino acids

urea

sugars

enters the bloodstream and is excreted by the kidneys

used to provide energy

converted to fat or glycogen for storage

10 Give some examples of foods containing:

  i animal proteins

  ii plant proteins.

Table 3 Foods containing protein

Animal products with high protein content	Plant products with high protein content
milk	peas and beans
cheese	nuts
eggs	bread
fish	cereals
meat	dried apricots

What are vitamins and minerals?

11 a Write down the difference between vitamins and minerals.

  b Why is it important to eat a varied diet?

  c What is a deficiency disease?

  d Give an example of a deficiency disease.

Vitamins are complex chemical substances made by living things, and **minerals** are simple chemical substances not made by living things. The human body is able to make a few vitamins, but most of them and all the minerals have to come from food. A varied diet provides all the vitamins and minerals needed to stay healthy. Only small quantities are required, so vitamins and minerals are known as **micronutrients**.

The recommended daily allowance (RDA) of vitamins and minerals is the amount needed to maintain good health. They can all be stored in the body for weeks or months, so a healthy person on an average diet is very unlikely to develop a deficiency disease. A **deficiency disease** is an illness caused by a lack of essential chemicals in the diet.

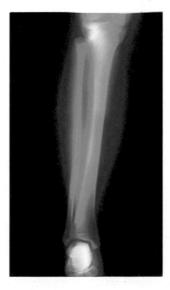

Bones in legs are normally strong and can bear the weight of the body. This coloured X-ray shows the lower half of a normal adult leg; the bones are straight and healthy.

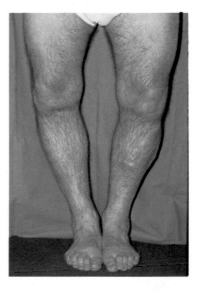

When this man was a child, his diet lacked vitamin D, and he developed rickets. In this deficiency disease, bones are soft and weak, and they bend under the weight of the body.

Why are vitamins needed in the diet?

The chief function of vitamins is to assist enzyme activity. When vitamins were first discovered, each was named by a letter – A, B and so on. Some of these early discoveries were not vitamins after all, and several (especially vitamin B) are now known to include two or more vitamins. Some vitamins are often referred to by their chemical names, particularly members of the B group. Vitamins are grouped into two classes.

12 a Name the vitamins in:

   i foods containing fat or oil

   ii green vegetables, fruit and cereals.

  b Say which vitamins are:

   i stored in the body

   ii not be stored in the body.

- **Fat-soluble vitamins – A, D, E and K**
  These are found in animal fats and vegetable oils. Any excess is stored in fatty tissue. High levels of these vitamins can be harmful.
- **Water-soluble vitamins – B and C**
  These are present in green vegetables, fruits and cereals. If the body takes in more of these vitamins than it needs, the excess is excreted in urine.

Lack of vitamins leads to a range of deficiency diseases (see Table 4).

Table 4 Vitamins required by the human body

Vitamin	Main sources in UK	Notes	Deficiency diseases
vitamin A (retinol)	foods containing fat (e.g. dairy foods, margarine, fish liver oils)	can be obtained from carotene, which occurs in carrots and some other vegetables and fruit	• night blindness • blindness in children • unhealthy skin
vitamin B_1 (thiamine)	bread, milk, vegetables, fruit, cereals	added to fortified cereals such as cornflakes	• beri-beri • nervous disorders • muscle weakness and heart failure
vitamin B_2 (riboflavin)	milk, meat, fortified cereals, egg	destroyed by ultra-violet light	• skin problems
niacin (nicotinic acid)	meat, potatoes, bread, fortified cereals	do not confuse niacin with nicotine	• pellagra (skin becomes dark and scaly)
vitamin B_6 (pyridoxine)	potatoes and other vegetables, milk, meat	sometimes taken for PMT (premenstrual tension)	• anaemia
vitamin B_{12} (cobalamine)	most animal products, especially liver	absent in plants, therefore absent in a vegan diet (one with no animal products)	• pernicious anaemia • weakened nerves of the leg
folic acid (folate)	green vegetables, liver, kidney, yeast, milk	increased amounts are required in early pregnancy destroyed by prolonged cooking	• impaired early development of the nervous system of the fetus
vitamin C (ascorbic acid)	fresh fruit and vegetables	disappears from food during storage and cooking	• scurvy (bleeding under the skin and from the gums) • wounds that do not heal
vitamin D (calciferol)	foods containing fat, (e.g. butter, margarine, herrings, egg yolk)	with good exposure to sunlight, enough can be produced in skin	• soft bones and muscle weakness in adults • rickets in children
vitamin E (tocopherol)	many foods including whole milk, fats and oils	never in short supply in the diet	
vitamin K	green vegetables	made by bacteria in the large intestine and never in short supply in a healthy person	• slow blood clotting

13 a Name two vitamins that can be made in the body.

  b Which vitamin is required in increased amounts in pregnancy?

  c Which vitamin is only found in animal foods?

  d Name three vitamins in foods containing fats.

  e Say which vitamin is destroyed by:

   i cooking   **ii** ultra-violet light.

  f Say which vitamin prevents:

   i beri-beri   **ii** scurvy   **iii** rickets.

  g Name two vitamins that:

   i help prevent anaemia

   ii are never in short supply in a healthy person.

  h Which vitamin is in short supply in the diet of people with pellagra?

Why are minerals needed in the diet?

About 15 minerals are known to be required by the human body and most foods contain a variety of them (see Table 5). People who have a balanced diet take in more minerals than are needed. Surplus minerals are either not absorbed or are excreted in the urine.

Table 5 Minerals required by the human body

Mineral	Main sources in UK	Required for	Deficiency disease
iron	meat, potatoes, white bread (added by government regulations)	haemoglobin	• anaemia
calcium	dairy foods, white bread, hard water	bones, teeth, and blood	• weak bones • poor teeth
magnesium	vegetables, meat, milk	bones and teeth	(no isolated problems)
sodium (usually taken in as sodium chloride – salt)	table salt, prepared foods containing salt	maintaining body water level	• low blood pressure causing fainting deficiency can result from excessive sweating, vomiting, diarrhoea and taking drugs to remove water
potassium	vegetables, meat, milk	nerve impulses and muscle action	• muscular weakness deficiency can occur when drugs are taken to remove water

What are trace elements?

Trace elements are minerals that are required in only very small quantities. They include:

- iodine, which is required for thyroid hormone; the main sources are iodised table salt, milk, and seafood; the deficiency disease is goitre
- fluorine, which hardens teeth and bones; fluorides are often added to the water supply and toothpaste
- zinc, which is required for some enzymes; the main source is red meat
- selenium, copper, chromium, molybdenum and manganese are other trace elements.

14 a How many minerals are essential for humans?
  b What are trace elements?
  c List:
    i three minerals required for healthy bones
    ii how the body obtains them.
  d Which mineral that the body needs is found in salt and why is it needed?
  e Which trace element can be added to salt?
  f Which foods are the main sources of potassium and what is it needed for?
  g Name the mineral:
    i required for thyroid hormone
    ii that can be added to toothpaste
    iii required for some enzymes.

5.2 Metabolism

What is energy?

15 a What is energy?
  b Give three examples of work.

Energy is the ability of a system to do work. Energy is invisible but it is easy to detect its *effects* when it transfers from one body to another. So, a transfer of energy can warm something up, or move it, or drive a chemical reaction. These different *effects* of energy are sometimes called energy forms. However, there is only one type of energy – it can just be used in a variety of ways.

What is metabolism?

Metabolism is the overall term for all the chemical reactions that occur in living cells (see Figure 5). Metabolism can be divided into two sets of reactions:

- **catabolic reactions** break down larger molecules into smaller ones; for example, glucose is broken down to carbon dioxide and water
- **anabolic reactions** build larger molecules from smaller ones; for example, amino acids are linked together to form protein molecules.

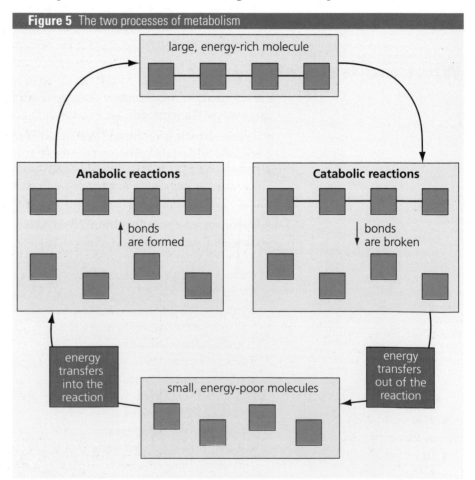

Figure 5 The two processes of metabolism

16 a What is metabolism?
  b What is the difference between anabolic and catabolic reactions?
  c Draw diagrams to show what happens in:
    i an anabolic reaction
    ii a catabolic reaction.
  d Starting with 'large energy-rich molecule' describe what is happening in Figure 5.

All chemical reactions involve transfer of energy. In catabolic reactions, energy is transferred out of the reaction and is then used to drive other reactions or is released as heat. In anabolic reactions, energy is transferred into the reaction and is used to hold the parts of the molecule together .

What part does energy play?

At any one time, an enormous number of chemical reactions are taking place inside each living cell in the body. All these reactions transfer energy. Energy is needed to:

* build larger molecules from smaller ones
* transport substances within the cell
* perform special functions in different types of cell; for example, contraction by muscle cells, transmission of impulses by nerve cells, movement of cilia by ciliated cells, secretion by gland cells
* keep the body warm in cool conditions.

17 Why does the body need energy?

How is energy transferred from food?

The energy needed to drive anabolic reactions comes from food. A living cell requires a continuous supply of glucose from which to transfer energy. Glucose from food is supplied to cells by the bloodstream. If the glucose supply runs out, stored glycogen is converted into glucose and used. Fats are used later if required, and protein from the muscles is used last.

Glucose is converted to carbon dioxide and water by a catabolic process that involves nearly 30 steps. Energy is transferred to ATP at several of these steps. Cells do not have large stores of ATP, so when energy is needed, the cycle shown in Figure 6 goes faster and faster. This delivers fresh supplies of ATP as they are needed and clears away the ADP and phosphate. (See also section 4.3 Respiration.)

Although most of the energy from food is transferred to ATP, some is transferred as heat. This helps to maintain the body temperature at 37 °C. (See also section 7.2 Homeostasis.)

18 a Where does the energy to drive anabolic reactions come from?

b What happens to most of the energy from food?

c What happens to the energy not transferred to ATP?

d Explain Figure 6 in your own words.

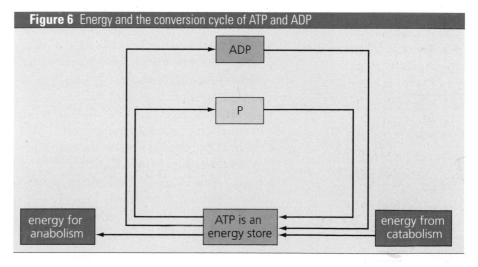

Figure 6 Energy and the conversion cycle of ATP and ADP

What is the metabolic rate?

The **metabolic rate** is the amount of energy used by the body in a set time. The faster cells work, the greater the demand for energy and the higher the metabolic rate (see Figure 7). The demand for energy results in an increase in the depth and rate of breathing, and speeds up the circulation in order to:

- supply more oxygen
- supply more glucose
- remove extra carbon dioxide
- remove excess heat.

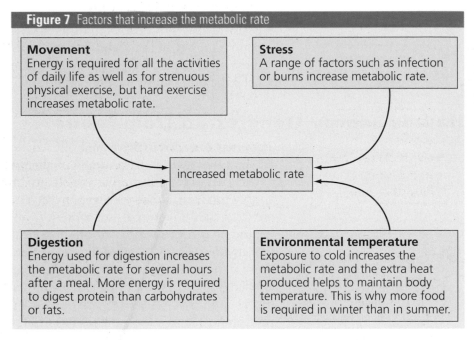

Figure 7 Factors that increase the metabolic rate

Movement
Energy is required for all the activities of daily life as well as for strenuous physical exercise, but hard exercise increases metabolic rate.

Stress
A range of factors such as infection or burns increase metabolic rate.

increased metabolic rate

Digestion
Energy used for digestion increases the metabolic rate for several hours after a meal. More energy is required to digest protein than carbohydrates or fats.

Environmental temperature
Exposure to cold increases the metabolic rate and the extra heat produced helps to maintain body temperature. This is why more food is required in winter than in summer.

The **resting metabolic rate** (RMR), also called the **basal metabolic rate** (BMR), is the amount of energy required to maintain life when the body is at complete mental and physical rest. RMR varies between individuals and is influenced by:

- **surface area** – small people have a relatively higher RMR than large people because they have a proportionally greater surface area through which heat can be lost
- **age** – RMR decreases with age
- **sex** – men have a higher RMR than women because they have a higher proportion of muscle tissue to fat
- **thyroid hormones** – more thyroid hormone speeds up RMR, less thyroid hormone slows RMR
- **body temperature** – RMR increases when the body temperature rises above normal due to fever
- **body weight** – the heavier the body, the greater the number of metabolising cells.

19 a What is the metabolic rate?
 b Name four factors that can increase metabolic rate and explain why in each case.
 c What is the resting metabolic rate also called?
 d Why does RMR vary between individuals?

How do enzymes control metabolism?

Enzymes are proteins. All enzymes are made inside cells. Enzymes that stay inside the cell are called **intracellular enzymes**; they speed up the many chemical reactions that take place in cells. **Extracellular enzymes** are secreted from the cells in which they are made and have an effect elsewhere in the body, for example, digestive enzymes. Wherever they work, all enzymes share the same four basic properties.

- **Enzymes are catalysts**
  They speed up chemical reactions but are not altered or used up by the reaction. Only a small quantity of an enzyme is required because it can be used over and over again.
- **Enzymes are specific**
  An enzyme usually acts on only one substance. Therefore, a very large number of enzymes are required for all the different chemical reactions that take place in the body.
- **Enzymes are affected by temperature**
  They work best at about body temperature (37 °C) and are destroyed by heat above 50 °C.
- **Enzymes are sensitive to pH**
  Most enzymes work best in nearly neutral conditions at pH 7.4. The digestive enzymes in the stomach are unusual because they require an acid medium and work best at pH 2.

20 a List four properties of enzymes.
  b Give the difference between intracellular and extracellular enzymes.

Summary of food and metabolism

- Food is a mixture of up to seven different types of substance: carbohydrates, fats, proteins, minerals, vitamins, fibre and water.
- Carbohydrates include sugars and starches and supply the body with energy.
- Fats and oils are made of fatty acids bound to glycerol molecules. They are used to supply and store energy, and in the manufacture of important parts of cells.
- Proteins are made of amino acids units joined together in long chains.
- There are 20 naturally occurring amino acids. This means that the possible range of protein molecules is almost infinite. Protein is needed to build many structures in the body and to form enzymes and antibodies.
- Vitamins and minerals are needed in small amounts to keep the body healthy. Different vitamins and minerals do different jobs. An illness caused by a lack of a particular vitamin or mineral is called a deficiency disease.
- Metabolism is the overall name given to the chemical reactions going on in the body. Catabolic reactions break down chemicals and transfer energy out. Anabolic reactions build larger chemical molecules by transferring energy into them.
- The metabolic rate is a measure of the energy used by the body in a set time.
- Enzymes are proteins and speed up chemical reactions. Enzymes are specific to particular reactions and are damaged by heat and change in pH. A particular enzyme will work best within a particular temperature and pH range.

5.3 The digestive system

How is the digestive system organised?

21 a List four functions of the digestive system.

b What does the digestive system consist of?

c What is the alimentary canal?

d How many salivary glands are there?

e Name the one part shown in Figure 8 that plays no part in digestion.

f Give the function of:
  i stomach
  ii gall bladder
  iii bile duct
  iv large intestine
  v anus.

The digestive system has a number of functions including:

- **ingestion**, taking food into the body
- **digestion**, breaking food down into very small particles
- **absorption**, movement of food from the gut to the bloodstream
- **egestion**, elimination of undigested food residue from the body.

To carry out these activities, the digestive system consists of:

- the mouth
- the **alimentary canal**, also called the **gut**, which is a muscular tube extending from the mouth to the anus; different parts are specialised for different functions
- the digestive glands linked to the gut.

The digestive system converts many complex food chemicals into a few simpler molecules that the body can absorb (see Figure 8).

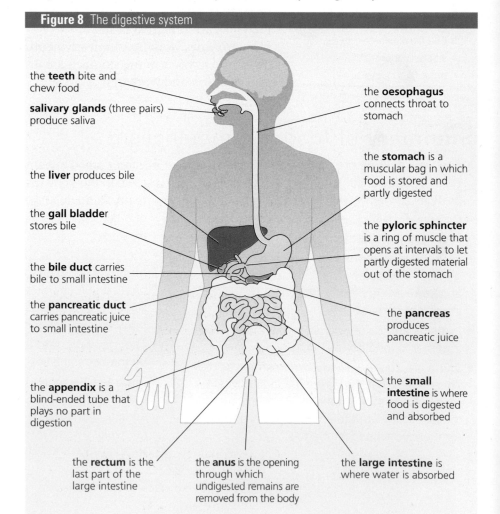

Figure 8 The digestive system

the **teeth** bite and chew food

salivary glands (three pairs) produce saliva

the **liver** produces bile

the **gall bladder** stores bile

the **bile duct** carries bile to small intestine

the **pancreatic duct** carries pancreatic juice to small intestine

the **appendix** is a blind-ended tube that plays no part in digestion

the **oesophagus** connects throat to stomach

the **stomach** is a muscular bag in which food is stored and partly digested

the **pyloric sphincter** is a ring of muscle that opens at intervals to let partly digested material out of the stomach

the **pancreas** produces pancreatic juice

the **small intestine** is where food is digested and absorbed

the **rectum** is the last part of the large intestine

the **anus** is the opening through which undigested remains are removed from the body

the **large intestine** is where water is absorbed

5.4 The mouth

What does the mouth do?

The mouth has a number of parts (see Figure 9). It takes in food and drink, chews food and mixes it with saliva to help with swallowing, tastes food, allows air to the lungs, and makes speech possible.

22 a Use a mirror to examine your mouth, then describe what you can see.

b Give five functions of the mouth.

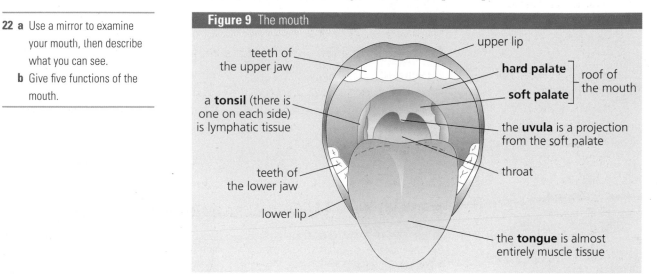

Figure 9 The mouth

- upper lip
- teeth of the upper jaw
- **hard palate** — roof of the mouth
- **soft palate**
- a **tonsil** (there is one on each side) is lymphatic tissue
- the **uvula** is a projection from the soft palate
- teeth of the lower jaw
- throat
- lower lip
- the **tongue** is almost entirely muscle tissue

How do teeth grow?

There are two sets of teeth. The first set are called the **milk teeth** or **deciduous teeth**. They begin to appear when a child is a few months old. There are 20 milk teeth, 10 in each jaw:

- 4 incisors
- 2 canines
- 4 molars.

From the age of five onwards, the milk teeth gradually fall out. They are replaced by larger, **permanent teeth**. When complete, the permanent set contains 32 teeth, 16 in each jaw... (see Figure 10).

23 a Name the two sets of teeth and say how many teeth are in each set.

b Draw a plan of the milk teeth in the lower jaw, using Figure 10 as a guide.

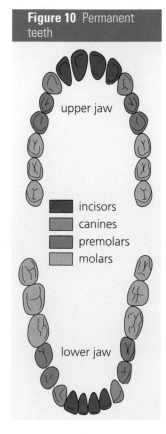

Figure 10 Permanent teeth

- upper jaw
- incisors
- canines
- premolars
- molars
- lower jaw

What do teeth do?

Teeth start the digestion of food by breaking it into smaller pieces. This increases the surface area of the food and makes it easier for the digestive enzymes to work. The different types of teeth have different functions (see Figure 11).

24 Draw and describe the four types of teeth.

Figure 11 Functions of the different types of permanent teeth

Incisors
These teeth are situated in the front of the mouth and have chisel-like edges for biting. They have a single root.

biting surface

Canines
Positioned towards the side of the mouth, these teeth are rather pointed and can be used for tearing off pieces of food. They have a single root.

point for tearing

Premolars
These teeth are found at the sides of the mouth. They have a flat surface and are used for grinding food into small pieces. Premolars have a single root.

grinding surface

Molars
Positioned behind the premolars, these teeth are similar to premolars but larger. The upper molars have three roots and lower molars have two roots.

grinding surface

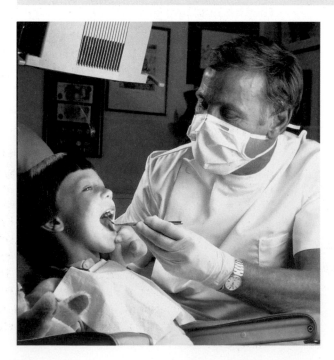

Regular visits to the dentist for check ups are essential for healthy teeth.

What is the inside of a tooth like?

The visible part of the tooth is called the crown. It is covered with **enamel**, the hardest substance in the body. The enamel protects the tooth and forms a hard biting surface. Under the enamel is the **dentine**, a hard, bone-like substance that forms the bulk of tooth (see Figure 12). Minute tubules run towards the outer surface of the tooth, each containing a fibre from a cell in the pulp cavity. Dentine is sensitive to touch, temperature, acids, and sugar because the fibres transmit information to nerve endings in the pulp cavity.

25 a Name the hardest substance in the body, and describe its functions.

b Describe dentine and explain why it is sensitive to touch and temperature.

c Draw a diagram of a section through a tooth and label: enamel, dentine, pulp cavity.

d From Figure 12, which two parts help to hold the tooth in position in the jaw?

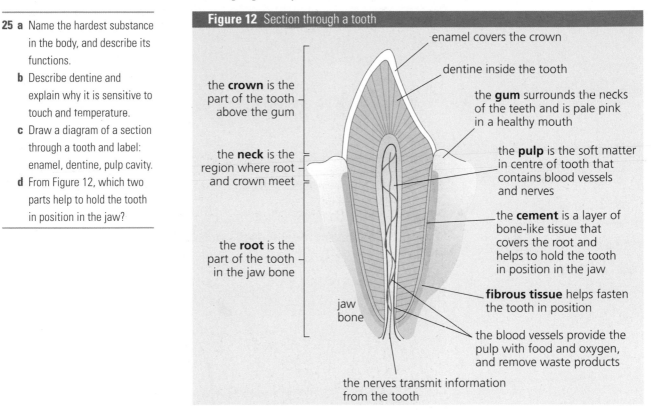

Figure 12 Section through a tooth

enamel covers the crown

dentine inside the tooth

the **gum** surrounds the necks of the teeth and is pale pink in a healthy mouth

the **pulp** is the soft matter in centre of tooth that contains blood vessels and nerves

the **cement** is a layer of bone-like tissue that covers the root and helps to hold the tooth in position in the jaw

fibrous tissue helps fasten the tooth in position

the blood vessels provide the pulp with food and oxygen, and remove waste products

the **crown** is the part of the tooth above the gum

the **neck** is the region where root and crown meet

the **root** is the part of the tooth in the jaw bone

jaw bone

the nerves transmit information from the tooth

What causes tooth decay?

26 a Describe the usual pattern of tooth decay.

b What is the difference between plaque and tartar?

c Explain why tooth decay is encouraged by:

i eating sweets

ii plaque

iii tartar.

Bacteria are always present in the mouth and some help to keep it healthy. However, the process of tooth decay (**caries**) starts with bacteria feeding on sugar in the mouth. The bacteria produce acids as they use the sugar. These acids cause tooth decay. Sugar remains in the mouth for about half an hour after eating sweet food, or longer if the food was sticky. The longer that sugar is in the mouth, the more chance there is of tooth decay.

Plaque consists of bacteria in a sticky paste that sticks to and between the teeth and is not washed away by saliva. It helps to hold the acids produced by the bacteria to the tooth surface, particularly at the gum margins. **Tartar** is plaque that has been made hard by calcium deposited on the teeth from saliva. Tartar provides shelter for bacteria and can also damage gums.

Toothache from dental caries results from the action of lactic acid (see Figure 13). Even more painful is an abscess.

An **abscess** is a collection of pus. Pus is a mixture of living and dead bacteria, debris, damaged tissue cells, white cells and serum. A root abscess is an abscess that forms on the root of a tooth. The bacteria that cause a root abscess usually enter the tooth through an area of decay and then spread through the pulp to the root (see Figure 14). The tooth may have to be extracted to relieve the pain and pressure caused by inflammation and pus.

27 a What is an abscess?
  b What is pus?
  c Draw diagrams to show the development of a root abscess.

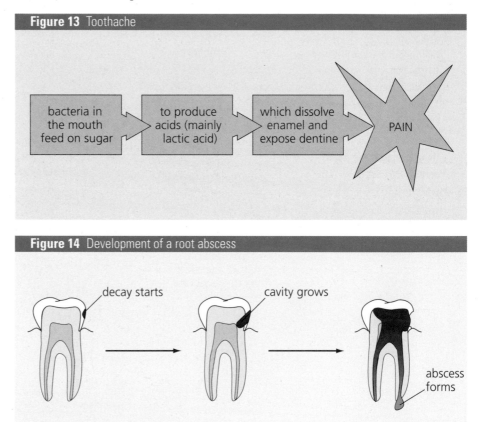

Figure 13 Toothache

bacteria in the mouth feed on sugar → to produce acids (mainly lactic acid) → which dissolve enamel and expose dentine → PAIN

Figure 14 Development of a root abscess

decay starts   cavity grows

abscess forms

What causes infected gums?

Gums infected by bacteria become swollen and sore, cause an unpleasant taste in the mouth, make the breath smell and may bleed when the teeth are brushed. This condition is called **gingivitis**. Gingivitis may develop because the teeth are not being cleaned properly, allowing plaque and tartar to build up.

If it is not severe, the condition can usually be cured by a new toothbrush, more thorough cleaning, and the repeated use of an anti-bacterial mouthwash and gel. However, if gingivitis is allowed to continue for a long time, the jaw bone around the teeth is destroyed, and the teeth may become loose and fall out.

28 a List the signs of infected gums.
  b Give three suggestions to help remedy this condition.

5.5 The gut

What is the structure of the gut wall?

The gut is basically a long, rather complex, tube. It is wider in some parts (the stomach) and narrower in others (the small intestine) but the basic structure of the wall is the same (see Figure 15).

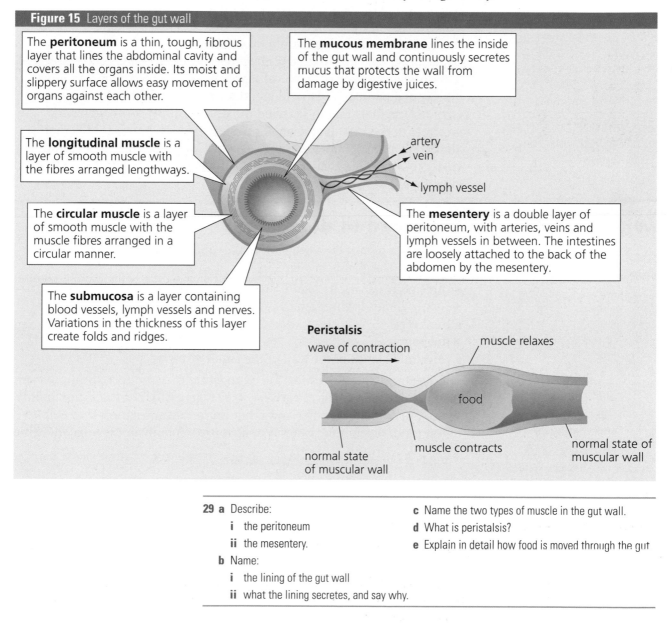

Figure 15 Layers of the gut wall

The **peritoneum** is a thin, tough, fibrous layer that lines the abdominal cavity and covers all the organs inside. Its moist and slippery surface allows easy movement of organs against each other.

The **mucous membrane** lines the inside of the gut wall and continuously secretes mucus that protects the wall from damage by digestive juices.

The **longitudinal muscle** is a layer of smooth muscle with the fibres arranged lengthways.

artery
vein
lymph vessel

The **circular muscle** is a layer of smooth muscle with the muscle fibres arranged in a circular manner.

The **mesentery** is a double layer of peritoneum, with arteries, veins and lymph vessels in between. The intestines are loosely attached to the back of the abdomen by the mesentery.

The **submucosa** is a layer containing blood vessels, lymph vessels and nerves. Variations in the thickness of this layer create folds and ridges.

Peristalsis

wave of contraction

muscle relaxes

food

normal state of muscular wall

muscle contracts

normal state of muscular wall

29 a Describe:

  i the peritoneum

  ii the mesentery.

b Name:

  i the lining of the gut wall

  ii what the lining secretes, and say why.

c Name the two types of muscle in the gut wall.

d What is peristalsis?

e Explain in detail how food is moved through the gut

How does food move through the gut?

Peristalsis is the rhythmic squeezing movement of the wall of the oesophagus and intestines. The squeezing is produced by alternate contraction and relaxation of the longitudinal and circular muscle layers.

5.6 Digestive glands and enzymes

What do digestive enzymes do?

Digestive enzymes are made in the digestive glands and secreted in the digestive juices. Their function is to increase the speed of the chemical reactions that break down large food molecules into smaller molecules. With the aid of these enzymes, food is digested in a few hours. Without them, the same processes would take months.

Like other enzymes, digestive enzymes are very specific. Each enzyme acts only in one type of chemical reaction, and each enzyme acts most rapidly at a particular pH: acid, neutral or alkaline. The pH at which any enzyme acts most rapidly is called the **optimum pH** for that enzyme. The enzymes in the mouth and small intestine have an optimum pH that is almost neutral (pH 6.5); the stomach enzymes have an acid optimum pH (pH 1 to 3). If the pH is not optimal for a particular enzyme, its action either slows down or stops.

30 a What is the function of digestive enzymes?
b What is meant by the optimum pH for an enzyme?

Which glands are involved in digestion?

A **gland** is a part of the body that makes and secretes substances that act elsewhere. The glands involved in digestion are:

- three pairs of salivary glands
- gastric glands in the stomach wall
- the liver
- the pancreas
- intestinal glands in the wall of the small intestine.

These glands secrete digestive juices; together they produce about 5 litres (5 dm^3) of digestive juices each day (see Figure 16). The juices are mainly water, but contain enzymes and other important substances that help to digest food. Most of the water is re-absorbed, mainly in the large intestine.

31 Copy Table 6 and complete it using Figure 16.

Table 6 Digestive glands, juices and enzymes

Gland	Digestive juice	Enzymes	Other substances
salivary glands			
gastric glands			
liver			
pancreas			
intestinal glands			

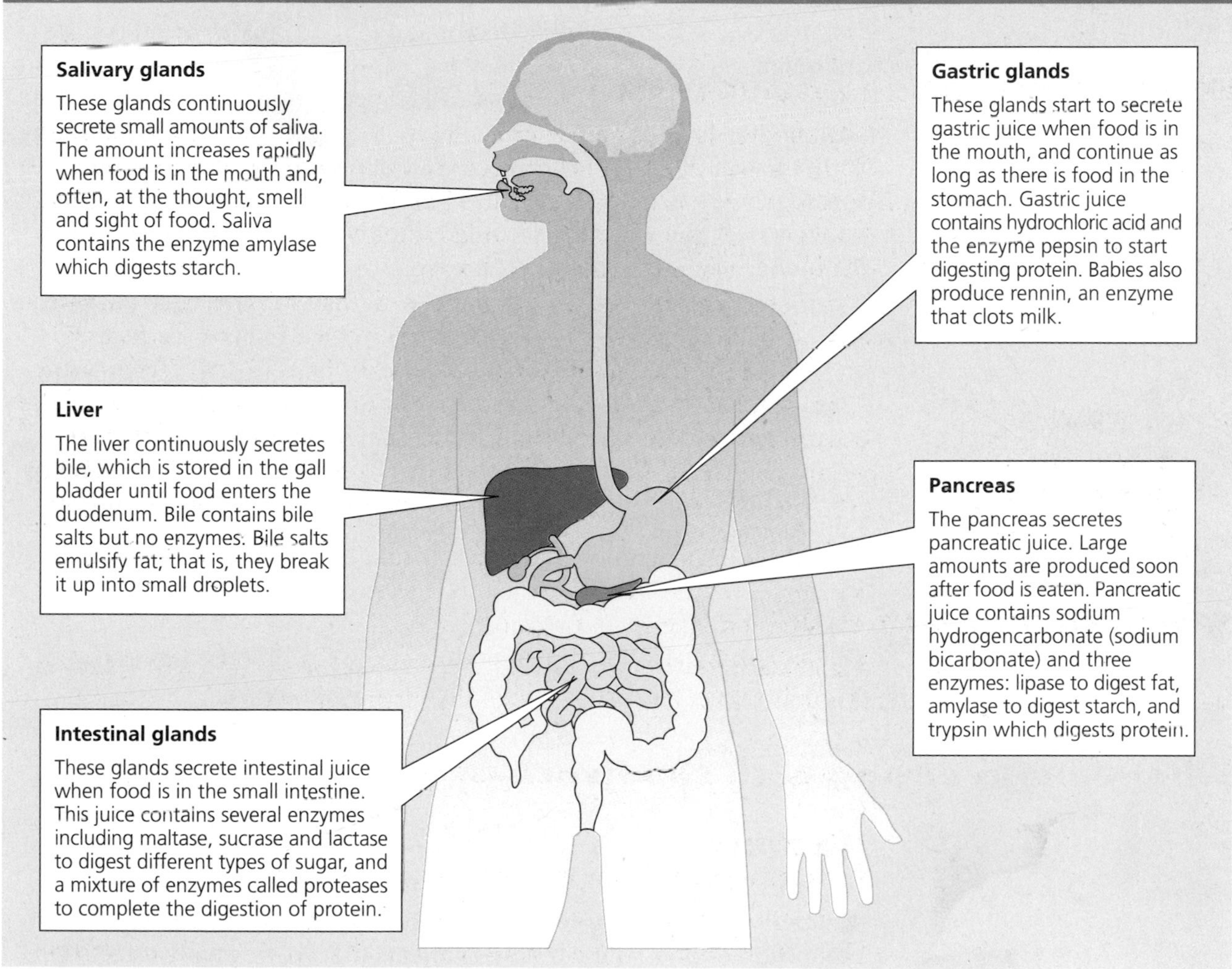

Figure 16 Digestive glands

Salivary glands

These glands continuously secrete small amounts of saliva. The amount increases rapidly when food is in the mouth and, often, at the thought, smell and sight of food. Saliva contains the enzyme amylase which digests starch.

Liver

The liver continuously secretes bile, which is stored in the gall bladder until food enters the duodenum. Bile contains bile salts but no enzymes. Bile salts emulsify fat; that is, they break it up into small droplets.

Intestinal glands

These glands secrete intestinal juice when food is in the small intestine. This juice contains several enzymes including maltase, sucrase and lactase to digest different types of sugar, and a mixture of enzymes called proteases to complete the digestion of protein.

Gastric glands

These glands start to secrete gastric juice when food is in the mouth, and continue as long as there is food in the stomach. Gastric juice contains hydrochloric acid and the enzyme pepsin to start digesting protein. Babies also produce rennin, an enzyme that clots milk.

Pancreas

The pancreas secretes pancreatic juice. Large amounts are produced soon after food is eaten. Pancreatic juice contains sodium hydrogencarbonate (sodium bicarbonate) and three enzymes: lipase to digest fat, amylase to digest starch, and trypsin which digests protein.

What is the liver?

The liver is the largest organ in the body and weighs about 1.5 kilograms. Four important vessels are linked to the liver (see Figure 17).

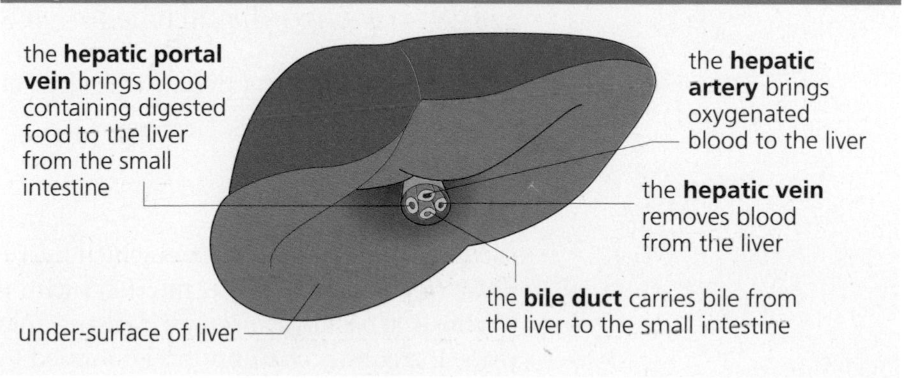

Figure 17 The under-surface of the liver

the **hepatic portal vein** brings blood containing digested food to the liver from the small intestine

the **hepatic artery** brings oxygenated blood to the liver

the **hepatic vein** removes blood from the liver

the **bile duct** carries bile from the liver to the small intestine

under-surface of liver

32 a Draw and label a diagram of the liver to show the four vessels connected to it.

b Which vessel brings glucose and amino acids to the liver?

What does the liver do?

The liver is found beneath the diaphragm in the upper right side of the abdomen, and is protected by the ribs. It is dark red-brown in colour and has a very smooth surface. It has a wide range of functions, many of which are concerned with **homeostasis**, that is, keeping conditions in the body within narrow limits. The hepatic portal vein carries glucose, amino acids, some fat droplets, fatty acids and glycerol from the intestine to the liver to be processed. Some fats are absorbed into the lymph and then pass into the bloodstream near the heart. The liver:

- helps to regulate the amount of glucose in the blood by converting the excess into glycogen or fat for storage
- converts the fats, fatty acids and glycerol into forms that can be used or stored by the body
- converts excess amino acids into urea for excretion by the kidneys.

The liver has a range of other functions. It:

- stores vitamins A and B_{12} and some iron
- secretes bile containing bile salts to help digest fat
- disposes (in the bile) of waste products from worn-out red cells
- makes fibrinogen
- helps remove alcohol and other drugs from the blood
- produces heat from many of its chemical activities.

33 a Describe the position of the liver in the body.

  b Say what happens in the liver to:

  i glucose

  ii fats

  iii amino acids.

  c List the other functions of the liver.

What can go wrong with the liver?

Hepatitis

Hepatitis is inflammation of the liver. It can be due to infection, chemicals such as cleaning fluid, or drugs. The disease interferes with the production of bile, so the yellow pigments that are normally excreted in the bile circulate in the bloodstream. This causes a number of symptoms: jaundice (yellowness of the skin and eyes), fever, discomfort and tenderness over the liver, nausea and vomiting, loss of appetite and weight.

The usual cause of hepatitis is a virus infection. There are three main viruses:

- **hepatitis A virus** is spread from person to person by food contaminated with faeces
- **hepatitis B virus** and **hepatitis C virus** are spread by blood, semen and vaginal secretions.

Cirrhosis

Cirrhosis is a liver disorder in which liver tissue is replaced by fibrous tissue (see Figure 18). This interferes with the normal working of the liver. Cirrhosis is usually caused by excessive intake of alcohol over several years. If alcohol consumption is stopped in time, the liver usually recovers.

In patients with jaundice, the whites of the eyes turn yellow and the urine is usually dark yellow or orange. If the patient has a white skin, the skin also looks yellow.

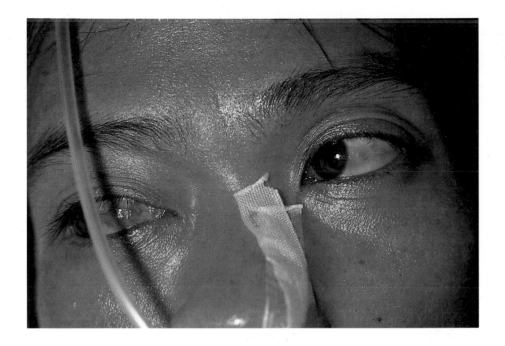

34 a What is hepatitis and what is the usual cause?

b List the symptoms of hepatitis.

c Name two viruses that cause hepatitis and say how they are spread.

d What is cirrhosis of the liver and what usually causes it?

e Draw a diagram to show where gallstones develop.

f How can gallstones cause pain?

g What treatment might be recommended for painful gallstones?

Gallstones

Gallstones develop in the gall bladder and are usually formed from cholesterol in the bile. They are quite common, especially in overweight women. Gallstones usually cause no symptoms, but they can:

- result in indigestion when fat is eaten
- irritate the gall bladder lining and cause pain in the upper right-hand side of the abdomen
- block the bile duct and cause pain and jaundice

If gallstones cause repeated pain or jaundice, they are usually removed by surgery.

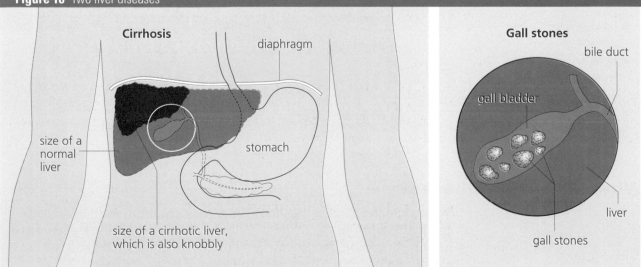

Figure 18 Two liver diseases

Cirrhosis

diaphragm

stomach

size of a normal liver

size of a cirrhotic liver, which is also knobbly

Gall stones

bile duct

gall bladder

liver

gall stones

What is the pancreas?

The **pancreas** is a large, pale gland about 20 to 25 centimetres long. It is at the back of the abdomen behind the lower part of the stomach. It is linked to the **duodenum**, the first part of the small intestine, by the pancreatic duct through which pancreatic juice flows during digestion (see Figure 19).

The pancreas has two functions. It produces:

- **pancreatic juice** to help with digestion
- **hormones** to control the amount of sugar in the blood.

The hormones are made in special groups of cells called **islets of Langerhans**. There are about 2 000 000 islets and these small nodules secrete two hormones:

- **insulin** to reduce the level of glucose in the blood
- **glucagon** to raise the level of glucose in the blood.

Insulin encourages muscle cells and liver cells to take up glucose for storage as glycogen. Glucagon encourages the liver cells to break down glycogen and release glucose into the blood.

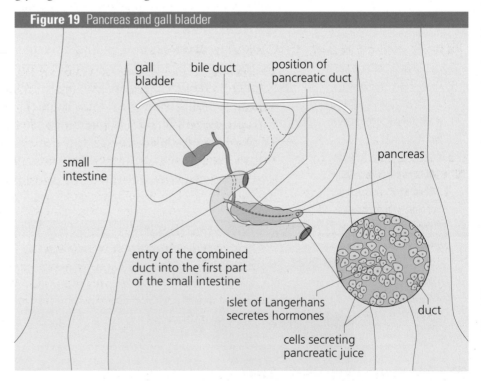

Figure 19 Pancreas and gall bladder

gall bladder

bile duct

position of pancreatic duct

small intestine

pancreas

entry of the combined duct into the first part of the small intestine

islet of Langerhans secretes hormones

duct

cells secreting pancreatic juice

35 **a** Draw and label a diagram of the pancreas to show its position in the body.

b Give two functions of the pancreas.

c Name the two pancreatic hormones and say what they do.

d How do the pancreatic hormones work?

What causes diabetes?

Sugar diabetes (*diabetes mellitus*) is the most common form of diabetes and it affects about 2% of the population. It is caused by lack of effective insulin. As a result, the glucose level builds up in the blood and the excess passes into the urine. There are two forms of sugar diabetes.

Type 1 diabetes occurs mainly in young people. The first symptoms are excessive thirst, frequent passing of urine, weight loss and general exhaustion. Treatment involves a controlled and healthy diet and regular injections of insulin, usually 2 to 4 times a day.

People with type 1 diabetes need a regular pattern of meals with a restricted amount of starchy food in each meal. They should also cut down on sugary foods and fatty foods, especially those containing saturated fatty acids. The diet should include foods containing fibre: vegetables, fruit, pulses and wholemeal bread. This is a healthy diet suitable for everyone.

Type 2 diabetes mainly comes on in middle or old age, often in people who are overweight. It can often be controlled by a diet similar to that for type 1 diabetes and medicines to lower the blood glucose level (but insulin injections are sometimes required).

Diabetic foods

Some foods are labelled 'for diabetics', but is probably better to eat smaller quantities of ordinary food: a small piece of ordinary chocolate is usually better than a large piece of diabetic chocolate.

36 a What causes diabetes?

b What are the first symptoms of type 1 diabetes?

c In which group of people does type 2 diabetes mainly occur?

d What diet is recommended for people with diabetes?

e Who might need insulin injections?

What causes a diabetic coma?

Coma is loss of consciousness from which, unlike a faint, the person cannot be roused. There are two types of diabetic coma depending on whether there is too little or too much glucose in the blood.

Hypoglycaemic coma, sometimes called a 'hypo', occurs when the level of glucose in the blood drops. This condition comes on quickly and makes the person pale, sweaty, and sometimes aggressive before they lose consciousness. Food or drink containing glucose should be taken immediately, and the patient recovers quickly. The reason for the 'hypo' is usually too much insulin, or not enough food, or too much physical exercise which uses up glucose very quickly.

Hyperglycaemic coma occurs when the blood glucose level stays too high for a day or two. The person passes a lot of water, becomes dehydrated, and then becomes more and more drowsy before passing into a coma. Urgent medical attention is required in hospital, and recovery can be slow and difficult.

37 a What is meant by a coma?

b What are the two types of diabetic coma and when do they occur?

c How can you recognise a 'hypo' and what action should you take?

d Give three reasons why a 'hypo' might develop.

Summary of the digestive system

- The digestive system consists of the teeth, the gut, and the digestive glands.
- Teeth start digestion by breaking up food into smaller pieces.
- The gut is a long tube with different areas modified to do different parts of the job of digestion.

- The liver is the largest organ in the body and has a range of functions concerned with the control of materials produced by the digestion of foods.
- The pancreas produces digestive enzymes and a pair of hormones, insulin and glucagon, which help to regulate the level of glucose in the blood.

5.7 Digestion

Digestion is the breaking down of large pieces of food containing complex molecules into smaller, simpler molecules that can pass through the wall of small intestine into the body. Digestion of food involves both physical and chemical processes.

Physical digestion involves:

- chewing to break solid food into smaller pieces
- churning by the stomach to help break up food and to mix it with gastric juice
- melting of fat by the body's heat.

Chemical digestion uses enzymes to break down:

- carbohydrates into simple sugars
- fats into fatty acids and glycerol
- proteins into amino acids.

Small molecules such as glucose, vitamins and minerals, and water can be absorbed without digestion. Fibre cannot be digested, but it is important for keeping the gut functioning properly.

38 a What is digestion?
  b List three physical and three chemical processes involved in digestion.
  c Which substances do not need to be digested, and why?

What happens in the mouth?

When food enters the mouth, it is chewed and mixed with saliva. Saliva moistens the food and makes it easier to swallow. The enzyme salivary amylase begins to change starch into a sugar called maltose.

The tongue rolls the food into a **bolus**, a ball of chewed food. This is pushed to the back of the mouth and into the oesophagus. Peristalsis pushes the food through the oesophagus into the stomach. The food cannot 'go the wrong way' because the soft palate closes the entrance to the nose and the epiglottis covers the entrance to the windpipe.

39 a Why does mixing food with saliva make it easier to swallow?
  b How is food swallowed?
  c How is food prevented from going into the windpipe?

What happens in the stomach?

Gentle movements of the stomach wall mix the food with gastric juice, and the warmth of the body melts the fats. The hydrochloric acid in gastric juice kills microbes and also enables the stomach enzymes to work. Pepsin starts to digest the protein by splitting it up into smaller units called peptides (see Figure 3 on page 76). Rennin is important in infancy because it clots milk.

At intervals, the pyloric sphincter, which is the ring of muscle at the entrance to the duodenum, opens to allow a little of the churned-up mixture to pass through into the small intestine.

40 a What happens when food enters the stomach?
  b Give two effects of hydrochloric acid in the stomach.
  c What does pepsin do?
  d When is rennin important and why?
  e How does the mixture from the stomach get into the small intestine?

What happens in the small intestine?

The small intestine is the region in which most digestion and absorption takes place. The mixture from the stomach is now mixed with bile, pancreatic juice and intestinal juice. The following actions occur:

- **sodium hydrogencarbonate** (sodium bicarbonate) neutralises the hydrochloric acid from the stomach; this stops the action of pepsin and allows the enzymes in the small intestine to work
- **bile salts** emulsify fat (fat becomes an emulsion of minute fat droplets suspended in the mixture)
- **lipase** splits fats into fatty acids and glycerol
- **trypsin** continues the digestion of proteins into peptides
- **protease** splits peptides into amino acids
- **amylase** continues the digestion of starch into maltose
- **maltase** splits maltose into glucose.

41 List the actions that take place in the small intestine.

Where does absorption take place?

42 a Draw a diagram of a villus.
  b Describe absorption into the capillaries.
  c Describe absorption into the lacteals.

Absorption is the movement of small molecules from digested food from the gut into the bloodstream.

Small amounts of water, glucose, alcohol and some other substances that do not need to be broken down can be absorbed in the stomach. Most of the absorption takes place through the wall of the small intestine (see Figure 20).

Figure 20 Wall of the small intestine

Section through the wall of the small intestine

villi
gland produces enzymes
submucosa
circular muscle layer
longitudinal muscle layer
peritoneum

Each villus has a very thin wall and contains capillaries and a lacteal. This means that the contents of the small intestine come very close to the bloodstream.

Part of a villus wall

mucus produced by goblet cell to protect the intestinal wall

microvilli increase the surface area for absorption

mucous membrane
network of blood capillaries
lacteal

Glucose, amino acids, vitamins and mineral pass through the villus wall into blood capillaries. They are then carried to the hepatic portal vein and taken to the liver.

Fats are absorbed as fat droplets or as fatty acids and glycerol. All of these pass into lacteals, are carried to lymph vessels and then enter the bloodstream near the heart.

→ to hepatic portal vein
→ to lymph vessel

Section through a villus

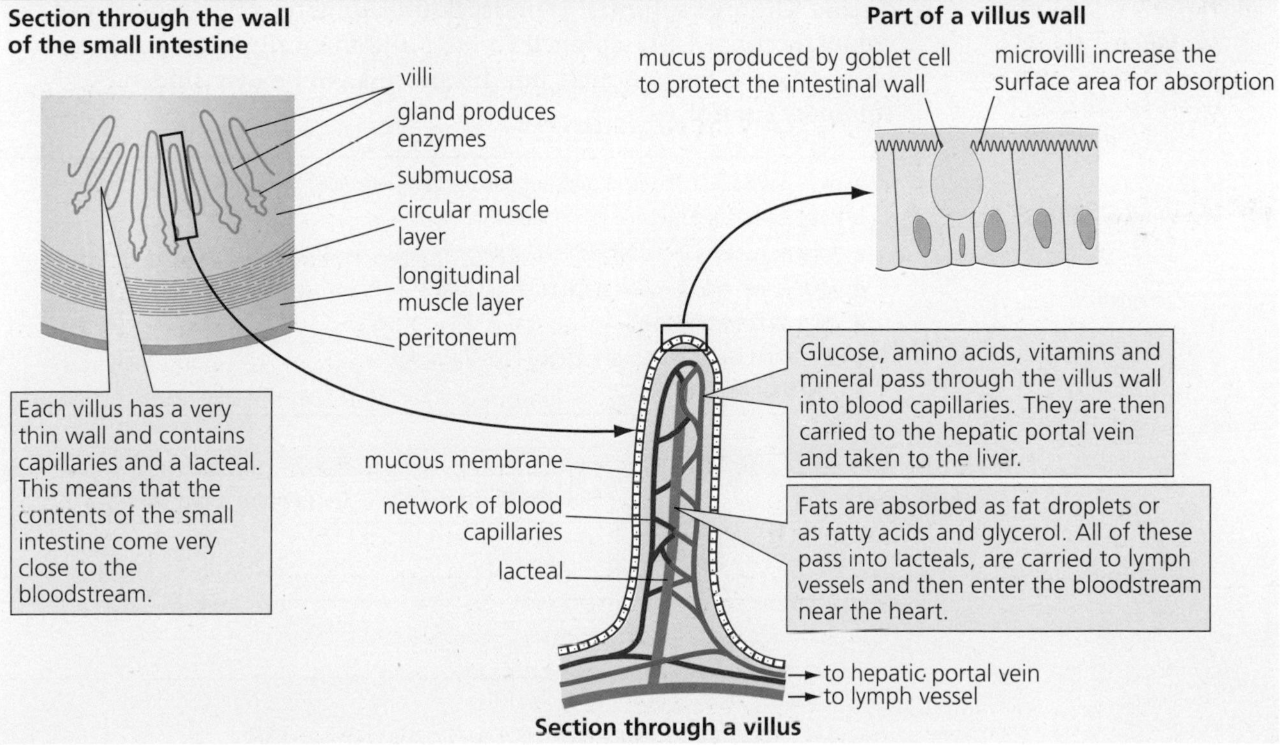

The wall of the small intestine provides a large surface area for absorption because:
- it is very long, about 5 metres in an adult
- the inner surface is much folded
- the inner surface is covered with finger-like projections called **villi** (singular: villus)
- the cells of each villus wall have **microvilli** (very small villi).

After absorption, nutrients are transported by the blood to the liver. After processing in the liver, they are transported to the tissues. Nutrients are assimilated into the body when they enter the cells of the tissues.

---

43 How does the wall small intestine provide a large surface area for absorption?

What happens in the large intestine?

The material that passes from the small intestine into the large intestine is mainly water and undigested matter such as fibre. As it moves slowly along, most of the water is absorbed through the wall of the large intestine. Enormous numbers of bacteria live in the large intestine. They feed on its contents and produce vitamin K.

The large intestine also acts as a storage place for waste matter, called **faeces** or **stools**. From time to time, faeces leave the body by passing through the rectum and out of the anus. Besides the undigested remains of food, faeces contain vast numbers of bacteria, both living and dead. Most are harmless, but some of the live bacteria are a possible source of disease. The anal sphincter is under both automatic reflex control and voluntary control. The sphincter relaxes automatically when the pressure of the faeces is high enough, but this process can be over-ridden by voluntary control.

---

44 a What passes from the small intestine into the large intestine?
   b What is absorbed from the large intestine?
   c What do bacteria in the large intestine do?
   d What is the other function of the large intestine?
   e What do faeces contain?
   f How is this waste matter discharged from the body?
   g Copy and complete Table 7.

Table 7 Summary of digestion

Part of gut	Secretions produced	Action on food
mouth		
stomach		
small intestine		

Summary of digestion

- Digestion is the breaking down of large pieces of food containing complex molecules into smaller molecules that can pass through the gut wall and into the body.
- Saliva helps to begin the digestion of starch.
- The stomach is strongly acid and begins the digestion of protein. The small intestine is neutral and completes the digestion of protein, fats and carbohydrates.

- Most absorption of food takes place in the small intestine. The wall of the small intestine has many villi to increase the surface area and so help absorption.
- The large intestine absorbs water and stores waste until it is passed out as faeces.

5.8 Digestive disorders

What causes indigestion?

Indigestion is a term for a variety of symptoms such as discomfort, feelings of distension (internal pressure or swelling), or other aches or pains associated with the digestive system. There are many causes of indigestion, but a doctor's advice is needed if indigestion lasts for more than a week, or if attacks recur regularly (see Table 8).

Table 8 Some causes of indigestion

Causes of occasional indigestion	Causes of frequent or persistent indigestion
over-eating	heartburn
hunger	gallstones
swallowing air	peptic ulcer
fatty foods, cucumber, onions	hiatus hernia
alcohol	irritable bowel syndrome
some medicines	
constipation	
diarrhoea	

45 a What is indigestion?
  b Give eight possible causes of occasional indigestion.
  c If indigestion is frequent or persistent, what could be the cause?

What can go wrong with the stomach?

46 a What is an ulcer?
  b What is a peptic ulcer?
  c Describe:
    i a hernia
    ii a hiatus hernia.

There are two main disorders of the stomach: ulcers and hernia. An **ulcer** is a break in any of the body surfaces in which healing is delayed. Ulcers affect the skin on the outside, or the mucous membrane on the inside. Ulcers of the stomach (gastric ulcers) or duodenum (duodenal ulcers) are called **peptic ulcers**. A **hernia** occurs when a part of the body pushes into the wrong place. A **hiatus hernia** occurs when part of the stomach pushes through the diaphragm into the thorax; it can cause heartburn. The stomach pushes through the opening through which the oesophagus passes.

Figure 21 Stomach disorders

Heartburn
The stomach lining is able to resist stomach acid, but the oesophagus lining is not. When acid from the stomach flows backwards into the oesophagus, it causes inflamation and pain.
Treatment:
• take small, regular meals
• wear loose-waisted clothes
• sleep propped up
• take medicines to reduce acid secretion
• take a special gel that lines and protects the oesophagus.

Hiatus hernia
Hiatus hernia occurs when a part of the stomach is pushed through the diaphragm next to the oesophagus. Hernias are more likely to occur in older people, and are encouraged by increased pressure in the abdomen caused by bending or coughing, tight clothes or being overweight.

Gastric ulcers
Peptic ulcers in the stomach cause pain in the middle of the abdomen; it is relieved by milk, food and antacids. The pain tends to come for a few days or weeks, then go for a few weeks or months. Most stomach ulcers are caused by long-term infection by bacteria.

Treatment
• stop smoking
• avoid foods that produce pain
• take antacids to neutralise stomach acid
• take medicines to stop acid secretion
• take antibiotics to kill bacteria

Bleeding from peptic ulcers needs urgent attention if blood is obvious. Blood in vomit can be bright-red, or dark like coffee grounds. Blood in faeces makes them black. When bleeding is only a slow trickle, it goes unnoticed, but anaemia slowly develops.

What are antacids?

47 a Using figure 21, describe:
  i the symptoms of a peptic ulcer
  ii treatment for a peptic ulcer
  iii the effects of bleeding from a peptic ulcer.
b Describe heartburn and four ways of relieving it.
c What encourages a hiatus hernia?
d What are antacids?
e What conditions do they relieve?
f List three other points about antacids.

Antacids neutralise acid produced by the stomach. They can relieve the pain of hiatus hernia, peptic ulcer and gastritis. **Gastritis** is inflammation of the stomach lining due to unwise eating or excessive alcohol intake. Many different types of antacid are available in liquid or tablet form and contain a variety of ingredients.

Although antacids give temporary relief from pain caused by acid they:
• do not cure the problem
• are ineffective for other digestive disorders
• can cause health problems if taken in large amounts over a long period of time.

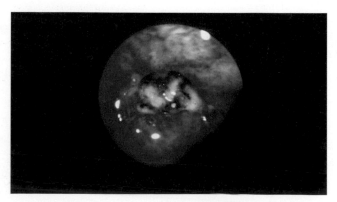

Some antacid preparations also relieve pain from an ulcer such as this one by covering the ulcer with a layer that protects it from acid attack.

What can go wrong with the intestines?

Figure 22 Intestinal disorders

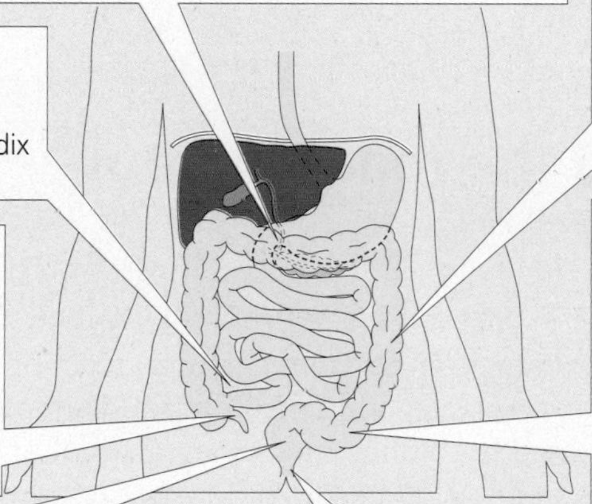

Flatulance
Gas in the stomach or intestines causes slight to severe discomfort. It can be relieved by burping, belching, or passing wind. The gas is often air that has been swallowed; sometimes, it is gas produced by bacteria acting on food in the large intestine.

Peritonitis
Inflamation of the peritoneum is serious and is usually caused by bacterial infection from a burst appendix or an abdominal wound.

Appendicitis
Inflammation of the appendix causes pain which usually starts in the middle of the abdomen and, 12 to 24 hours later, moves to the lower right side. Other symptoms are slight fever, nausea, occasional vomiting, loss of appetite and constipation.

Haemorrhoids (piles)
Swollen veins in the side of the rectum are often painful and can bleed, causing anaemia. Small veins can be treated by injection. Larger or protruding veins may have to be removed surgically.

Diarrhoea
Diarrhoea is the frequent passing of loose, watery faeces. Most short-term diarrhoea is due to infection by bacteria or viruses. People with long-term diarrhoea need medical advice.

Irritable bowel syndrome (IBS)
The muscles of the colon wall go into spasm (tighten) and cannot maintain peristalsis. This causes pain in the lower left side of the abdomen.There may be diarrhoea or constipation. It is eased by more fibre in the diet, and there are various medicines that help.

Constipation
Passing of hard, dry faeces can be painful, and might tear the anus and cause bleeding. Constipation can be due to repeatedly ignoring signals to empty the bowel, a diet lacking fibre, repeated use of laxatives or some pain-relievers, lack of exercise, and illness. A diet rich in fibre helps to prevent constipation. It can be treated with a gentle laxative for a short time (but laxatives are drugs and repeated use can cause dependence). Normal frequency of bowel action is between three times a day and three times a week.

48 a Using Figure 22, describe:
  i irritable bowel syndrome
  ii where the pain is felt
  iii other possible symptoms
  iv how it can be eased.
 b Describe:
  i appendicitis
  ii where pain is usually felt
  iii the other symptoms.
 c What is the difference between constipation and diarrhoea?
 d What is the cause of most short-term diarrhoea?
 e List six causes of constipation.
 f What is the recommended treatment for constipation and why should it only be used for only a short time?
 g Describe:
  i peritonitis
  ii what causes it.
 h What are piles and how can they be treated?
 i Describe flatulence and two reasons for the presence of gas in the digestive system.

Summary of digestive disorders

- Indigestion is a term for a variety of symptoms and there are many causes. If it occurs frequently or lasts for more than a week, medical advice is needed.
- Stomach disorders include ulcers, hernia and heartburn.
- Anfracids neutralise stomach acid. They give relief from pain but do not cure any problems.

- Intestinal disorders include flatulence, irritable bowel syndrome, constipation, appendicitis, peritonitis, haemorrhoids and diarrhoea.
- The treatments for the range of intestinal disorders are very varied.

5.9 Excretion and the renal system

What is excretion?

Excretion is the removal from the body of:

- waste products from chemical reactions
- excess water and salts from food and drink
- used hormones, medicines, alcohol and drugs of abuse.

The kidneys are the main organs of excretion, but waste substances are also excreted through the skin, lungs and liver (see Table 9).

The undigested food waste in faeces is not excreted because it has never been a part of the body; it simply passes though the alimentary canal. Only the bile in faeces is truly excreted. However, many people mistakenly refer to faeces as being excreted.

Table 9 Waste products and organs of excretion

Excretory organ	Substance excreted	Waste substance
kidneys	urine	urea
		excess water and salts
		hormones, medicines, alcohol, drugs of abuse
skin (sweat glands)	sweat	water
		salt
		urea (small amount)
lungs	carbon dioxide	
liver	bile	bile pigments from haemoglobin of destroyed red cells

How is the renal system organised?

The **renal system** consists of two kidneys and two ureters leading to a bladder and a urethra (see Figure 23). About 600 cm^3 (or 1 pint) of blood passes through the kidneys every minute, and they are so efficient that it is possible for the body to function with only one. This could happen if a kidney is removed because of disease or accident, or for transplanting into another person.

Urine drips into the bladder through the ureters. The bladder has a muscular wall and as it fills the muscles relax. From time to time, the sphincter muscle that closes the bladder relaxes and urine runs into the urethra.

In men, the urethra is about 20 centimetres long and opens at the end of the penis. In women, the urethra is about 4 centimetres long and opens into the vulva.

49 a Draw a diagram of the renal system showing the kidneys and their blood supply, the ureters and the bladder.

b Give the function of:

i renal artery

ii renal vein

iii ureter

iv bladder

v sphincter muscle

vi urethra.

c Using Figure 23 as a guide, draw a diagram showing the three regions of a kidney.

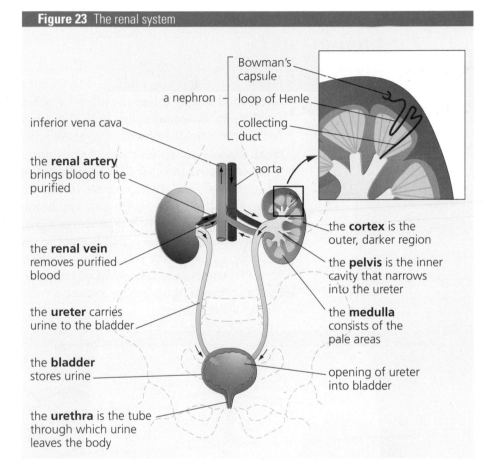

Figure 23 The renal system

Bowman's capsule

a nephron — loop of Henle

collecting duct

inferior vena cava

the **renal artery** brings blood to be purified

aorta

the **cortex** is the outer, darker region

the **renal vein** removes purified blood

the **pelvis** is the inner cavity that narrows into the ureter

the **ureter** carries urine to the bladder

the **medulla** consists of the pale areas

the **bladder** stores urine

opening of ureter into bladder

the **urethra** is the tube through which urine leaves the body

The kidneys are dark reddish-brown in colour, bean-shaped, about 11 centimetres long, 6 centimetres wide and 3 centimetres thick. They are situated high up on the back wall of the abdomen, one on each side of the backbone. The right kidney is usually slightly lower than the left kidney.

The kidneys are delicate organs but are well protected by:

• a tough membrane that encloses each kidney

• a layer of fat surrounding each kidney

• the abdominal wall and intestines

• the bones of the lower ribs and spine

• the bulky muscles of the back.

Each kidney has three different, specialised regions: cortex, medulla and pelvis (see Figure 23).

50 a Describe the position, size and colour of the kidneys.

b How are the kidneys protected in the body?

c What are the functions of the kidneys?

What do the kidneys do?

The kidneys help to maintain **homeostasis**; that is, they help to keep conditions in the body within narrow limits by:

- regulating the salt and water balance in the body
- removing urea and other nitrogenous waste from the blood
- removing excess sodium chloride and other minerals from the blood
- controlling the pH of the blood.

What are nephrons?

Each kidney contains about a million tubules called nephrons (see Figure 24). A nephron is about 3 to 5 centimetres long and each has its own blood supply called the **afferent artery**, which is a branch of the renal artery. **Bowman's capsule** is the cup-shaped blind end of a nephron in the cortex. Inside Bowman's capsule, the afferent artery splits into a small knot of capillaries called the **glomerulus**. The blood pressure in these capillaries forces most of the liquid part of the blood through the capillary walls and into the space in Bowman's capsule. This liquid is called the filtrate (see Figure 25). The blood capillaries then join up to form the **efferent** artery, which leaves Bowman's capsule, then divides into a network of capillaries surrounding the rest of the nephron. Behind Bowman's capsule, the tubule coils, then forms a U-shaped loop into the medulla; this is called the **loop of Henle**. The tubule then returns to the cortex and coils again before joining a collecting duct that leads to the centre of the kidney.

Figure 24 Structure of a nephron

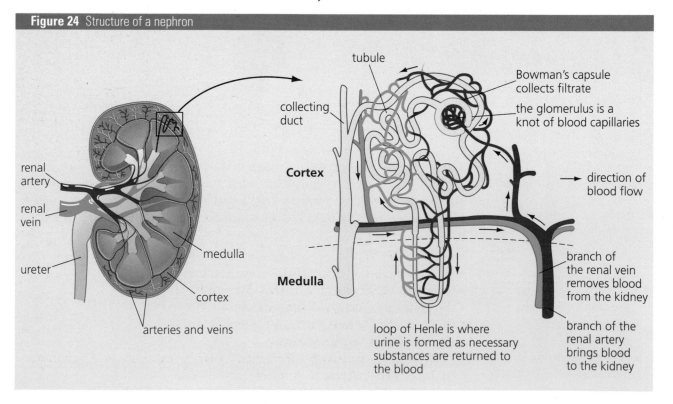

How does the kidney work?

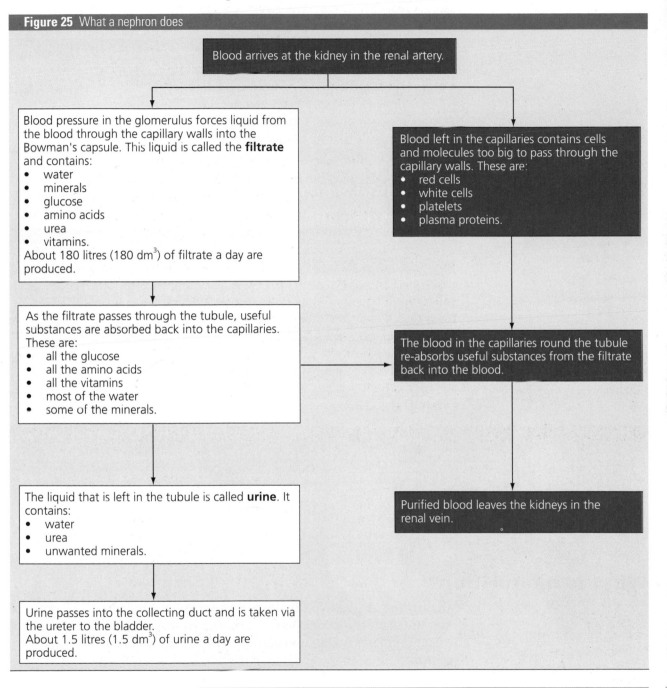

Figure 25 What a nephron does

Blood arrives at the kidney in the renal artery.

Blood pressure in the glomerulus forces liquid from the blood through the capillary walls into the Bowman's capsule. This liquid is called the **filtrate** and contains:
- water
- minerals
- glucose
- amino acids
- urea
- vitamins.

About 180 litres (180 dm³) of filtrate a day are produced.

Blood left in the capillaries contains cells and molecules too big to pass through the capillary walls. These are:
- red cells
- white cells
- platelets
- plasma proteins.

As the filtrate passes through the tubule, useful substances are absorbed back into the capillaries. These are:
- all the glucose
- all the amino acids
- all the vitamins
- most of the water
- some of the minerals.

The blood in the capillaries round the tubule re-absorbs useful substances from the filtrate back into the blood.

The liquid that is left in the tubule is called **urine**. It contains:
- water
- urea
- unwanted minerals.

Purified blood leaves the kidneys in the renal vein.

Urine passes into the collecting duct and is taken via the ureter to the bladder.
About 1.5 litres (1.5 dm³) of urine a day are produced.

51 a Use Figure 25 to say which artery brings blood to the kidney.

b In which part of the kidney is the blood filtered?

c List six substances in the filtrate.

d Name four items that stay in the blood.

e Which substances are absorbed back into the blood as the filtrate passes through the tubule?

f Name the liquid left behind in the kidney.

What does urine contain?

Urine is the watery yellow fluid produced by the kidneys. Its quanity, colour and smell can vary (see Figure 26). Its composition varies widely because it contains varying amounts of:

- waste substances from metabolism, for example, urea and hormones
- excess substances absorbed from the gut
  - 1 to 5 litres (1 to 5 dm^3) of water per day
  - up to 15 gram of salt (sodium and chloride ions) per day
  - other minerals such as potassium and calcium
- drugs, for example, medicines, alcohol, drugs of abuse
- a range of other chemicals that are absorbed from the gut and pass unchanged through the body, for example, red colouring from beetroot, some spices.

52 a What does urine contain?

  b What can give urine a strong smell?

  c Say why urine might be:

  i pink

  ii yellow or orange.

  d Give four reasons why the daily output of urine varies.

Figure 26 A sample of urine

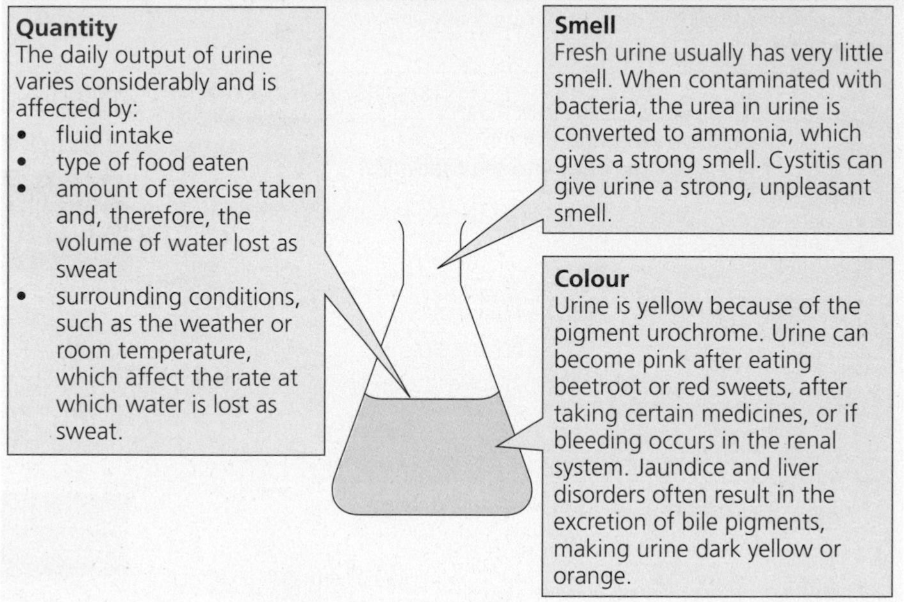

Quantity
The daily output of urine varies considerably and is affected by:
- fluid intake
- type of food eaten
- amount of exercise taken and, therefore, the volume of water lost as sweat
- surrounding conditions, such as the weather or room temperature, which affect the rate at which water is lost as sweat.

Smell
Fresh urine usually has very little smell. When contaminated with bacteria, the urea in urine is converted to ammonia, which gives a strong smell. Cystitis can give urine a strong, unpleasant smell.

Colour
Urine is yellow because of the pigment urochrome. Urine can become pink after eating beetroot or red sweets, after taking certain medicines, or if bleeding occurs in the renal system. Jaundice and liver disorders often result in the excretion of bile pigments, making urine dark yellow or orange.

What is micturition?

53 a What is micturition?

  b What is incontinence?

  c What controls the outlet from the bladder?

  d What triggers the automatic reflex?

  e What can over-ride the automatic reflex?

Micturition, also called **urination**, is the act of passing urine. The outlet from the bladder is controlled by a ring of muscle called a **sphincter**, which is under is under both automatic reflex control, and voluntary control.

When the pressure of urine in the bladder reaches a certain level, it automatically triggers the reflex to relax the sphincter. As the sphincter relaxes, the muscles in the bladder wall contract, and urine is released into the urethra and is then expelled from the body. However, this automatic process can be over-ridden by voluntary control that prevents the sphincter from relaxing, so urine is not released.

Voluntary control of micturition has to be learned. **Incontinence** is the loss of this voluntary control.

What can a urine test detect?

54 a What is the urinary tract?

b Write down which substance in urine might indicate:

  i kidney stones

  ii sugar diabetes

  iii slimmings

  iv jaundice

  v infection of the urinary tract (two answers).

A urine test is part of a routine health check. It can give information about:

- the state of the kidneys
- the state of the **urinary tract**, that is, the tubes in the kidneys, the ureters, bladder, and urethra
- the blood.

The blood often shows changes due to other conditions in the body, for example, diabetes, starvation, and jaundice. Urine is filtered from blood, so a urine test is a diagnostic tool for a range of conditions. A urine test is performed by dipping a test strip into the urine (see Figure 27).

Figure 27 Sample positive results for substances in urine

pH	Urine is usually acid.
Glucose	If present, often a sign of sugar diabetes.
Ketones	Present in the urine of people who are slimming or starving, and in poorly controlled diabetes.
Protein	Usually a sign of infection of the urinary tract.
Blood	Can be a sign of kidney stones or cancer in the urinary tract.
Bilirubin	Normally present in very small quantities, and in increased amounts in people with jaundice.
Nitrites	A sign of infection of the urinary tract.

What can go wrong with the renal system?

Urinary tract infection

Infection can occur in any part or along the entire tract.

Cystitis

Cystitis is inflammation of the bladder, usually caused by an infection. It causes pain in the lower abdomen and the frequent passing of small amounts of stinging urine. It is quite a common complaint, especially in women. This is because the urethra is much shorter in females than males. There are more bacteria present in the outlet area, and the bacteria can more easily pass up into the bladder. Drinking large quantities of water can reduce the symptoms, but medical advice should be sought.

Kidney stones

Occasionally stones form in the kidneys and interfere with kidney function (see Figure 28).

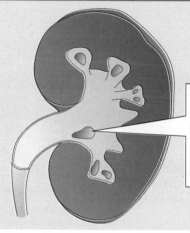

Figure 28 Kidney stones

Kidney stones can also cause bleeding into the urine. If a kidney stone becomes loose and passes down into a ureter, it causes severe pain. Kidney stones can be removed by surgery. Another treatment, called **lithotripsy**, uses ultrasound to break up the hard stone.

55 a What is cystitis and what causes it?

b Why is cystitis more common in women than in men?

c Where do kidney stones form and what effect can they have?

d Study Figure 28, then name two ways that kidney stones can be treated.

e What happens in kidney failure?

Kidney failure (renal failure)

When the kidneys fail, they are unable to clear waste substances from the blood or keep the various chemicals in the blood balanced. The cells of the body can then become poisoned. In severe cases of kidney failure, dialysis or a kidney transplant is necessary. Kidney failure can occur when:

- the kidneys are inflamed or irritated
- the urethra is obstructed, for example, by an enlarged prostate gland
- the blood supply to the kidneys is reduced, for example after an accident.

How does kidney dialysis work?

If the kidneys are not working, the removal of toxic substances from blood can be done by dialysis through a membrane. There are two dialysis techniques: **haemodialysis** uses an artificial kidney with selectively permeable membranes (see Figure 29); **peritoneal dialysis** uses the peritoneum in the abdomen as a membrane.

Haemodialysis

Blood from an artery, usually in the patient's arm, is pumped to the artificial kidney. Inside the machine, selectively permeable membranes separate the blood from the dialysis fluid. As the blood passes over the membranes, urea and other unwanted substances diffuse into the dialysis fluid and are carried away. The blood is then returned to a vein. Although it is time-consuming and requires bulky machinery, this technique can be carried out in the patient's home.

Figure 29 Haemodialysis

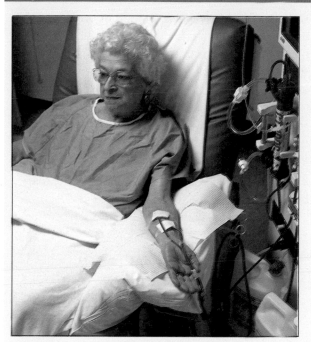

Haemodialysis is carried out for several hours, two or three times a week.

An artificial kidney

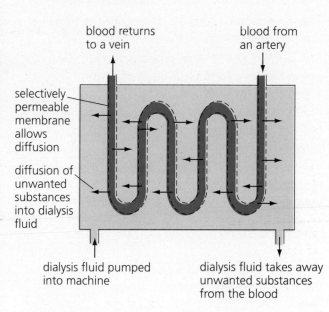

blood returns to a vein

blood from an artery

selectively permeable membrane allows diffusion

diffusion of unwanted substances into dialysis fluid

dialysis fluid pumped into machine

dialysis fluid takes away unwanted substances from the blood

Peritoneal dialysis

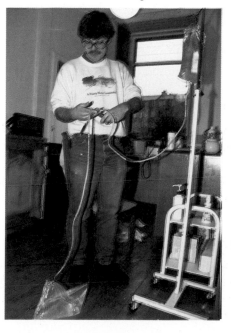

The inside walls of the abdominal cavity and the outside walls of the intestines are covered by a thin membrane, the peritoneum, which contains blood vessels. In peritoneal dialysis, fluid is passed into the abdominal cavity and toxic substances in the blood in the peritoneum diffuse into it. The fluid is then drained off.

Peritoneal dialysis can be repeated as often as necessary and is usually carried out by the patient at home.

56 a When is dialysis necessary?
  b Name the dialysis technique that uses:
   i an artificial kidney
   ii the abdominal cavity.
  c Draw and label a diagram of an artificial kidney.

Summary of excretion

- Excretion is the removal of the waste products of metabolism from the body.
- The lungs, the skin, the liver and kidneys all have an excretory function. The kidneys are the most important excretory organs in the body.
- The renal system consists of the kidneys, the ureters, bladder and urethra.
- The kidneys filter a large amount of material out of the blood and return only the useful substances to the blood.
- The body regulates the water balance in the blood by controlling how much water is reabsorbed before the urine leaves the body.
- The maintenance of conditions inside the body within narrow limits is called homeostasis. The kidneys are responsible for homeostatic control of water and a range of chemicals.

- A kidney nephron consists of a Bowman's capsule, connecting tubule, a loop of Henle and a collecting duct to pass urine to the ureters and the bladder.
- Urine tests can give an indication of problems in the urinary system and in the blood. Since the blood passes through every part of the body it can show indications of a range of illnesses. This is why urine tests are so useful to doctors.
- Problems of the renal system include infection anywhere along the urinary tract, inflammation of the bladder (cystitis), kidney stones, and kidney failure.
- Kidney failure can be treated by dialysis using a kidney machine or through peritoneal dialysis.

The *nervous system and senses*

6

Learning objectives

By the end of this chapter you should be able to:

- **describe** the organisation of the nervous system into the central nervous system and the peripheral nervous system
- **describe** the structure of a sensory neurone, motor neurone, and a relay neurone
- **describe** the structure of a typical nerve
- **explain** how a nerve carries an impulse and passes it across a synapse
- **list** the five senses and their relevant sense organs
- **describe** the structure and functioning of the nose and tongue
- **describe** the structure and functioning of the eye

- **describe** the symptoms and treatment of common vision problems
- **describe** the structure and functioning of the ear
- **list** the commonest causes of deafness
- **describe** the functioning of a reflex arc
- **explain** the differences between reflexes and voluntary actions
- **describe** the organisation and function of the autonomic nervous system
- **describe** the organisation of the brain, linking function to particular areas
- **describe** the symptoms of the common disorders of the nervous system.

6.1 The nervous system

What is the nervous system?

The **nervous system** is a network of millions of cells. It:

- carries impulses rapidly to all parts of the body
- controls the action of muscles
- learns about the environment
- makes decisions about survival
- learns from experience and decides on new ways to behave.

Acrobatics and juggling involve hearing, balance and sight and touch. Some activities may be associated with particular smells and tastes. To hear, move, see, touch, smell and taste, you need sense organs to collect information and a nervous system to process it.

1 What are the functions of the nervous system?

111

2 What are the two regions of the nervous system?

The nervous system penetrates to all parts of the body, and is organised into two regions:

- the **central nervous system** or **CNS** containing the brain and spinal cord
- the **peripheral nervous system** consisting of the nerves (see Figure 1).

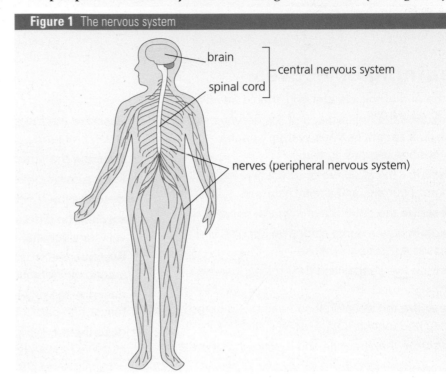

Figure 1 The nervous system

brain

spinal cord

central nervous system

nerves (peripheral nervous system)

What is a neurone?

3 a Name three types of neurone, and give the function of each.

b Draw and label a motor neurone.

c Which type of neurone:

 i is found only in the CNS

 ii has its cell body, but not its nerve fibre, in the CNS

 iii does not have its cell body in the CNS

 iv is connected to a muscle or gland?

d What is the difference between dendrites and axons?

e Where is a myelin sheath found and what is its function?

Neurones are cells found in the nervous system (see Figure 2). There are three main types:

- **sensory neurones** carry impulses from sense organs to the central nervous system
- **motor neurones** carry impulses away from the central nervous system to the muscles and glands
- **relay neurones** carry impulses within the central nervous system.

Each neurone has a cell body with several thin strands or processes coming from it (see Figure 2). The processes coming from a neurone are:

- **dendrites**, which are short and branched and carry impulses towards the cell body
- an **axon**, also called a **nerve fibre**, which is often much longer and carries impulses away from the cell body.

Many nerve fibres are surrounded by a **myelin sheath**. This insulates the fibre and allows impulses to be conducted along it more quickly. Myelin is a white fatty substance. The myelin sheath is in sections. Each section is formed from a single cell called a Schwann cell that wraps itself round the nerve fibre. The junctions between sections of the sheath are called nodes of Ranvier.

Figure 2 Neurones, nerve impulses and myelin

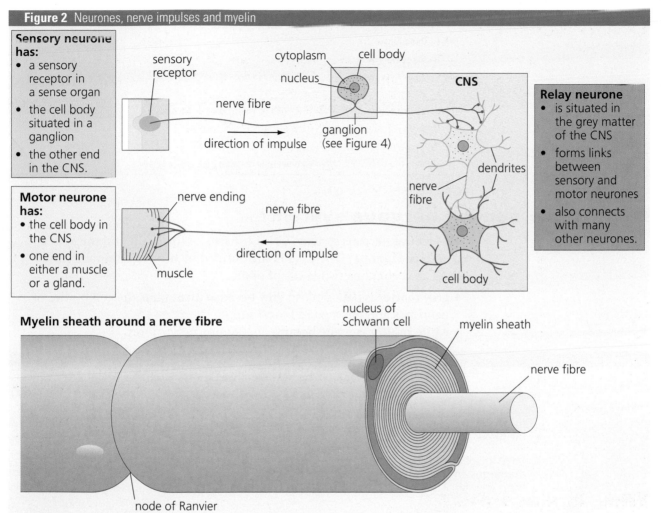

Sensory neurone has:
- a sensory receptor in a sense organ
- the cell body situated in a ganglion
- the other end in the CNS.

Motor neurone has:
- the cell body in the CNS
- one end in either a muscle or a gland.

Relay neurone
- is situated in the grey matter of the CNS
- forms links between sensory and motor neurones
- also connects with many other neurones.

Myelin sheath around a nerve fibre

What is a nerve?

Figure 3 Structure of a nerve

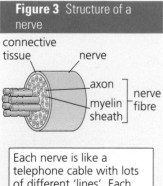

Each nerve is like a telephone cable with lots of different 'lines'. Each 'line' is the nerve fibre of a single neurone, insulated from all the others by its own myelin sheath.

A **nerve** is a bundle of nerve fibres (see Figure 3). A nerve reaching from the toe to the spinal cord may be over a metre long and some neurones have fibres that reach the full length of the nerve.

There are 43 pairs of nerves that come directly from the central nervous system:

- 12 pairs of **cranial nerves** are connected to the under-surface of the brain and pass outwards through holes in the skull
- 31 pairs of **spinal nerves** are connected to the spinal cord and pass outwards between the vertebrae of the backbone.

All the other nerves in the body are branches of these 43 pairs.

Nerves vary in thickness from very thin threads to the thickness of a little finger. This depends on how many nerve fibres they contain. Most large nerves are **mixed nerves** and contain both sensory and motor nerve fibres running to and from particular parts of the body. The other nerves are either sensory or motor nerves.

4 a Write down how many pairs of nerves are connected to:

    i the brain

    ii the spinal cord.

  b Describe how nerves connected to the CNS pass through:

    i the skull

    ii the backbone.

  c Draw and label a diagram to show the structure of a nerve.

  d What is a mixed nerve?

  e What is the difference between a neurone, a nerve fibre and a nerve?

What is the central nervous system?

The central nervous system (CNS) consists of the brain and the spinal cord (see Figure 4). The CNS is surrounded by bone, membranes and fluid, and contains two kinds of tissue:

- **grey matter** is pale pinkish grey because it contains the cell bodies of neurones and has a good blood supply
- **white matter** is white because it contains nerve fibres.

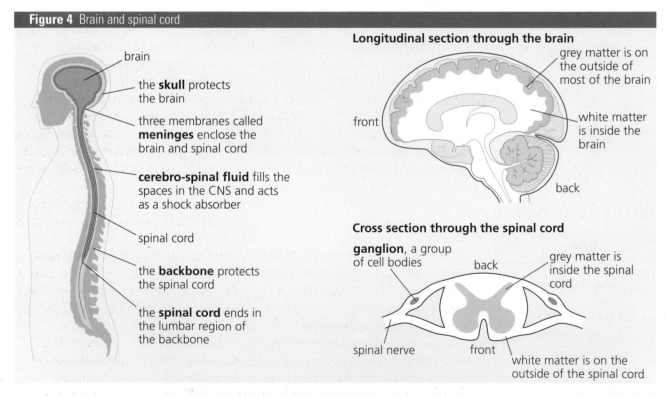

Figure 4 Brain and spinal cord

brain

the **skull** protects the brain

three membranes called **meninges** enclose the brain and spinal cord

cerebro-spinal fluid fills the spaces in the CNS and acts as a shock absorber

spinal cord

the **backbone** protects the spinal cord

the **spinal cord** ends in the lumbar region of the backbone

Longitudinal section through the brain

grey matter is on the outside of most of the brain

front

white matter is inside the brain

back

Cross section through the spinal cord

ganglion, a group of cell bodies

back

grey matter is inside the spinal cord

spinal nerve

front

white matter is on the outside of the spinal cord

5 a Name the two parts of the central nervous system.

  b Draw and label a diagram to show the position of the central nervous system in the body.

  c What is the difference between grey matter and white matter?

  d Where is grey matter found in the brain?

  e Draw and label a section through the spinal cord to show the grey and white matter.

What are nerve impulses?

The nervous system works continuously to help control the activities in the body, whether we are awake or asleep. Nerve impulses carry information through the network of neurones that make up the nervous system (see Figure 5).

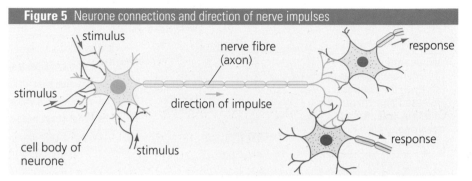

Figure 5 Neurone connections and direction of nerve impulses

6 Figure 5 shows one complete neurone. Write down how many neurones it is:

i receiving impulses from

ii transmitting impulses to.

A **nerve impulse** is an electrical signal that passes along a neurone. A **stimulus** is anything that makes a neurone produce a nerve impulse. Examples of stimuli are heat, pressure, pain, certain chemicals, or an impulse from another neurone.

There is an all-or-nothing response by the neurone. This means that if the stimulus does not reach a certain level called the threshold level, the neurone does not produce a nerve impulse. Every individual nerve impulse produced by the neurone is the same size. It is the number of impulses that the neurone produces in a given time which indicates the strength of the stimulus it has received. Thus, a strong stimulus may produce a stream of 100 impulses per second from the neurone, whereas a weak stimulus may produce only 20 impulses per second. It is important to remember that there are no big impulses or small impulses, only many impulses or few impulses.

Nerve impulses always pass through a neurone in the same direction. For a message to be sent in the opposite direction, the impulses must pass through other neurones.

7 a What is a nerve impulse?

b What is a stimulus?

c Name five stimuli.

d What is meant by an 'all or nothing response by the neurone'?

e How does a myelin sheath affect the speed of a nerve impulse?

f Describe the response of a muscle and a gland to receiving impulses.

g What does the strength of response by a muscle or gland depend on?

The speed at which nerve impulses travel depends on the thickness of the nerve fibre and the presence or absence of a myelin sheath. The fastest impulses, in thick fibres with myelin sheaths, travel at a rate of 130 metres per second. In thin fibres without myelin sheaths, nerve impulses travel at about 0.5 metres per second.

When nerve impulses reach the end of a neurone, they either cross a synapse to another neurone, or stimulate a muscle or a gland. Another neurone responds by sending on the impulse, a muscle responds by contracting, a gland responds by secreting. The strength of the response depends on the number of impulses received per second.

How do impulses get from one neurone to another?

A **synapse** is the junction between two neurones. Although very close together, the cells do not quite touch. There is a gap between them of

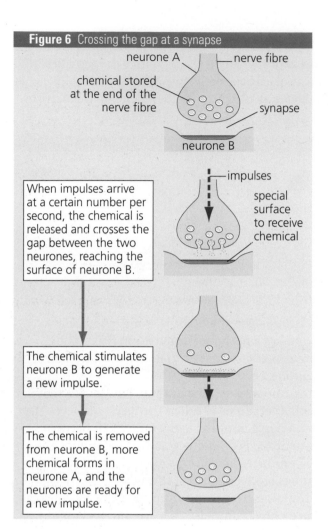

Figure 6 Crossing the gap at a synapse

neurone A — nerve fibre

chemical stored at the end of the nerve fibre

synapse

neurone B

impulses

special surface to receive chemical

When impulses arrive at a certain number per second, the chemical is released and crosses the gap between the two neurones, reaching the surface of neurone B.

The chemical stimulates neurone B to generate a new impulse.

The chemical is removed from neurone B, more chemical forms in neurone A, and the neurones are ready for a new impulse.

about 20 nanometres (nm). When a nerve impulse reaches a synapse, it stimulates the release of **neuro-transmitters**. These are chemicals such as acetylcholine or dopamine. They cross the gap and cause a new impulse to start travelling along the next neurone (see Figure 6).

8 a What is a synapse?
   b Draw and label a synapse.
   c Describe how an impulse crosses the gap at a synapse.
   d What type of chemical is dopamine?
   e What do chemicals of this type do?

Summary of the nervous system

- The central nervous system (CNS) consists of the brain and spinal cord. The rest of the nervous system is called the peripheral nervous system.
- A nerve is a collection of nerve fibres linking a part of the body with the central nervous system.
- Schwann cells wrap around the fibre of a neurone. Schwann cells contain large amounts of the fatty substance myelin. Myelin insulates each nerve fibre from others running alongside it. Nerves with myelin sheaths carry impulses more quickly than non-myelinated ones.
- An axon carries impulses away from the neurone cell body. Dendrites carry impulses towards the neurone cell body.

- White matter in the nervous system consists mainly of myelinated fibres. Grey matter consists largely of cell bodies and blood vessels.
- A nerve impulse is an electrical signal that passes along a neurone. All impulses are the same size. A neurone can carry impulses in one direction only.
- The strength of the signal passing along a neurone depends on the number of impulses that pass in a given time.
- The junction between two neurones is called a synapse. There is a very small gap between the two neurones. Chemicals called neuro-transmitters carry the signal across the gap.

6.2 Sense organs

What are sense organs?

The nervous system works with the sense organs to collect information. This information is passed to the central nervous system for processing.

Sense organs are organs containing sensory cells or sensory nerve endings called receptors. A **receptor** responds to a particular stimulus by producing nerve impulses. Different receptors monitor conditions outside the body, the **external environment**, and conditions inside the body, the **internal environment**.

Receptors sensitive to the external environment are those of the four special sense organs and the skin. They include:

- **rods** and **cones** in the eyes that are sensitive to light
- **organs of Corti** in the ears that are sensitive to sound
- **taste buds** on the tongue that are sensitive to chemical stimuli
- **olfactory cells** in the nose that are sensitive to chemical stimuli
- **receptors** in the skin that are sensitive to touch, pressure, pain, heat and cold.

Receptors sensitive to the internal environment fall into two groups:

- proprioceptors
- receptors in the internal organs.

Proprioceptors include: receptors in the semicircular canals of the inner ear, and receptors in the muscles, ligaments, joints and tendons. The proprioceptors supply information to the brain about the position and movement of the body and joints. The brain can then coordinate the muscles to keep the body balanced when standing or moving.

Receptors in the internal organs (heart, gut, lungs) help to coordinate automatic muscle contractions, such as the heart beat and gut movement.

Proprioceptors provide the information that enables the brain to make the adjustments necessary when balancing or holding an object that is changing its weight, for example a kettle being filled with water.

9 a Copy and complete Table 1.

b What is a sense organ?

c What do receptors do?

d What is the difference between the internal and external environment?

d Give two examples of receptors that monitor the internal environment.

e What are proprioceptors?

Table 1 Sense organs, receptors and stimuli

Sense organ	Receptor	Stimulus
eye	rods and cones	light
ear		
tongue		
nose		
skin		

How do sense organs work?

Sense organs all work in the same way. When the sensory nerve endings in the organ are stimulated, they send nerve impulses to the brain. All the nerve impulses are the same. The brain can correctly interpret each impulse, for example as sound or light or taste, because it can identify where the impulse comes from. The more impulses that arrive in a given time, the stronger the sensation.

When a stimulus is applied continuously or frequently to a sense receptor, its effect is reduced with time. This is called **sensory adaptation**. The degree of adaptation depends on the type of sense receptor. Touch adapts rapidly; for example, we soon forget we are wearing a wrist-watch. Warning sensations such as pain and cold adapt very slowly and incompletely.

---

10 a Nerve impulses from sensory cells are identical. How do we know whether a stimulus is sound, light or taste?

b What is sensory adaptation?

Summary of sense organs

- The five senses are taste, smell, touch, sight and hearing. These provide information about the environment outside the body.
- Internal receptors provide information about the internal environment and include nerve endings sensitive to pain and stretch receptors in muscles.

- Sense organs convert stimuli into nerve impulses. The brain interprets these impulses as particular sensations depending on which sense organ sends them.

6.3 Tongue, nose and skin

How does the tongue work?

The tongue is made of muscle fibres that run in several directions. This enables the tongue to alter its shape and position to help with chewing,

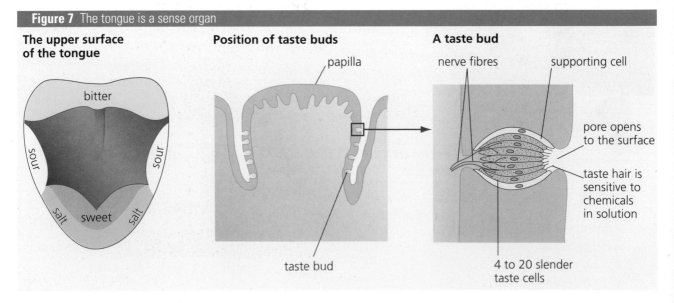

Figure 7 The tongue is a sense organ

The upper surface of the tongue

bitter

sour

sour

salt

sweet

salt

Position of taste buds

papilla

taste bud

A taste bud

nerve fibres

supporting cell

pore opens to the surface

taste hair is sensitive to chemicals in solution

4 to 20 slender taste cells

swallowing and speech. The tongue is also sensitive to taste, touch and temperature.

The upper surface of the tongue looks rough, but feels smooth. It is covered with tiny projections of different sizes called papillae. They are sometimes mistaken for taste buds, but the taste buds are very much smaller and found in the sides of the papillae.

Saliva moistens food in the mouth. As it does so, some of the chemical substances in the food dissolve in the saliva and reach the taste buds. When the chemicals stimulate the taste cells, impulses pass along nerve fibres to the brain. Taste buds are arranged on the tongue in such a way that different areas are sensitive to the four basic tastes (see Figure 7).

11 a What is the tongue made of?

    b List four functions of the tongue.

    c Describe the upper surface of the tongue.

    d Draw a section through a papilla to show the position of the taste buds.

    e Draw a section through a taste bud.

    f Describe the process of tasting.

    g Draw and label a diagram showing the taste areas of the tongue.

    h Design an experiment to find out if your tongue has similar taste areas to those shown in Figure 7.

How does the nose work?

The nose extends from the face to the end of the hard palate. It is divided into two nasal cavities and lined with mucous membrane (see Figure 8). The surface area within the nose is increased by three flaps of bone that extend inwards from the sides. A small area in the upper part of each nasal cavity contains olfactory cells that are sensitive to chemicals in solution.

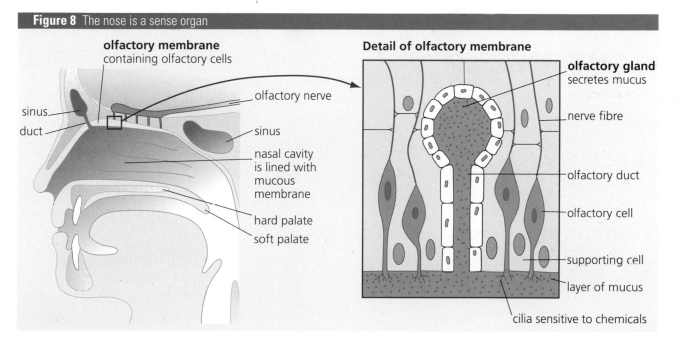

Figure 8 The nose is a sense organ

olfactory membrane
containing olfactory cells

olfactory nerve

sinus

duct

sinus

nasal cavity
is lined with
mucous
membrane

hard palate

soft palate

Detail of olfactory membrane

olfactory gland
secretes mucus

nerve fibre

olfactory duct

olfactory cell

supporting cell

layer of mucus

cilia sensitive to chemicals

12 a How far back does the nose extend from the face?

b Where are the olfactory cells situated?

c Draw a diagram of olfactory cells and an olfactory gland.

d Describe the process of smelling.

e Which two senses does flavour depend on?

13 Draw and label the five types sensory nerve ending found in the skin. Say what each detects.

The inner surface of the nose is kept moist by mucus. Chemicals in the air entering the nose dissolve in the mucus and stimulate the olfactory cells to send impulses to the brain. The brain interprets the impulses as smell. The olfactory area of the brain can distinguish between many smells.

Our sense of taste depends on the sense of smell as well as the taste buds. This becomes obvious when the nose is blocked due to a cold, and food seems to have little flavour.

Sinusitis

This is inflammation of the **sinuses**, air-filled cavities opening into the nasal cavity. It can be caused by infection with bacteria or viruses, or by an allergy, for example to dust or pollen. The mucous membrane lining the sinuses becomes inflamed, swells, and produces abundant mucus which causes a headache.

Why is the skin sensitive?

The skin is a sense organ (see Figure 9). It contains nerve endings that are sensitive to touch, pain, pressure and temperature (heat and cold).

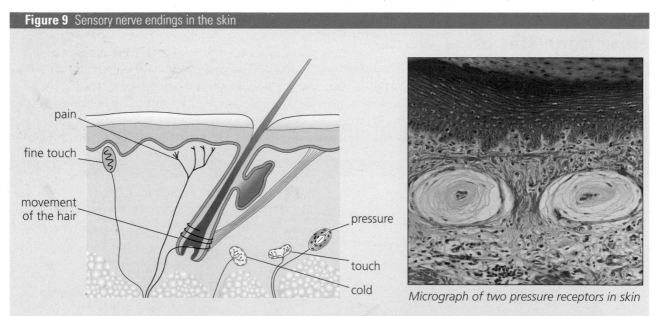

Figure 9 Sensory nerve endings in the skin

pain

fine touch

movement of the hair

pressure

touch

cold

Micrograph of two pressure receptors in skin

Summary of tongue, nose and skin

- The four basic tastes are sweet, sour, salt and bitter. Different areas of the tongue are better at detecting each of these tastes.

- Chemicals dissolve in the mucus lining the inner surfaces of the nose and stimulate olfactory cells. The olfactory cells pass nerve impulses to the brain.

- The skin acts as a sense organ and is able to detect heat, cold, touch, pressure and pain.

6.4 Eyes

What do the eyes do?

14 a What is the function of the eyes?

b Where are the tear glands?

c Give three functions of the fluid secreted by the tear gland, and two reasons why extra fluid might be secreted.

d Study your right eye in the mirror, then draw what you see. Label your drawing, using Figure 10 as a guide.

e Study Figure 10, then describe three ways in which the eye is protected.

f How many muscles are attached to the eyeball?

g Describe how you can:

  i look out of the corner of your eye

  ii roll your eyes.

The eyes convert light into nerve impulses which are then sent to the brain, where they are interpreted as sight. Each eye is a small sphere about 2 to 2.5 centimetres in diameter, with a transparent bulge at the front through which light enters.

Above the upper outer corner of each eye is a **tear gland**, also called a lachrymal gland (see Figure 10). It continuously secretes fluid that:

- keeps the eyeball moist
- cleans the surface of the eyeball
- prevents infection because it contains an enzyme called **lysozyme** that is antiseptic and destroys bacteria.

Blinking spreads this fluid over the eyeball. The fluid drains away through a duct from each lower eyelid into the side of the nose. If the eye is irritated by particles such as dust, or by chemicals such as onion juice or tear gas, the tear glands secrete extra fluid (called tears) to wash the irritant away. The tears also enter the duct to the nose, and can cause a 'runny nose'. Emotions such as sadness or happiness can also cause tears.

Eye movements are controlled by six muscles attached to the eye (see Figure 10). When all these muscles relax, the eyeball faces forwards. Contraction of one or more of these muscles causes the eye to move. Contraction of all six muscles in succession makes the eye 'roll'.

Figure 10 The eye in its socket

Left eye seen from the front

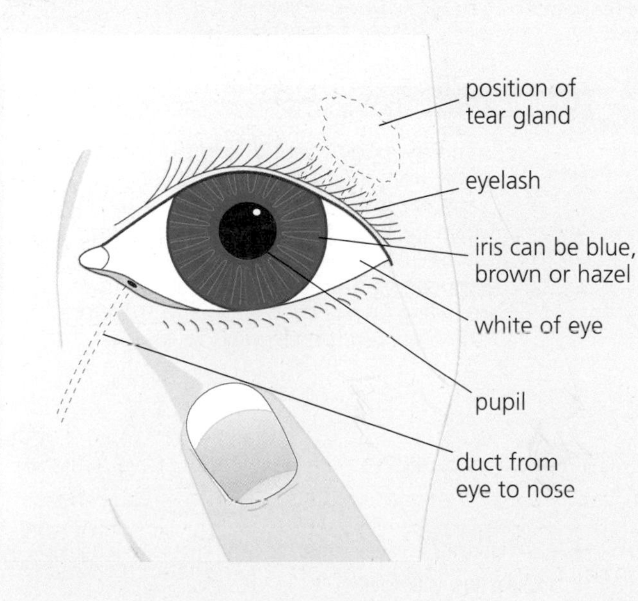

position of tear gland

eyelash

iris can be blue, brown or hazel

white of eye

pupil

duct from eye to nose

Protection and movement of the eyeball

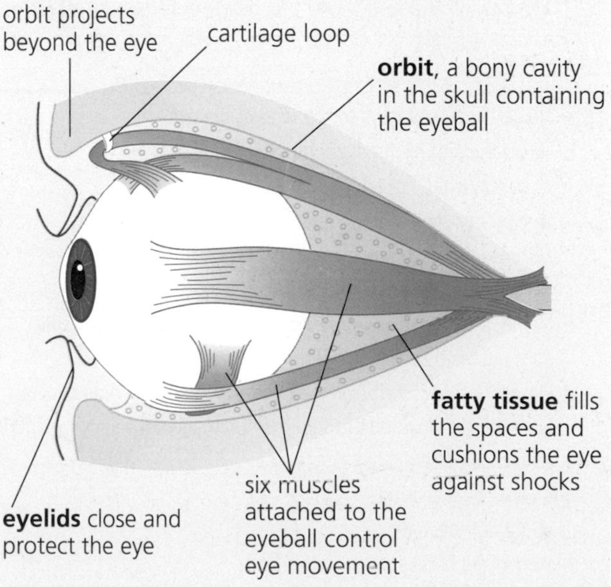

orbit projects beyond the eye

cartilage loop

orbit, a bony cavity in the skull containing the eyeball

fatty tissue fills the spaces and cushions the eye against shocks

six muscles attached to the eyeball control eye movement

eyelids close and protect the eye

What is the inside of the eye like?

Figure 11 Transverse section through the eyeball

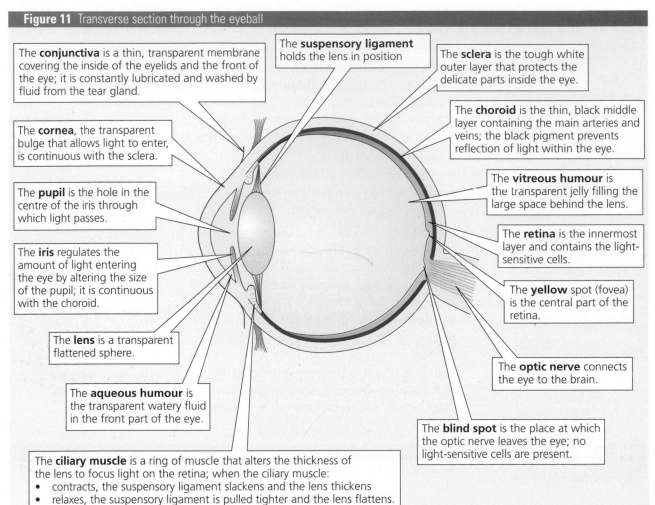

The **conjunctiva** is a thin, transparent membrane covering the inside of the eyelids and the front of the eye; it is constantly lubricated and washed by fluid from the tear gland.

The **suspensory ligament** holds the lens in position

The **sclera** is the tough white outer layer that protects the delicate parts inside the eye.

The **cornea**, the transparent bulge that allows light to enter, is continuous with the sclera.

The **choroid** is the thin, black middle layer containing the main arteries and veins; the black pigment prevents reflection of light within the eye.

The **pupil** is the hole in the centre of the iris through which light passes.

The **vitreous humour** is the transparent jelly filling the large space behind the lens.

The **iris** regulates the amount of light entering the eye by altering the size of the pupil; it is continuous with the choroid.

The **retina** is the innermost layer and contains the light-sensitive cells.

The **yellow** spot (fovea) is the central part of the retina.

The **lens** is a transparent flattened sphere.

The **optic nerve** connects the eye to the brain.

The **aqueous humour** is the transparent watery fluid in the front part of the eye.

The **blind spot** is the place at which the optic nerve leaves the eye; no light-sensitive cells are present.

The **ciliary muscle** is a ring of muscle that alters the thickness of the lens to focus light on the retina; when the ciliary muscle:
* contracts, the suspensory ligament slackens and the lens thickens
* relaxes, the suspensory ligament is pulled tighter and the lens flattens.

15 a Name the three layers of the wall of the eyeball.

  b Name the part of the eyeball that:

    i contains the light-sensitive cells

    ii contains the main blood vessels and a black pigment

    iii holds the lens in position

    iv alters the thickness of the lens.

  c Name, in order, the five transparent parts of the eyeball that light passes through to reach the retina.

  d Figure 11 shows a transverse section through the right eyeball. Consider the position of the optic nerve, then explain why Figure 11 could not be:

    i a vertical section

    ii the left eyeball.

  e Why is the blind spot so-called?

Figure 12 Finding the blind spot

Hold the book about 20 cm (8 inches) away from the face. Cover the left eye and focus the right eye on the cross. Move the book towards and away from the face. At one point, the black circle will disappear. At this point the light rays from it are falling on the blind spot, and therefore the brain is not registering an image.

16 Use Figure 12 to demonstrate the blind spot in your right eye and explain how you did this.

What is the structure of the retina?

17 a Comparing rods with cones, say which:

   i are sensitive to colour

   ii work best in bright light

   iii work best in poor light.

  b Where is the yellow spot?

  c From Figure 13, describe the distribution in the retina of:

   i cones

   ii rods.

The retina contains cells that are sensitive to light: rods and cones. **Rods** are very sensitive to light intensity, but are not sensitive to colour. Rods work best in dim light. **Cones** are sensitive to colour and work well only in good light. There are three types of cone: one type is sensitive to red light, another to green light, and the third type to blue light. All colours are a mixture of these three primary colours. Equal stimulation of all three types of cone gives a sensation of white.

The light-sensitive cells are connected to nerve fibres that pass across the surface of the retina to the blind spot. The nerve fibres then leave the eye as the optic nerve.

False-colour scanning electron micrograph of rod cells (coloured blue) and cone cells (coloured turquoise). At dusk we cannot see in as much detail or as strong colours as we see during the day, because we are using rods rather than cones.

The cones are most numerous in the part of the retina opposite the pupil. The **yellow spot** (fovea) is in the centre of the retina opposite the pupil and has only cones (see Figure 13). Moving outwards from the yellow spot, the number of cones decreases and the number of rods increases. In daylight, an object is most clearly seen when the light from it is focused directly on the yellow spot. This happens when it is looked at directly. Other nearby objects are indistinct.

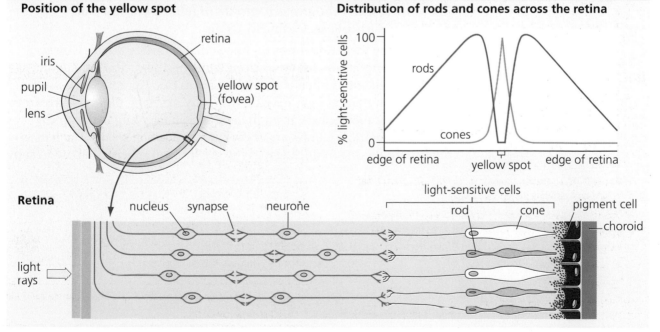

Figure 13 Structure of the retina and distribution of rods and cones

Position of the yellow spot

iris, pupil, lens, retina, yellow spot (fovea)

Distribution of rods and cones across the retina

% light-sensitive cells — rods, cones — edge of retina, yellow spot, edge of retina

Retina

light rays — nucleus, synapse, neurone — light-sensitive cells: rod, cone, pigment cell, choroid

How does the eye adapt to different light conditions?

At dusk, colours tend to fade to grey as there is no longer have enough light for the cones function and the rods take over. The rods only function when a substance called **visual purple** is present in them. Visual purple breaks down in bright light and re-forms when the light becomes dim (see Figure 14).

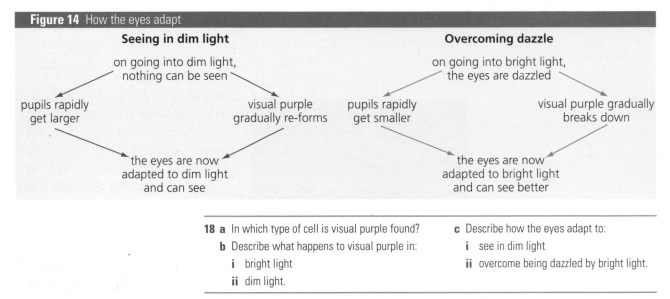

Figure 14 How the eyes adapt

Seeing in dim light

on going into dim light, nothing can be seen

pupils rapidly get larger

visual purple gradually re-forms

the eyes are now adapted to dim light and can see

Overcoming dazzle

on going into bright light, the eyes are dazzled

pupils rapidly get smaller

visual purple gradually breaks down

the eyes are now adapted to bright light and can see better

18 a In which type of cell is visual purple found?
  b Describe what happens to visual purple in:
   i bright light
   ii dim light.
  c Describe how the eyes adapt to:
   i see in dim light
   ii overcome being dazzled by bright light.

How does the eye focus light?

Light entering the eye is refracted (bent) and brought into focus on the retina by:

• the cornea, where the greatest amount of refraction takes place
• the lens, which adjusts for fine focusing.

Light reaching the retina forms an image that is upside down. However, the brain interprets the impulses from light-sensitive cells in the retina as an image of the object that is the right way up (see Figure 15).

People with normal sight have no difficulty in seeing things clearly from about 20 centimetres away from the eye. The shape of the lens rapidly adjusts so that the light rays are always focused on the retina. The lens is continually altering in thickness as the eye looks at objects that are nearer

19 a Why is light entering the eye refracted?
  b Name two parts of the eye where refraction takes place.
  c Put the following in order to explain how we see:
   • impulses are carried by the optic nerve to the brain
   • an image is formed on the retina
   • light from an object enters the eye
   • impulses are interpreted as a picture of the object
   • the light passes through the pupil
   • light-sensitive cells convert light into impulses
   • the lens focuses the light on to the retina
   • cornea focuses light rays towards the pupil.
  d What part of the eye changes shape so that light is focused on the retina?

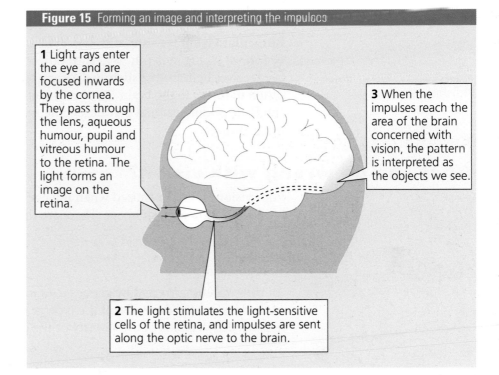

Figure 15 Forming an image and interpreting the impulses

1 Light rays enter the eye and are focused inwards by the cornea. They pass through the lens, aqueous humour, pupil and vitreous humour to the retina. The light forms an image on the retina.

3 When the impulses reach the area of the brain concerned with vision, the pattern is interpreted as the objects we see.

2 The light stimulates the light-sensitive cells of the retina, and impulses are sent along the optic nerve to the brain.

or further away. To focus on near objects, the lens thickens. The thicker, more convex shape refracts the light more. To focus on distant objects, the lens flattens and causes less refraction (see Figure 16).

As the eyes watch an object that is approaching:

- the eyeballs turn inwards to keep the pupils pointed at the object
- the pupils contract (get smaller)
- the lens thickens to bend the light rays more.

When watching an object moving away from the eyes, the opposite happens.

20 a Draw diagrams to show focusing on a near object and a distant object.

b As the eyes keep an approaching object in focus, what happens to the eyeballs, the pupils, and the lenses?

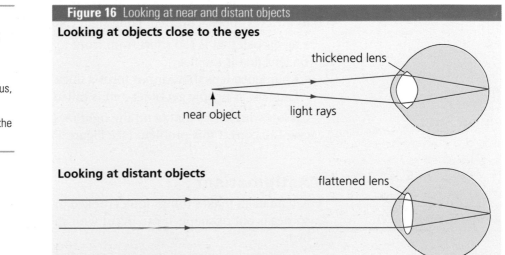

Figure 16 Looking at near and distant objects

Looking at objects close to the eyes

thickened lens

near object   light rays

Looking at distant objects

flattened lens

How do we see in three dimensions?

Binocular vision is seeing with two eyes. It is necessary for **stereoscopic vision**, or seeing in depth. When an object is viewed with both eyes, each eye receives light from a slightly different angle and sends a slightly different image to the brain. The brain combines the two images to give a single three-dimensional picture. Seeing in three dimensions enables us to judge distance.

21 Define:
  i binocular vision
  ii stereoscopic vision.

What can go wrong with vision?

Poor vision is usually caused when the eye is unable to focus light on the retina and form a sharp image. There are three common problems:

• short sight
• long sight
• astigmatism.

All three can be corrected by glasses containing suitable lenses. The shape of the lens needed depends on the type of problem. The strength of the lens needed depends of the severity of the problem.

Short sight (myopia)

People who have short sight can only clearly see things that are close to the eyes; everything else is blurred. Short sight can be caused by:

• an eyeball that is too long from front to back
• a lens that is too rounded.

Glasses with lenses that bend the light rays outwards before they reach the eyes can correct this problem (see Figure 17).

Long sight (hypermetropia)

People with long sight can see distant things clearly but everything close to the eyes appears blurred. Long sight can be caused by:

• an eyeball that is too short from front to back
• a lens that is too flat
• a hardened lens that cannot form a thick enough shape; this often happens as people get older and is called **presbyopia**.

Glasses with lenses that bend the light rays inwards before they reach the eyes can correct this problem (see Figure 17).

Astigmatism

22 What is astigmatism?

Astigmatism makes things look crooked or out of shape because the cornea is out of shape. It can occur with short sight, long sight, or on its own.

Glasses with lenses shaped to correct the fault can improve this condition.

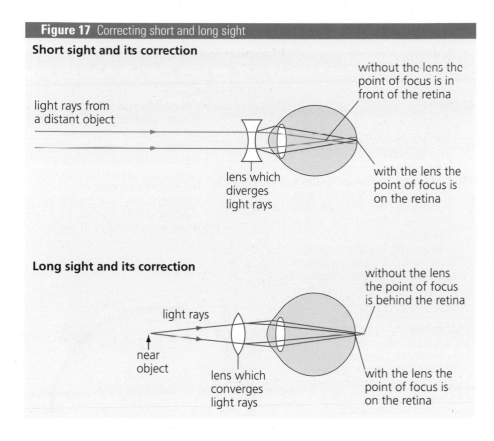

Figure 17 Correcting short and long sight

Short sight and its correction

light rays from a distant object

lens which diverges light rays

without the lens the point of focus is in front of the retina

with the lens the point of focus is on the retina

Long sight and its correction

light rays

near object

lens which converges light rays

without the lens the point of focus is behind the retina

with the lens the point of focus is on the retina

23 a Use Figure 17 to draw diagrams showing:

i short sight and how a lens can correct it

ii long sight and how a lens can correct it.

Colour-blindness

Colour-blindness is inherited and cannot be corrected. People who are colour-blind cannot distinguish between certain colours. The most common form of colour-blindness affects red and green. This is due to an absence of cones that are sensitive to red light and it affects about 8% of males and 0.4% of females.

People with normal colour vision see a ribbon of green dots in the left-hand chart and a ribbon of red dots in the right-hand chart. Those with red–green colour-blindness cannot distinguish these patterns.

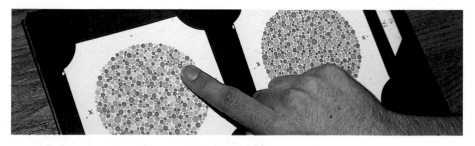

Blindness

Blindness is the absence of *useful* sight. Most registered blind people can see a little, but their sight is so poor that it cannot be adequately corrected to give useful vision. Total blindness is rare. It can be due to injury, a detached retina, diabetic eye disease or degeneration of the retina due to old age. Damage to the optic nerve or the visual area of the brain can also cause blindness.

24 What is blindness?

What can go wrong with the eyes?

Figure 18 Eye defects

Squint
The eyes look in different directions because the muscles controlling the eyeballs (Figure 10) are not working together properly. A mild squint is normal in the first six months of life, but if it persists after that, or develops in later life, corrective treatment is necessary to prevent blindness developing in one eye.
Treatment: exercises for the eye muscles, and wearing glasses; surgery may be necessary to shorten one or more of the eyeball muscles.

Conjunctivitis
Also called 'pink eye', this is an infection or irritation of the conjunctiva by such things as smoke or dust. The eyes look red and inflamed, and feel gritty and painful.
Treatment: apply the correct antibiotic or avoid the irritant.

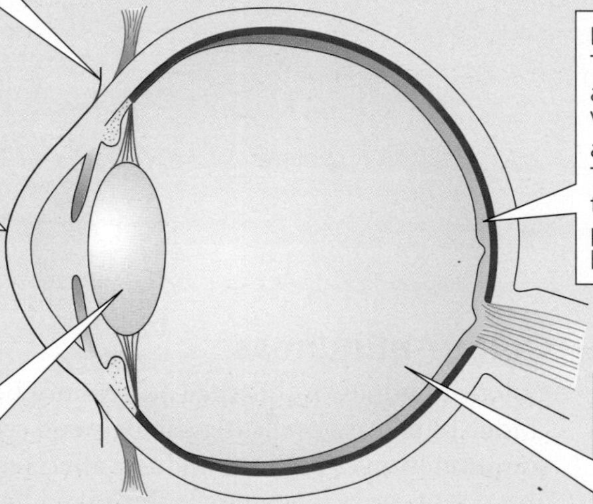

Detached retina
The retina, or part of it, comes away from the wall of the eye. Vision is lost from the affected area.
Treatment: it is often possible to 'stick' the retina back in place by surgery using a laser beam.

Scratches
Slight scratches on the cornea are painful but heal quickly. If the scratch is deep, a doctor should check it because a scar on the cornea can interfere permanently with vision.

Cataract
The lens becomes cloudy, making the pupil look milky white. Effective vision is blurred or lost completely in the affected eye.
Treatment: the lens is removed from the eye and a plastic lens must be implanted to focus light on the retina.

Glaucoma
Too much fluid within the eyeball causes pressure on the optic nerve. The result is pain, blurred vision and, if not treated, blindness.
Treatment: eye drops, tablets, or surgery to reduce the fluid.

Eye-strain
Tired and sore eyes result from working in a poor light or not wearing glasses when they are needed.
Permanent damage to the eyes does not occur.

25 a Using Figure 18, name the eye condition due to:
  i too much fluid
  ii eyeball muscles not working properly
  iii infection
  iv a cloudy lens
  v poor light.

b Name the eye condition that can be treated by:
  i exercises
  ii eye drops
  iii surgery and a plastic implant
  iv surgery with a laser beam
  v antibiotic.

Summary of the eyes

- The eye converts light into nerve impulses. The brain interprets these impulses as images to give vision.
- The retina has a layer of light-sensitive cells that can convert light into nerve impulses. The rods detect only light intensity and provide black and white vision. Rods are sensitive to low light levels.
- Cones both detect light intensity and distinguish between wavelengths of light. There are three types of cone each responding to red, green or blue light. The brain interprets impulses from these three cell types to give full colour vision.
- The fovea, or yellow spot, has only cones and gives the sharpest vision in bright light.
- Visual purple breaks down in bright light and reforms in dim light. Seeing in dim light depends on visual purple.

- The cornea of the eye provides most of the focusing power. The lens is used for fine adjustment and bringing objects at different distances from the eye into focus.
- Short sight (myopia) means objects at a distance are blurred. Short sight can be treated with a convex lens.
- Long sight (hypermetropia) means objects close to the eyes are blurred. Long sight can be treated with a concave lens.
- Colour-blindness affects men more often than women and is the inability to distinguish colours accurately. Red–green colour-blindness is the most common form.

6.5 Ears

What do the ears do?

The ears have two functions: hearing and balance. One part of the ear converts sound waves into nerve impulses that are sent to the brain and interpreted as sounds. Another part detects movements of the head. These movements are converted into nerve impulses and sent to the brain to provide information about the position of the head.

With two ears, a person can estimate from which direction sounds are coming. Sound waves from a source reach one ear before the other. The first ear sends impulses to the brain before the other; the brain can then decide on the direction of the sound.

26 a State two functions of the ear.
  b Why is it an advantage to have two ears?

How is the ear organised?

There are three parts to each ear: the outer ear, middle ear and inner ear. Only the pinna and the opening of the ear canal, which are parts of the outer ear, are visible. The middle ear and the inner ear are small and delicate, and are inside the bones of the skull. Glands in the wall of the ear canal secrete wax which:

- lubricates the ear drum and keeps it supple
- keeps insects away
- keeps the ear clean because dirt sticks to it and is removed when the wax falls out, as it does naturally.

27 State three functions of wax in the ear.

Figure 19 Structure of the ear

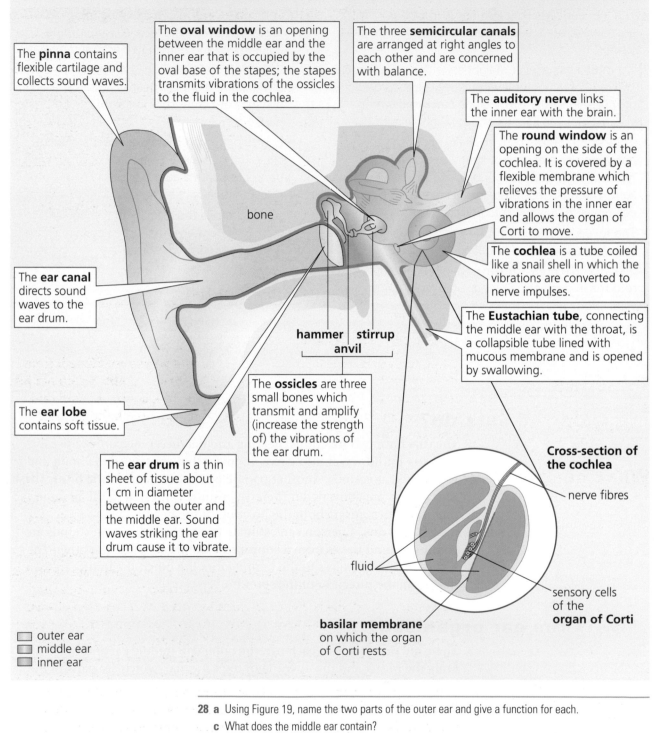

The **pinna** contains flexible cartilage and collects sound waves.

The **oval window** is an opening between the middle ear and the inner ear that is occupied by the oval base of the stapes; the stapes transmits vibrations of the ossicles to the fluid in the cochlea.

The three **semicircular canals** are arranged at right angles to each other and are concerned with balance.

The **auditory nerve** links the inner ear with the brain.

The **round window** is an opening on the side of the cochlea. It is covered by a flexible membrane which relieves the pressure of vibrations in the inner ear and allows the organ of Corti to move.

bone

The **cochlea** is a tube coiled like a snail shell in which the vibrations are converted to nerve impulses.

The **ear canal** directs sound waves to the ear drum.

hammer   stirrup
anvil

The **Eustachian tube**, connecting the middle ear with the throat, is a collapsible tube lined with mucous membrane and is opened by swallowing.

The **ossicles** are three small bones which transmit and amplify (increase the strength of) the vibrations of the ear drum.

The **ear lobe** contains soft tissue.

The **ear drum** is a thin sheet of tissue about 1 cm in diameter between the outer and the middle ear. Sound waves striking the ear drum cause it to vibrate.

Cross-section of the cochlea

nerve fibres

fluid

sensory cells of the **organ of Corti**

basilar membrane on which the organ of Corti rests

☐ outer ear
☐ middle ear
☐ inner ear

28 a Using Figure 19, name the two parts of the outer ear and give a function for each.

   c What does the middle ear contain?

   d What is the function of the ossicles?

   e What does the inner ear consist of?

   f Draw a diagram of the cochlea to show the position of the sensory cells.

How do we hear?

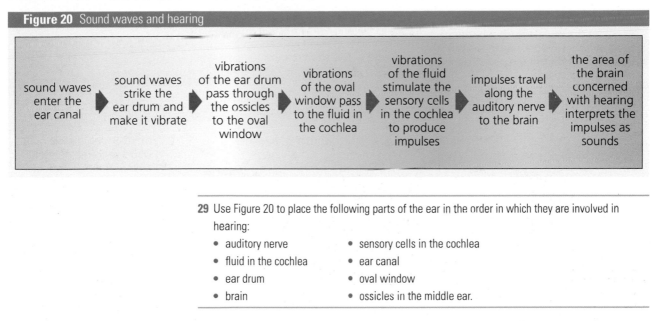

Figure 20 Sound waves and hearing

sound waves enter the ear canal ▶ sound waves strike the ear drum and make it vibrate ▶ vibrations of the ear drum pass through the ossicles to the oval window ▶ vibrations of the oval window pass to the fluid in the cochlea ▶ vibrations of the fluid stimulate the sensory cells in the cochlea to produce impulses ▶ impulses travel along the auditory nerve to the brain ▶ the area of the brain concerned with hearing interprets the impulses as sounds

29 Use Figure 20 to place the following parts of the ear in the order in which they are involved in hearing:

- auditory nerve
- fluid in the cochlea
- ear drum
- brain
- sensory cells in the cochlea
- ear canal
- oval window
- ossicles in the middle ear.

Why don't we recognise our own voice?

30 Explain why we do not recognise our own voice.

When we hear a recording of our voice, we find we sound different from the way we think we sound. This is because when we speak, we do not just hear the sound through our ears. At the same time, sound is conducted from the larynx through the skull bones and resonates in the air-filled sinuses before it reaches the cochlea.

What causes deafness?

Hearing depends on a chain of events. Damage to or disorder of any link in this chain results in deafness. Deafness can occur in one or both ears and can be of several types.

In total deafness, no sounds can be heard. It is rare for deaf people to be totally deaf. Partial deafness is more common. Some sounds are heard but not others. This makes it difficult to understand what people are saying.

Temporary deafness is due to an ear infection or to a build-up of wax. Normal hearing returns when the infection is cured or the wax removed. Permanent deafness results from damage to the ear, auditory nerve, or a part of the brain responsible for hearing. Normal hearing never returns.

There is a gradual loss of hearing from adolescence onwards. The ability to hear high-pitched sound is affected most, so it becomes difficult to distinguish consonants from each other, but vowel sounds can still be heard. It also becomes more difficult to distinguish foreground noise from background noise. For example, at parties where there is a lot of noise, it can be difficult to hear what a person near to you is saying.

Tinnitus is ringing, buzzing or hissing sounds in the ear. It might be due to any of the causes of deafness, or there may be no known cause.

31 a What is the difference between total and partial deafness?
  b What is the difference between temporary and permanent deafness?
  c What is tinnitus?

Figure 21 Causes of deafness

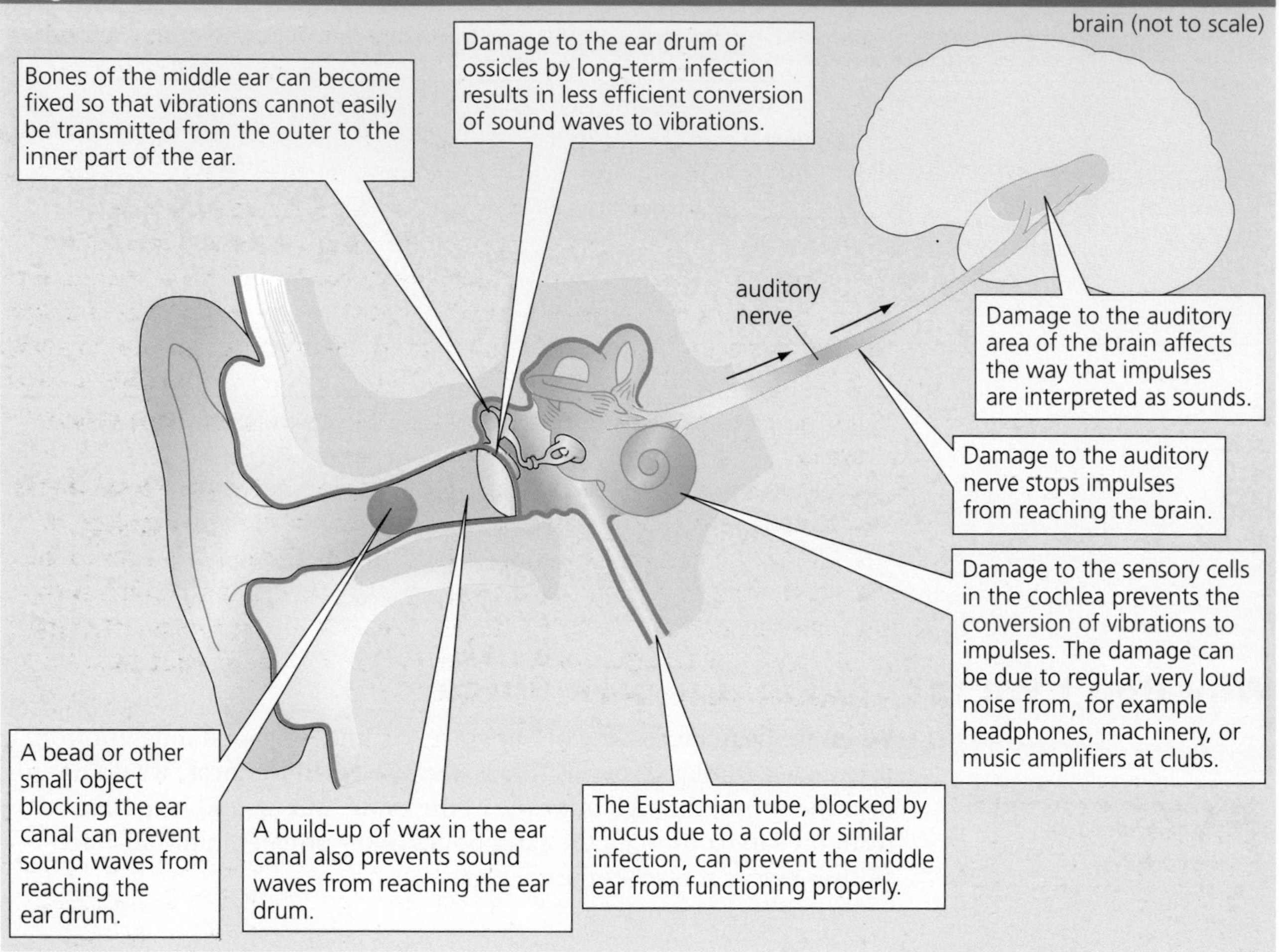

brain (not to scale)

Bones of the middle ear can become fixed so that vibrations cannot easily be transmitted from the outer to the inner part of the ear.

Damage to the ear drum or ossicles by long-term infection results in less efficient conversion of sound waves to vibrations.

auditory nerve

Damage to the auditory area of the brain affects the way that impulses are interpreted as sounds.

Damage to the auditory nerve stops impulses from reaching the brain.

Damage to the sensory cells in the cochlea prevents the conversion of vibrations to impulses. The damage can be due to regular, very loud noise from, for example headphones, machinery, or music amplifiers at clubs.

A bead or other small object blocking the ear canal can prevent sound waves from reaching the ear drum.

A build-up of wax in the ear canal also prevents sound waves from reaching the ear drum.

The Eustachian tube, blocked by mucus due to a cold or similar infection, can prevent the middle ear from functioning properly.

32 Using Figure 21, say what can prevent:

   i sound waves from reaching the ear drum (give two examples)

   ii the efficient conversion of sound waves to vibrations

   iii easy transmission of sound waves across the middle ear

   iv conversion of sound waves to impulses

   v transmission of impulses to the brain.

Why do ears 'pop'?

33 a What happens when air pressure in the outer ear rises?

  b Why does yawning or swallowing help to stop pain in the ears when landing in an aeroplane?

  c What is happening when the ears 'pop'?

If the pressures on either side of the ear drum are unequal, the ear drum bulges towards the lower pressure. For example, the slight reduction of pressure in aeroplanes before take-off causes air pressure in the outer ear to fall and the ear drum to bulge outwards. This stretching is painful and causes temporary, partial deafness. Swallowing, yawning or sucking a sweet all help to equalise the pressure by opening the Eustachian tube. This allows air to move into or out of the middle ear and a slight 'popping' is felt as the ear drum returns to its flat position. The reduced pressure is maintained during the flight, but on landing, normal pressure is restored. The air pressure in the outer ear then rises and the ear drum bulges inwards. Again, the pressure can be equalised by opening the Eustachian tube.

What causes dizziness?

The three semicircular canals are positioned at right angles to each other (see Figure 19 on page 130). They are filled with fluid, and at one end of each canal are sensory cells that are sensitive to movement.

When the position of the head changes, the sensory cells move with the head, but the fluid in the semicircular canals stays still. The movement of the sensory cells against the fluid stimulates the cells to sends nerve impulses to the brain. The brain uses this information to work out how the head is moving – even if the eyes are closed and movement cannot be seen. The brain responds by sending impulses to the appropriate muscles to keep the body balanced. So, when a person stumbles and loses balance, the brain immediately sends impulses to the appropriate muscles so that they can restore the body to its correct position (see proprioceptors on page 117).

Spinning round and round and then stopping causes dizziness. This is because the fluid in the semicircular canals continues moving after the head has stopped, so the sensory cells continue to send impulses to the brain. The impulses from the sensory cells in the ear may conflict with impulses from the eyes. So, after spinning around, the ears may tell the brain the body is still moving but the eyes show that it is not. This confusion helps to produce dizziness.

34 a Where are the sensory cells involved with balance?

 b What stimulates these cells to send impulses to the brain?

 c What type of movement causes dizziness, and why?

Summary of the ears

- The ears convert sound waves into nerve impulses, and provide information about balance and movement of the body.

- The ear is divided into three areas: outer ear, middle ear and inner ear. The outer and middle ears are air-filled but the inner ear is filled with fluid.

- Sound waves make the ear drum vibrate. The ear drum passes these vibrations on to three small bones in the middle ear called the ossicles. These pass the vibrations on to the inner ear.

- In the cochlea of the inner ear, pressure waves in the fluid stimulate nerve cells to pass impulses to the brain along the auditory nerve.

- Damage to or a disorder of any link in the chain of events that starts with sound waves entering the ear, leads to deafness.

- Deafness can be partial or total, and temporary or permanent. Hearing degenerates with age; the ability to hear high-pitched sounds is affected most.

- When we speak, we hear the sound of our own voice partly through the ears and partly by conduction through the bones of the skull.

- The semicircular canals of the inner ear are able to detect movement of the head. Information supplied to the brain by sense cells in the semicircular canals is essential for keeping the body balanced. Confusing impulses from the inner ear, perhaps due to rapid movement of the head, can cause dizziness.

6.6 The brain

The brain weighs about 1500 grams in an adult and sits within the skull in a bath of fluid called the cerebrospinal fluid (CSF). The CSF both supports the brain (like water in a swimming pool supports your body), and acts as a shock absorber. The brain needs protection because brain tissue is very delicate. When neurones are destroyed they are not replaced. The brain has four main functions:

- receiving information from the sense organs
- controlling muscle movements
- linking the nervous system with the endocrine system
- providing consciousness, intelligence, reasoning, memory, personality and self-awareness.

Areas of the brain are specialised for different functions (see Figure 22).

35 a Draw a diagram of the brain. Label the cerebrum, a cerebral hemisphere, cerebellum, brain stem.

b Give four functions of the brain.

c Why is it necessary to protect the brain?

d How is the brain protected?

e Write down which part of the brain controls:

  i breathing and heartbeat

  ii walking and balance.

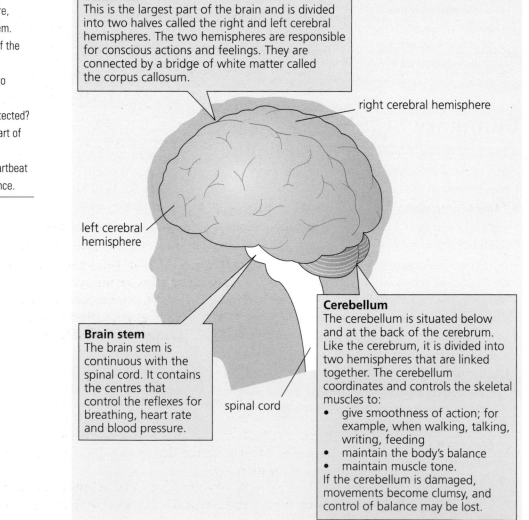

Figure 22 The main parts of the brain

Cerebrum
This is the largest part of the brain and is divided into two halves called the right and left cerebral hemispheres. The two hemispheres are responsible for conscious actions and feelings. They are connected by a bridge of white matter called the corpus callosum.

right cerebral hemisphere

left cerebral hemisphere

Brain stem
The brain stem is continuous with the spinal cord. It contains the centres that control the reflexes for breathing, heart rate and blood pressure.

spinal cord

Cerebellum
The cerebellum is situated below and at the back of the cerebrum. Like the cerebrum, it is divided into two hemispheres that are linked together. The cerebellum coordinates and controls the skeletal muscles to:
- give smoothness of action; for example, when walking, talking, writing, feeding
- maintain the body's balance
- maintain muscle tone.
If the cerebellum is damaged, movements become clumsy, and control of balance may be lost.

What is the inside of the brain like?

Most of the brain is covered with a layer of grey matter with many folds. The folding allows the number of neurones in the layer to be greatly increased. Each neurone connects with many others, and the millions and millions of neurones form a complex and elaborate network that is still not fully understood. The inner areas of the brain consist mostly of white matter. The brain is surrounded by three membranes called the **meninges** (see Figure 23).

36 a Give a reason for the many folds in the layer of grey matter.

b What are the meninges?

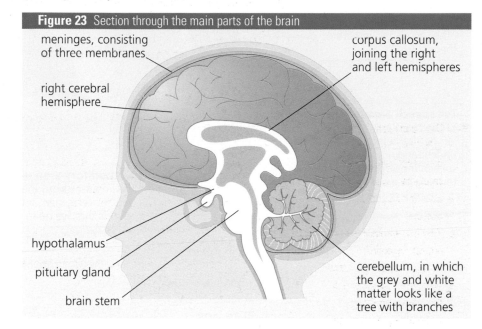

Figure 23 Section through the main parts of the brain

meninges, consisting of three membranes

corpus callosum, joining the right and left hemispheres

right cerebral hemisphere

hypothalamus

pituitary gland

brain stem

cerebellum, in which the grey and white matter looks like a tree with branches

What do the cerebral hemispheres do?

The two cerebral hemispheres have slightly different functions. The left cerebral hemisphere is more concerned with language, mathematical ability and logic. The right is more concerned with colour, shape, creativity, imagination and day-dreaming.

In each hemisphere, the motor, sensory and visual areas relate to the opposite side of the body. For example, if the motor area in the right cerebral hemisphere is damaged, the left side of the body is paralysed.

How does the brain remember?

37 a What are the differences in function between the two cerebral hemispheres?

b What happens if the motor area on the left side of the brain is damaged?

Information goes into the brain as nerve impulses which form an electrochemical pattern that can be stored and later recalled. **Short-term memory** recalls information about recent events, such as what you did yesterday. Most of this information is then lost, but some is stored away as **long-term memory.**

Elderly people often remember occasions from their childhood more easily than recent events. This is because short-term memory tends to reduce with age.

Figure 24 Map of functions of the left cerebral hemisphere

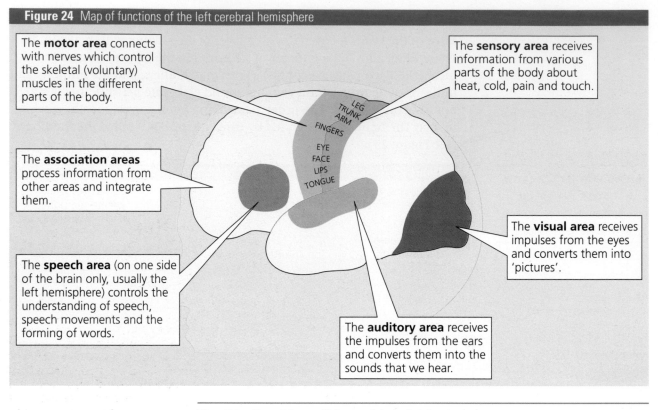

The **motor area** connects with nerves which control the skeletal (voluntary) muscles in the different parts of the body.

The **sensory area** receives information from various parts of the body about heat, cold, pain and touch.

The **association areas** process information from other areas and integrate them.

The **visual area** receives impulses from the eyes and converts them into 'pictures'.

The **speech area** (on one side of the brain only, usually the left hemisphere) controls the understanding of speech, speech movements and the forming of words.

The **auditory area** receives the impulses from the ears and converts them into the sounds that we hear.

LEG
TRUNK
ARM
FINGERS
EYE
FACE
LIPS
TONGUE

38 a Using Figure 24, say which area of the brain is involved when:

  i you feel something cold touch you

  ii you hear music

  iii you speak

  iv you look at something

  v muscles are used

  vi information from the various areas is processed.

Summary of the brain

- The brain is protected by the bones of the skull and the cerebrospinal fluid.
- The two cerebral hemispheres are responsible for conscious actions and feelings. The hemispheres are joined by the corpus callosum.
- The cerebellum coordinates movement, balance and muscle tone.
- The brain stem controls many of the internal conditions of the body.

- Different areas of the cerebral hemispheres are responsible for different parts of the body. Damage to a part of the cerebral hemisphere is shown as paralysis or loss of feeling on a corresponding part of the body. The left side of the brain controls the right side of the body, while the right side of the brain controls the left side of the body.
- Memory can be short-term (what happened yesterday) or long-term (what happened weeks or years ago). Short-term memory becomes less efficient with age.

6.7 Behaviour

What is a reflex action?

38 What is the difference between a reflex action and a reflex arc?

A **reflex action** is an automatic response to a stimulus. An example is the knee-jerk reflex. A **reflex arc** is the pathway along which impulses travel from the receptor of the stimulus, into the CNS and out to the effector that carries out the response (see Figure 25).

Figure 25 Knee-jerk reflex and the parts of a reflex action

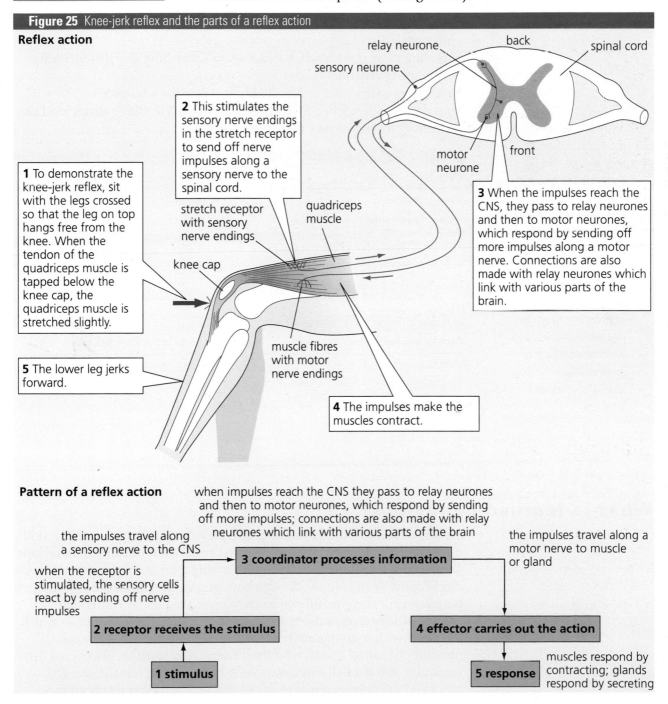

Reflex action

relay neurone

back

spinal cord

sensory neurone

2 This stimulates the sensory nerve endings in the stretch receptor to send off nerve impulses along a sensory nerve to the spinal cord.

motor neurone

front

1 To demonstrate the knee-jerk reflex, sit with the legs crossed so that the leg on top hangs free from the knee. When the tendon of the quadriceps muscle is tapped below the knee cap, the quadriceps muscle is stretched slightly.

stretch receptor with sensory nerve endings

quadriceps muscle

3 When the impulses reach the CNS, they pass to relay neurones and then to motor neurones, which respond by sending off more impulses along a motor nerve. Connections are also made with relay neurones which link with various parts of the brain.

knee cap

5 The lower leg jerks forward.

muscle fibres with motor nerve endings

4 The impulses make the muscles contract.

Pattern of a reflex action

when impulses reach the CNS they pass to relay neurones and then to motor neurones, which respond by sending off more impulses; connections are also made with relay neurones which link with various parts of the brain

the impulses travel along a sensory nerve to the CNS

the impulses travel along a motor nerve to muscle or gland

when the receptor is stimulated, the sensory cells react by sending off nerve impulses

3 coordinator processes information

2 receptor receives the stimulus

4 effector carries out the action

1 stimulus

5 response

muscles respond by contracting; glands respond by secreting

Reflex actions are made quickly and without thinking: when the body receives a certain stimulus it always gives the same response. The response is made by muscles or glands.

Reflex actions are inherited and do not have to be learned. Such reflexes are usually very rapid and often protect the body from harm. Examples are:

- the pupil reflex in which the pupil changes in size according to changes in the amount of light entering the eye (see Figure 27 on page 141)
- blinking when something moves close to the eye quickly and unexpectedly
- moving away quickly when treading on something sharp or touching something very hot
- coughing when solid or liquid matter enters the windpipe
- producing saliva when food enters the mouth (thinking about food or smelling it can produce the same result).

39 a Copy and complete Table 2.

b Demonstrate the knee-jerk reflex.

c Describe how the knee-jerk reflex happens.

d Copy and complete Table 3. You might wish to refer back to Figure 25.

e Using Figure 25 as a guide, describe the reflex action that follows standing on a pin. Start with: sensory nerve endings in the foot react by sending nerve impulses.

Table 2 Some reflex actions

Stimulus	Response
food in the mouth	produce saliva
solid or liquid matter in the windpipe	
treading on something sharp	
sudden movement close to the eye	
amount of light entering the eye changes	

Table 3 Parts of a reflex action

Parts of a reflex action	Equivalent parts in the knee-jerk reflex
stimulus	a tap below the knee-cap
receptor	
coordinator	
effector	
response	

What is learned behaviour?

Talking, reading, writing, dancing, and playing an instrument are all skills that have to be learned; they are **learned responses**, or learned behaviour. Some learned responses, for example driving a car and riding a bicycle, can become nearly automatic after enough practice. Once these skills have been learned, they are difficult to change and not usually forgotten.

A **conditioned response** is a special sort of learned behaviour in which the response has no natural relationship to the stimulus. A Russian physiologist called Pavlov, who lived from 1849 to 1936, discovered this. He found that if a bell was always rung before a dog was fed, the dog produced saliva in response to the sound of a bell even whithout food.

40 a List some skills that you do almost automatically.

b Describe a conditioned response.

41 a What are habits?

  b List some of your habits.

Habits are a type of conditioned response. They are actions that have been repeated so often, they have become automatic; for example, smoking after a meal, swearing, nail biting, and saying 'thank you'.

What are voluntary actions?

42 a What are voluntary actions?

  b Name four voluntary actions that you have carried out today.

Voluntary actions are actions that require conscious thought. We choose whether or not to them carry out. They can be altered, stopped or repeated. Voluntary actions are carried out by skeletal muscles. Examples of voluntary actions are: getting up in the morning, having breakfast, going out or staying indoors, and so on throughout the day.

What is the autonomic nervous system?

The **autonomic nervous system** is the part of the nervous system that regulates internal functions (see Figure 26).

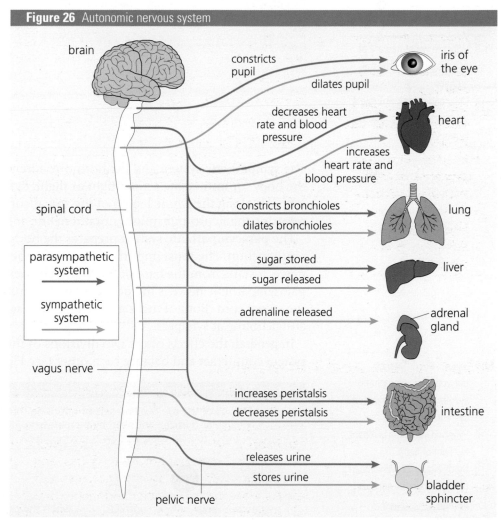

Figure 26 Autonomic nervous system

The autonomic nervous system consists of nerves which link the brain and spinal cord with various organs in the head and trunk. These nerves control the activities of smooth muscle, cardiac muscle, endocrine glands and sweat glands. The actions controlled by the autonomic nervous system are almost entirely reflex actions, so we are often not conscious that they are taking place. Examples are:

- maintaining heart rate and blood pressure
- breathing
- digestion
- excretion
- hormone production.

The autonomic nervous system is divided into two parts:

- the sympathetic system • the parasympathetic system.

Table 4 Some actions of the autonomic nervous system

Part of body	Action of sympathetic nerve	Action of parasympathetic nerve
iris	dilates	constricts
heart		
lung		
liver		
intestine		
bladder sphincter		

43 a Why are we not aware of actions controlled by the autonomic nervous system?

b Copy and complete Table 4. You might wish to refer to Figure 26.

The **sympathetic system** and the hormone adrenaline together prepare the body for immediate action: fight or flight. Sympathetic nerves arise at intervals along the whole length of the spinal cord. These nerves act by releasing the neuro-transmitter noradrenaline at synapses.

The **parasympathetic system** prepares the body for rest, excretion and reproduction. The most important parasympathetic nerve is the vagus nerve. It starts from the base of the brain. The next most important parasympathetic nerve is the pelvic nerve. It starts from the lower end of the spinal cord. Both of these nerves act by releasing the neuro-transmitter acetylcholine at synapses.

In general, the effects of the two divisions of the autonomic nervous system counteract and balance each other (see Figure 27).

44 a Explain the difference between the sympathetic system and parasympathetic system.

b What do you think is meant by 'fight or flight'?

c Study Figure 27. Which part of the autonomic nervous system:

 i dilates the pupil

 ii constricts the pupil?

Figure 27 Effects of the autonomic nervous system on the pupil

The iris of the eye has two sets of opposing muscles:
- circular muscle controlled by the parasympathetic nervous system
- radial muscle controlled by the sympathetic nervous system.

Dilated pupil — iris — pupil

when the radial muscle contracts, the pupil enlarges, so more light enters the eye

Constricted pupil

when the circular muscle contracts, the pupil becomes smaller, so less light enters the eye

Summary of behaviour

- A reflex action is an automatic response to a stimulus. It is not learned and is passed from parents to offspring through the genes.

- Reflex actions do not need to involve the brain. Reflexes are often concerned with protecting the body from harm.

- Conditioning is a form of learned behaviour in which an animal associates one stimulus with another and produces the same response to either one.

- Actions that require conscious thought are called voluntary actions.

- The autonomic nervous system controls a range of processes inside the body. It is not under conscious control.

- The sympathetic system works with the hormone adrenaline to prepare the body for flight or fight.

- The parasympathetic system prepares the body for rest.

6.8 Disorders of the nervous system

Disorders of the nervous system include:

- mental disability
- mental illness (psychiatric disorder)
- diseases of the nervous system (neuropathology).

45 List three types of disorder that affect the nervous system.

What can cause mental disability?

People with mental disability have reduced powers of learning, reasoning, and memory. There are two causes: interrupted brain development and brain damage.

- **Interrupted brain development**
  This might be caused by a genetic defect, for example by Down's syndrome (page 166), untreated phenylketonuria (page 204) or thyroid deficiency (page 204). Unsuitable conditions in the womb, caused for example by a German measles infection during early pregnancy, can affect development of the brain. Oxygen starvation during birth can also affect development of the brain.

- **Brain damage**
  This can be caused by head injury, meningitis, and carbon monoxide poisoning.

46 a List the effects of a mental disability.

  b What can cause failure of the brain to develop normally?

  c What can cause brain damage later in life?

  d What help can be given to people with a mental disability?

The 7-year-old boy on the left has Down's syndrome; his older brother does not. Brain cells that are undeveloped or damaged are not replaced. However, special training can often help in the development of the skills needed for daily life.

What is mental illness?

In mental illness, the brain has usually developed normally and is not damaged, but there is a behaviour disorder. The disorder may last for weeks, months or years, and during this time, the affected person's behaviour differs from socially accepted norms.

There are two types of mental illness:

- neurosis
- psychosis.

It is normal to feel anxious, worried or depressed from time to time. These are normal responses to difficult circumstances such as the illness of a close relative, stress at work or school, or money problems. However, a person whose anxiety or depression interferes with normal life, may be suffering from **neurosis**. Such a person is fully aware of both the problem and its effects.

There are different forms of neurosis.

- **Anxiety neurosis**
  A person with this condition becomes so anxious about trivial matters that their normal life style is seriously affected. The anxiety can cause fainting, dizziness, headache, tremor, sweating, poor concentration, diarrhoea, breathlessness and sexual difficulties. The anxiety may be sufficiently severe to interfere with normal relationships with family and friends.
- **Depression**
  Depression results in a loss of interest in other people and activities, and a lack of self-confidence with feelings of being inadequate, hopeless and helpless. Often the patient feels very tired and suffers from insomnia. Appetite may increase or decrease.
- **Phobia**
  A phobia is an extreme and irrational fear. Almost anything can be the object of a phobia. For example, animals such as spiders, snakes, or birds; activities such as flying; being in certain conditions such as open spaces (agoraphobia), or enclosed spaces (claustrophobia).

In **psychosis**, the sufferers are out of touch with reality and are unaware that their behaviour is considered abnormal.

There are different forms of psychosis.

- **Schizophrenia**
  A person with schizophrenia is emotionally distant and cool and withdraws into a private, unreal world with delusions and hallucinations. This illness usually starts in adolescence, and its cause is unknown. A complete cure is unusual but treatment can result in long periods of normal behaviour.
- **Manic depression**
  The behaviour of people with this condition swings between being extremely over-active, often to no purpose (mania), and extremely depressed to the point of immobility and complete withdrawal.

47 a What is mental illness?
  b Describe the difference between neurosis and psychosis.
  c List three forms of neurosis.
  d Give some examples of phobias.
  d Name two forms of psychosis.

Spike Milligan is a successful comedian who has had a lifelong career in comedy. He also suffers from manic depression and has spent time in hospital on a number of occaisions.

What diseases affect the nervous system?

Like other parts of the body, the brain, spinal cord and nerves can be affected by disease. If disease destroys neurone cell bodies, they cannot be replaced. However, if a nerve is damaged, the nerve fibres may be able to regenerate and heal themselves. If a nerve is cut, the ends can be sewn together and will heal, but the nerve fibres may not connect up again in the right way. When this happens, the part of the body served by the nerve cannot function normally.

Multiple sclerosis (MS)

This condition develops when small scattered patches of nerve tissue in the brain and spinal cord degenerate. The nerve fibres lose their myelin sheaths and so cannot conduct impulses. The symptoms of MS depend on which parts of the CNS are affected: perhaps blurred vision, unco-ordinated movements, slurred speech and unsteady walking.

MS usually starts between the ages of 20 and 50. The disease comes and goes, affecting different parts of the nervous system in turn. Recovery between episodes is often not complete. In severe cases, the episodes recur after short intervals and the patient becomes more and more disabled.

48 a What is the age range in which multiple sclerosis usually starts?

b What happens in the CNS in multiple sclerosis and what are the symptoms?

Dementia

Dementia is the slow, progressive loss of the abilities to know and to reason. It results in absent-mindedness, confusion, and inability to think. Dementia usually occurs in older people, often due to Alzheimer's disease. Less commonly, it can occur as a result of many small strokes, which damage parts of the brain.

Epilepsy

The characteristic of this disorder is temporary loss of consciousness. An absence of consciousness for a few seconds is known as **petit mal**. When unconsciousness is accompanied by convulsion (a fit or seizure), it is known as **grand mal**. Grand mal has three stages.

- **First stage**
  The patient goes rigid, becomes unconscious and falls, often with a cry. This stage lasts about half a minute.
- **Second stage**
  The patient makes jerking movements of the body, arms, legs, face and jaw. He or she may froth at the mouth and urinate. This stage lasts from half a minute to two minutes, during which the patient remains unconscious.
- **Third stage**
  The patient relaxes and usually goes into a deep sleep for up to an hour.

It is now possible to control epilepsy with drugs. Figure 28 shows the recommended procedure should you find someone who is having an epileptic fit.

Figure 28 What to do during an epileptic fit

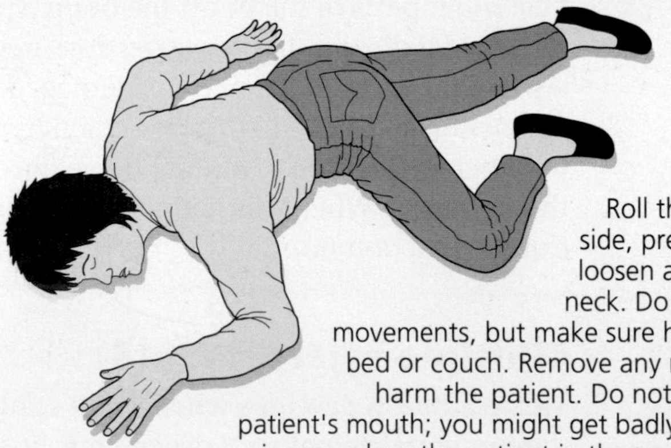

The recovery position

Roll the patient onto his or her side, preferably on the floor, and loosen anything tight around the neck. Do not restrain the patient's movements, but make sure he or she cannot fall off a bed or couch. Remove any nearby objects that could harm the patient. Do not put your fingers into the patient's mouth; you might get badly bitten. When the attack is over, place the patient in the recovery position as shown.

Meningitis

Meningitis is inflammation of the meninges covering the CNS (see Figure 23 on page 135). It is caused by infection with viruses or, less often but more seriously, with bacteria.

49 a What is dementia and what does it result in?

b Name two causes of dementia.

c Write down:
  i the characteristic of epilepsy
  ii the difference between the two forms of epilepsy
  iii how epilepsy can be controlled.

d What procedure is recommended for an epileptic fit?

e What is meningitis and what is it caused by?

What causes headaches?

Headaches are very common and can have many causes (see Figure 29). Rest and relaxation or a mild analgesic (pain reliever) can often help. If a headache lasts for more than a few days, the sufferer should go to a doctor.

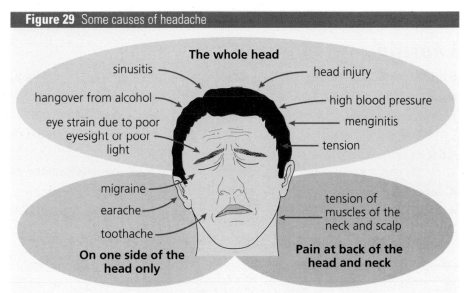

Figure 29 Some causes of headache

The whole head
- sinusitis
- hangover from alcohol
- eye strain due to poor eyesight or poor light
- head injury
- high blood pressure
- menginitis
- tension

On one side of the head only
- migraine
- earache
- toothache

Pain at back of the head and neck
- tension of muscles of the neck and scalp

50 a List seven possible causes when the whole head aches.

b What might be the cause of headache on one side only?

c What might cause pain at the back of the head and neck?

d What distinguishes a migraine from other forms of headache?

Migraine usually takes the form of a severe headache lasting from a few hours to a day or longer. A migraine often begins with the patient seeing 'flashing lights', and is associated with nausea, vomiting, and dislike of bright light. A migraine is sometimes brought on by certain foods such as chocolate, cheese and red wine, and by the contraceptive pill.

Summary of disorders of the nervous system

- Disorders of the nervous system include mental disability, mental illness, and diseases of the nervous system.
- Mental disability can be caused by genetic problems, conditions in the womb, damage during birth or an accident or illness after birth.
- Some forms of mental illness do not appear to have corresponding physical damage to a part of the brain.

- A person suffering from a neurosis knows that he or she has a mental problem and can understand how this affects mental state. A person suffering from a psychosis is not aware that he or she is mentally ill.
- Multiple sclerosis, dementia, epilepsy and meningitis are illnesses that physically affect nervous tissue.

The *endocrine* system

7

Learning objectives

By the end of this chapter you should be able to:

- **define** the word hormone
- **describe** the organisation of the endocrine system
- **list** the functions of the hypothalamus, pituitary, thyroid and adrenal glands
- **describe** the role of the sex hormones
- **define** the term homeostasis

- **explain** how the level of thyroid hormone is maintained
- **explain** how the pancreas maintains blood sugar level
- **explain** how the body maintains body temperature
- **explain** how the pituitary gland and kidneys maintain water balance.

7.1 The endocrine system

What are hormones?

The **endocrine system** produces hormones (see Figure 1). A **hormone** is a chemical produced by an endocrine gland in one part of the body and transported in the bloodstream to affect organs or tissues in another part. Although hormones travel to all parts of the body, each only affects certain tissues or organs called **target organs**.

Hormones control a wide variety of processes. Some hormones act quickly, for example adrenaline; others, such as growth hormone, produce a slower response and control many important long-term processes.

1 a What is a hormone and how does it travel around the body?

b After studying Figure 1, copy and complete Table 1.

Table 1 Endocrine glands			
Endocrine gland	Position in body	Hormone(s)	Function of hormone
pituitary gland			
hypothalamus			
thyroid gland			
parathyroid glands			
pancreas			
adrenal glands			
ovaries			
testes			

Figure 1 Endocrine glands and their hormones

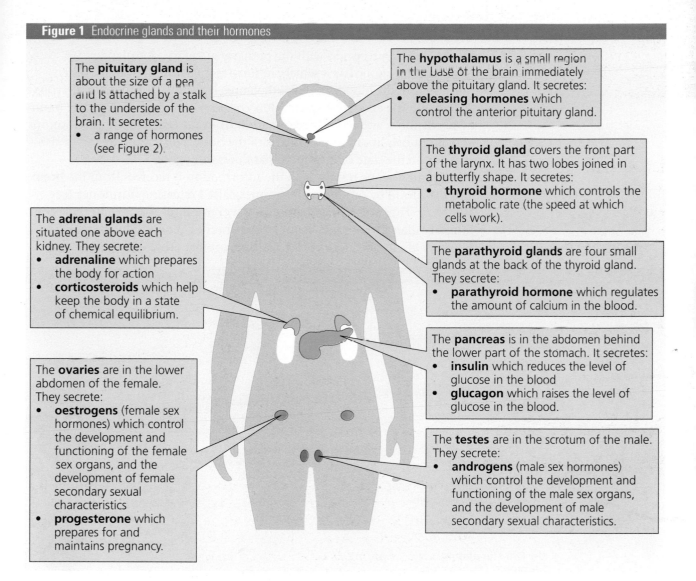

The **pituitary gland** is about the size of a pea and is attached by a stalk to the underside of the brain. It secretes:
- a range of hormones (see Figure 2).

The **hypothalamus** is a small region in the base of the brain immediately above the pituitary gland. It secretes:
- **releasing hormones** which control the anterior pituitary gland.

The **thyroid gland** covers the front part of the larynx. It has two lobes joined in a butterfly shape. It secretes:
- **thyroid hormone** which controls the metabolic rate (the speed at which cells work).

The **adrenal glands** are situated one above each kidney. They secrete:
- **adrenaline** which prepares the body for action
- **corticosteroids** which help keep the body in a state of chemical equilibrium.

The **parathyroid glands** are four small glands at the back of the thyroid gland. They secrete:
- **parathyroid hormone** which regulates the amount of calcium in the blood.

The **pancreas** is in the abdomen behind the lower part of the stomach. It secretes:
- **insulin** which reduces the level of glucose in the blood
- **glucagon** which raises the level of glucose in the blood.

The **ovaries** are in the lower abdomen of the female. They secrete:
- **oestrogens** (female sex hormones) which control the development and functioning of the female sex organs, and the development of female secondary sexual characteristics
- **progesterone** which prepares for and maintains pregnancy.

The **testes** are in the scrotum of the male. They secrete:
- **androgens** (male sex hormones) which control the development and functioning of the male sex organs, and the development of male secondary sexual characteristics.

How do endocrine and exocrine glands differ?

Glands make and release substances that have an effect elsewhere in the body. **Endocrine glands** secrete hormones directly into the bloodstream. Endocrine glands are ductless glands. **Exocrine glands** release secretions into ducts through which the secretions pass to the place where they are required, for example, sweat glands, salivary glands and tear glands.

The pancreas, ovaries and testes have both endocrine and exocrine functions.

2 a Give one difference between endocrine glands and exocrine glands.

  b Give two examples of:

    i endocrine glands

    ii exocrine glands

    iii glands that have both endocrine and exocrine functions.

What do the hypothalamus and pituitary gland do?

The hypothalamus works with the pituitary gland to control many important hormone levels which, in turn, regulate the amount of other hormones in the blood. The hypothalamus is the link between the nervous system and the endocrine system. It is connected to many areas of the brain by nerve fibres, and receives information from the brain about the emotions and about conditions in other parts of the body. The hypothalamus is also sensitive to the state of the blood that flows through it.

The hypothalamus responds to the information it receives from the brain and the blood by producing hormones called releasing hormones (see Figure 2). These releasing hormones travel the short distance to the pituitary gland where they regulate the anterior pituitary hormones. The pituitary gland produces hormones that control other endocrine glands.

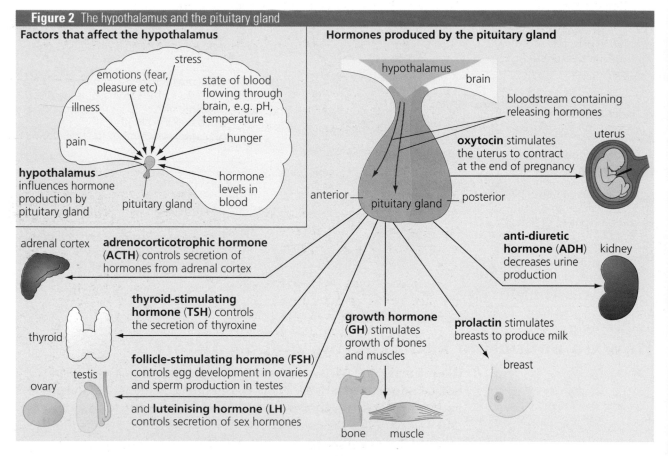

Figure 2 The hypothalamus and the pituitary gland

Why is the thyroid gland important?

The thyroid gland produces thyroid hormone. It is essential for normal development in children and the control of metabolic rate.

A baby with an inactive thyroid develops into an individual who is under-sized and whose brain is under-developed. The medical term for this condition is **cretinism**. To prevent cretinism, blood is tested at birth for thyroid hormone. If none is present, regular doses of thyroid hormone are given to enable the baby to grow and develop normally.

In some adults the thyroid gland may not function properly and can be either over-active or under-active. An **over-active thyroid** produces too much thyroid hormone, so the body then burns up energy too fast. This results in restlessness, irritability, increased appetite and weight loss. The condition can be treated by:

- tablets to slow down the production of thyroid hormone
- surgery to remove part of the gland
- radioactive iodine to destroy part of the gland.

An **under-active thyroid** produces too little thyroid hormone. This results in slower movements, a placid nature, an increase in weight, feeling the cold, no sweating, a gruff voice, and dry skin and hair. The condition can be treated by regular doses of thyroid hormone.

Iodine is required to make thyroid hormone. A shortage of iodine in the diet causes enlargement of the thyroid gland, and this enlargement is called **goitre**.

---

3 a Where is the hypothalamus?

b What sort of information does the hypothalamus receive from the blood flowing through the brain?

c What information does the hypothalamus receive from other parts of the brain?

d List the four hormones secreted by the anterior pituitary that affect other endocrine glands, and name the glands they target.

e Name the other two hormones produced by the anterior pituitary and say which body part each affects.

f Name the two hormones secreted by the posterior pituitary, and say what each does.

4 a What effect does an inactive thyroid have on the development of a baby?

b Contrast the effect of over-activity and under-activity of the thyroid gland in an adult.

c Describe goitre and give one cause of this condition.

Why is the adrenal gland important?

There are two separate parts to each adrenal gland: the **adrenal cortex** is the outer part surrounding the central **adrenal medulla** (see Figure 3).

The adrenal medulla continuously produces small amounts of adrenaline. When a person feels angry, excited or frightened, extra adrenaline is secreted to prepare the body for physical action. This extra secretion of adrenaline is sometimes called the 'fight or flight' reaction and has the following effects:

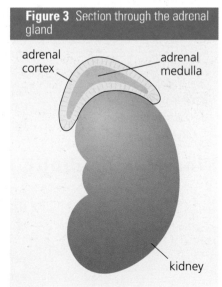

Figure 3 Section through the adrenal gland

adrenal cortex

adrenal medulla

kidney

- rate of heartbeat increases
- rate and depth of breathing increase
- glycogen is converted to glucose
- blood is diverted from the skin and gut to the muscles (people turn 'white with anger' or 'pale with fear' and get a 'sinking feeling' in the gut)
- there is an urge to remove faeces and urine (in extreme cases this urge cannot be controlled)
- pupils dilate.

5 a What are the two parts of the adrenal gland?

b What does extra adrenaline prepare the body for?

c List the effects of extra adrenaline secretion.

The adrenal cortex secretes a number of hormones called corticosteroids. Corticosteroids are often just called steroids. They include:

- **cortisol** which regulates the metabolism of carbohydrates, fats and proteins
- **aldosterone** which helps to control blood pressure and salt balance.

6 Name two steroids and say what each does.

What are the sex hormones?

Male sex hormones are called androgens, and female sex hormones are called oestrogens. Normal males also have small amounts of oestrogens, and normal females have small amounts of androgens.

Testosterone is the most important male sex hormone. It increases protein production and the formation of muscle tissue, and is responsible for the development of the male secondary sexual characteristics.

Oestradiol is the most important female sex hormone. It is necessary for the development of female secondary sexual characteristics. During pregnancy, the placenta acts as an endocrine gland. It secretes several hormones including human chorionic gonadotrophin (HCG). HCG is the hormone tested for in a pregnancy test.

What is hormone replacement therapy (HRT)?

The menopause usually occurs in middle age when production of the female sex hormones controlling the menstrual cycle declines. This change in hormone balance can produce 'hot flushes', sweating and depression. Women may be offered HRT to relieve symptoms. Doctors prescribe cycles of female sex hormones that correspond with the menstrual cycle and so reduce the symptoms.

7 a Which hormone is tested for in a pregnancy test?

b What is HRT?

c Which bone condition does HRT help to prevent?

After the menopause, calcium is lost from the skeleton at an increased rate. This can lead to a weakening of the bones called **osteoporosis**. HRT can reduce the rate of calcium loss and is sometimes given to women to help slow down osteoporosis.

What are anabolic steroids?

Anabolic steroids are artificial hormones. They resemble testosterone in that they increase muscle tissue, but they have less effect on other male characteristics.

Athletes who take 'steroids' or other drugs to increase the bulk and power of their muscles are disqualified from competitions when they are found out. They also risk grave side-effects. When men take anabolic steroids, sperm production declines and impotence is more likely.

8 a What are the effects of testosterone?

b What are anabolic steroids?

c Why do some athletes take steroids?

d List two side-effects of anabolic steroids in males and four in females.

The side-effects of anabolic steroids in women are more obvious than in men: skin becomes coarse and more hairy, voice deepens, and periods become irregular. There is also an increased build up of cholesterol in blood vessels. It is thought that the former East German olympic women swimmers were given steroids by their trainers.

7.2 Homeostasis

What is homeostasis?

Homeostasis means maintaining a steady state (homeo = same, stasis = state). Conditions outside the body, the **external environment**, are continuously changing, but conditions inside the body, **the internal environment**, must be kept within narrow limits. For example, cells are surrounded by tissue fluid. When its condition is kept within narrow limits, the tissue fluid allows the cells to function well and the body to remain healthy.

Each of the conditions that together make up the body's internal environment can vary slightly, but too great a change to any of them leads to ill-health. These conditions include:

9 a Give the meaning of:
  i homeostasis
  ii internal environment
  iii external environment.
  b Why is homeostasis important?

- pH of blood
- hormone levels
- blood glucose level
- temperature
- water balance.

Because the body can maintain each of the conditions of its internal environment in a steady state, it is possible for people to live in a wide variety of places from the arctic to the tropics, and to move from one to the other without ill effects.

10 a Why are skeletal muscles controlled by nerves and not hormones?

b Why is growth controlled by hormones and not nerves?

The nervous system and endocrine system work together to maintain the internal environment and achieve homeostasis.

The nervous system:

- works quickly
- controls short-term activities, such as movement, by making rapid adjustments
- sends impulses along nerves to stimulate particular muscle fibres or gland cells.

The endocrine system:

- works more slowly
- controls on-going processes such as metabolism and growth
- sends hormones, which each stimulate cells in a target organ, via the blood to all parts of the body.

What is pH?

The pH scale is used to express the degree of acidity or alkalinity of a solution. The scale runs from 1 to 14 and the mid-point, pH 7, is neutral. The lower figures, from pH 6.9 down to pH 1, are increasingly acid; the higher figures are increasingly alkaline.

The pH of blood is 7.4. The range of blood pH compatible with life is about 6.8 to 7.8. An incorrect pH slows down enzyme action and therefore the rate of activity within living cells.

11 Are the following neutral, acid or alkaline: pH 12, pH 3, pH 8.5, pH 6.9, pH 7?

How is the level of thyroid hormone controlled?

The pituitary gland produces a hormone called thyroid stimulating hormone (TSH). TSH stimulates the thyroid gland to produce thyroid hormone (see Figure 4). When the level of thyroid hormone in the blood rises above a certain level, it switches off the pituitary gland. This leads to a fall in the level of TSH, so the thyroid gland is not stimulated and stops producing thyroid hormone.

12 a Name the two hormones involved in control of the thyroid gland.

b Which hormone controls the secretion of thyroid hormone?

c Describe what happens when the level of thyroid hormone rises beyond a certain level.

How is the level of blood glucose maintained?

The amount of glucose in the blood is kept within limits by the activity of two hormones (see Figure 5). Glucagon increases the amount of glucose in the blood; insulin decreases the level of glucose in the blood.

13 a Name two hormones produced by the pancreas and say what each of these hormones does.

b Give two ways in which the amount of glucose in the blood is increased.

c Give one way in which the amount of glucose in the blood is reduced.

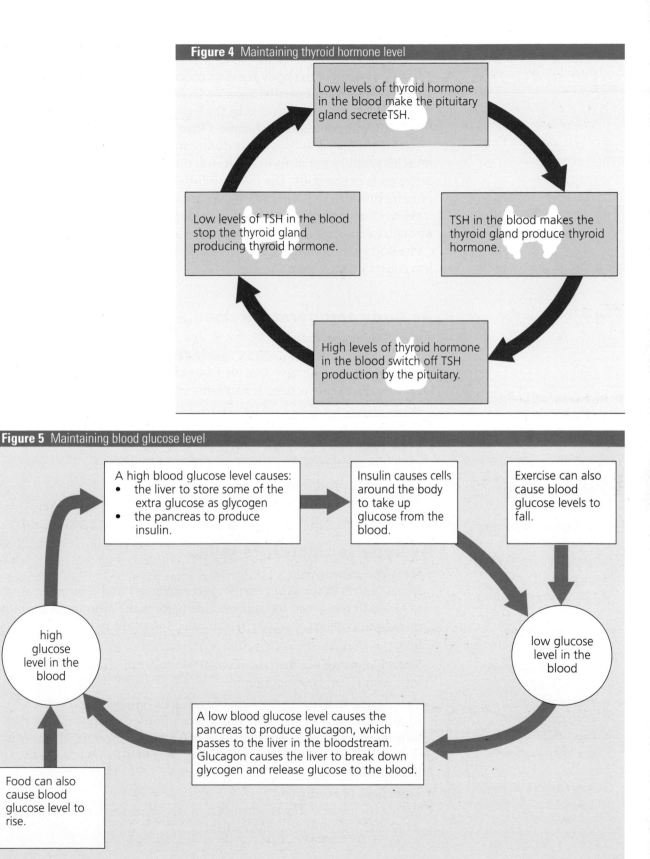

Figure 4 Maintaining thyroid hormone level

Low levels of thyroid hormone in the blood make the pituitary gland secreteTSH.

TSH in the blood makes the thyroid gland produce thyroid hormone.

High levels of thyroid hormone in the blood switch off TSH production by the pituitary.

Low levels of TSH in the blood stop the thyroid gland producing thyroid hormone.

Figure 5 Maintaining blood glucose level

A high blood glucose level causes:
- the liver to store some of the extra glucose as glycogen
- the pancreas to produce insulin.

Insulin causes cells around the body to take up glucose from the blood.

Exercise can also cause blood glucose levels to fall.

high glucose level in the blood

low glucose level in the blood

A low blood glucose level causes the pancreas to produce glucagon, which passes to the liver in the bloodstream. Glucagon causes the liver to break down glycogen and release glucose to the blood.

Food can also cause blood glucose level to rise.

How is body temperature maintained?

The temperature of the body remains remarkably constant at about 37 °C, a little higher in the late afternoon and a little lower in the early morning. Body temperature is controlled by the hypothalamus in the brain. The hypothalamus continuously balances heat production with heat loss.

Heat is produced in living cells during metabolism. The liver and muscles produce the most heat because they are the largest and most active parts of the body. The liver produces heat continuously, whereas muscles produce heat only when they are working.

Heat is lost from the body mainly through the skin; a little heat is lost through breathing, and a very small amount with urine and faeces.

The skin plays an important part in keeping body temperature more or less constant (see Figure 6).

As body temperature rises...

- **Heat loss is increased**
  Blood vessels in the skin dilate (get wider) and allow more blood to flow close to the surface. This increases the amount of heat lost by radiation and convection. It also causes the skin to look flushed.

  Sweat glands increase the rate of sweat production so that a continuous layer of moisture covers the skin. Heat from the body is used up as the sweat evaporates. If the air is both hot and humid (as, for example, in a sauna) evaporation is much more difficult.

- **Less heat is produced**
  People are less active in hot conditions.

As body temperature falls...

- **Heat loss is reduced**
  Blood vessels in the skin constrict (get narrower) and reduce the amount of blood flowing near the surface. This reduces the amount of heat lost by radiation and convection. It also causes the skin to look pale and blue.

  Sweat glands reduce the rate of sweat production. The skin is dry and little heat is lost by evaporation.

  The muscle attached to the base of each hair follicle also contracts, causing the hairs to stand up and 'goose pimples' to appear. This has little effect in humans but may have had a larger effect in ancestors with more fur. The raised hairs trap a thicker layer of air which helps to insulate the body.

- **More heat is produced**
  People use muscle movements such as stamping the feet, swinging the arms, and shivering to generate heat.

14 a What is normal body temperature?

b In what way is it controlled by the hypothalamus?

c Where in the body is heat produced?

d How is heat lost from the body?

e What causes goose pimples?

f What causes skin to look pale and blue?

g What happens during evaporation of sweat?

h Draw a diagram to show how heat is lost from the skin.

i Draw a diagram to show how heat loss from the skin is reduced.

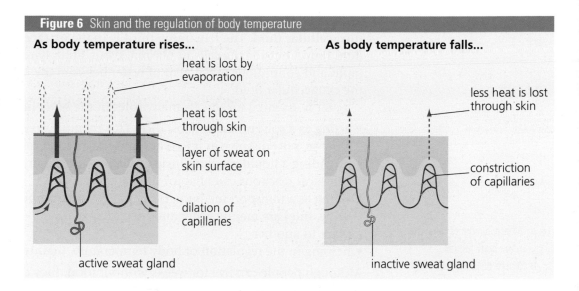

Figure 6 Skin and the regulation of body temperature

As body temperature rises...

heat is lost by evaporation

heat is lost through skin

layer of sweat on skin surface

dilation of capillaries

active sweat gland

As body temperature falls...

less heat is lost through skin

constriction of capillaries

inactive sweat gland

How is water balance maintained?

Water accounts for 60% to 70% of body weight. A person weighing 70 kilograms contains about 42 litres (42 dm^3) of water (see Figure 7). Younger people contain a higher percentage of water than older people, men contain a higher percentage than women, and thin people contain a higher percentage than fat people.

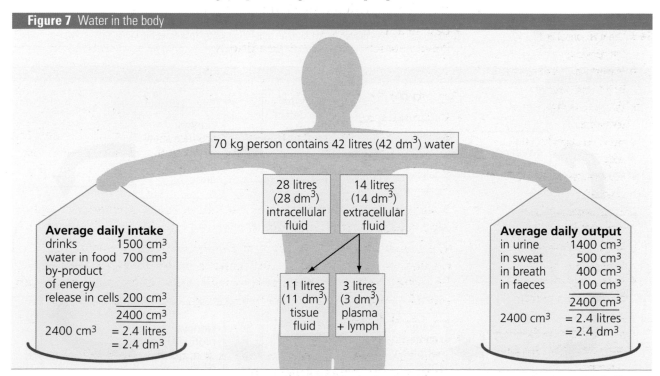

Figure 7 Water in the body

70 kg person contains 42 litres (42 dm^3) water

28 litres (28 dm^3) intracellular fluid

14 litres (14 dm^3) extracellular fluid

Average daily intake
drinks	1500 cm^3
water in food	700 cm^3
by-product of energy release in cells	200 cm^3

2400 cm^3

2400 cm^3 = 2.4 litres = 2.4 dm^3

11 litres (11 dm^3) tissue fluid

3 litres (3 dm^3) plasma + lymph

Average daily output
in urine	1400 cm^3
in sweat	500 cm^3
in breath	400 cm^3
in faeces	100 cm^3

2400 cm^3

2400 cm^3 = 2.4 litres = 2.4 dm^3

About two-thirds of the water in the body is in the cells. This is called **intracellular fluid**. The remaining third is in the **extracellular fluid**, the fluid found outside the cells in plasma, tissue fluid, lymph etc. There is rapid and continuous movement of water between the intracellular and the extracellular fluid.

Water is essential for life. Its many roles in the body include:

- acting as a solvent; many substances (for example, oxygen, carbon dioxide, glucose, salt) dissolve in it to enter and leave blood capillaries and cells
- providing a liquid medium inside cells in which many thousands of chemical reactions essential for life take place
- acting as a transport medium; body fluids (for example, blood, lymph, urine, bile) are mainly water and they carry many substances from one place to another
- helping in the regulation of body temperature, mainly through sweat.

Although people can live for weeks without food, they can survive for only a few days without water, especially in hot climates. Water is lost from the body in exhaled air, urine, sweat and faeces. The body tries to conserve water by reducing the volume of urine produced when sweating increases or diarrhoea occurs.

The brain continuously monitors the amount of water in the blood. When the water content drops below a certain level, the person feels thirsty and antidiuretic hormone (ADH) is released from the pituitary gland. ADH reduces the amount of water that the kidneys remove from the blood (see Figure 8). Drinking increases the amount of water in the body.

15 a Where is most of the water in the body found?

b Where does the rest of the water in the body occur?

c How long can a person survive without water?

d Give five reasons why water is essential to life.

16 Describe the part played by the brain in regulating water loss from the kidneys.

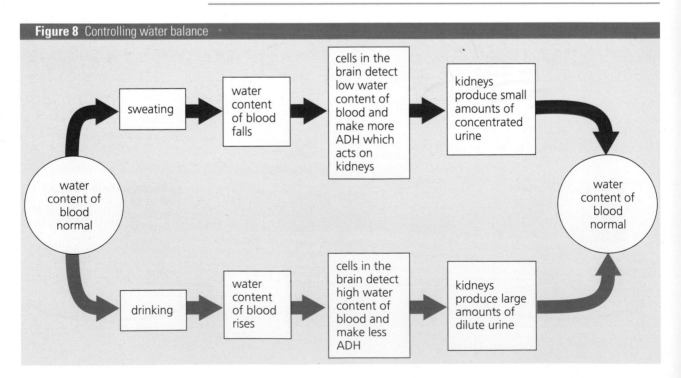

Figure 8 Controlling water balance

Summary of the endocrine system

- A hormone is a chemical secreted by an endocrine gland. It travels to all parts of the body and changes the action of the target organ. Hormones are transported in the bloodstream.

- The main endocrine glands are the hypothalamus, pituitary, thyroid, parathyroid, adrenal, pancreas, testes and ovaries.

- The hypothalamus is a part of the brain that monitors the internal state of the body. It controls the actions of the pituitary gland.

- The thyroid gland secretes thyroid hormone, which controls the metabolic rate of the body.

- The adrenal medulla secretes adrenaline, which prepares the body for fight or flight. The adrenal cortex secretes a range of corticosteroid hormones that affect glucose use and salt balance in the body.

- The testes produce testosterone, which controls the development of male sexual characteristics.

- The ovaries produce oestrogen and progesterone, which control the development of female sexual characteristics and regulate the menstrual cycle.

- Exocrine glands release secretions into ducts which lead to the place where the secretions are required. Examples are the sweat glands, salivary glands and tear glands.

- The pancreas, ovaries and testes have both endocrine and exocrine functions.

- Homeostasis means keeping conditions within the body within certain narrow limits that allow the body cells to survive. Both the nervous and endocrine systems are involved in maintaining homeostasis.

- Body temperature is maintained by balancing heat production by the body with heat loss through the skin.

- Water balance is maintained by the kidneys. They control the amount of water passed out in urine.

Variation and *genetics* 8

Learning objectives

By the end of this chapter you should be able to:

- **define** the term variation
- **list** environmental factors that produce variation in human beings
- **classify** variation as continuous or discontinuous
- **define** the terms chromosome, gene and allele
- **define** and use the terms dominant and recessive
- **predict** the likely characteristics of offspring for factors controlled by a single gene

- **explain** how gender is inherited in human beings
- **list** some of the common inherited illnesses
- **explain** how haemophilia is inherited in human beings
- **describe** the structure of the DNA molecule
- **describe** mitosis and meiosis.

8.1 Variation

Why is everybody different?

There are about 6 billion people on Earth, but no two people are exactly alike. They differ in appearance, personality, behaviour, physiology and lifestyle.

---

1 Why are no two people exactly alike?

Differences between people are due to the combined effects of genes and environment. Each child inherits a unique set of **genes**, except for pairs of identical twins, who have identical genes. The genes provide a set of instructions for growth and development. **Environment** is the word used to sum up the complete range of conditions in which an individual lives.

Almost everything in our environment affects us in some way and differences in the environment affect different people in different ways. Environmental differences include:

- cultural differences
- food and water supply
- shelter and security
- illness and accident
- quality of available medical care
- educational opportunity
- love and companionship.

2 List seven environmental differences that can cause of differences in people.

How are differences classified?

Biologists use the term **variation** to describe the differences between individuals. Variation can be classified as continuous or discontinuous (see Figure 1).

Continuous variation is seen, for example, in weight, height and foot length. Continuous variation:

- shows gradation from one extreme to the other without any break
- is produced by the combined effects of many genes
- is affected by environmental conditions.

A characteristic, or feature, showing continuous variation usually has a frequency distribution similar to the graph shown in Figure 1. When a sufficient number of people are measured, most of them will fall into the middle range, with fewer people at either end. This bell-shaped curve is called a **normal distribution curve**.

Discontinuous variation is found, for example, in blood groups, finger prints, tongue-rolling ability, and sex of the individual. Discontinuous variation:

- shows clearly defined differences with no intermediate stages
- is usually controlled by one or two genes
- is usually unaffected by environmental conditions.

3 a Name the two forms of variation, and give examples of each.

b Give three differences between continuous and discontinuous variation.

c Using Figure 1, draw an example of:

i a normal distribution curve

ii a bar chart.

Figure 1 Continuous and discontinuous variation

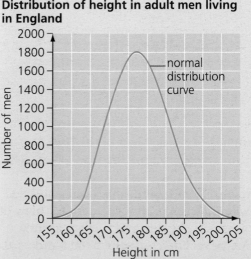

Distribution of height in adult men living in England

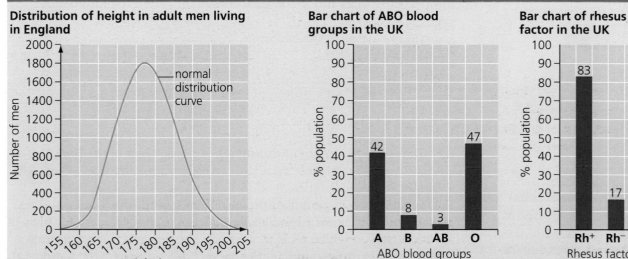

Bar chart of ABO blood groups in the UK

Bar chart of rhesus factor in the UK

Summary of variation

- All human beings are slightly different. These differences are due to differences inherited from their parents and differences in the environment in which they live.

- Variation is the name given to the differences between living things. Continuous variation occurs where the different forms cover a broad range with many intermediate types, for example weight or height in humans. Continuous variation is typically produced by a number of genes acting together.

- Discontinuous variation occurs where the different forms can be clearly distinguished, for example eye colour and blood groups in humans. Discontinuous variation is usually controlled by single genes.

8.2 Genetics

What are inherited characteristics?

Genetics is the study of genes and their effects on growth and development. It explains the way in which certain characteristics 'run in families' and are passed from parents to their children. Characteristics that are passed on from parent to child by the genes are said to be inherited.

The entire group of genes that a person possesses is called the **genotype**. The way a person looks, his or her visible characteristics, is called the **phenotype**. Phenotype depends on the genes and on the effects of the environment.

What are genes?

A **gene** is a segment of a chromosome that contains the code for a particular characteristic, for example eye colour, blood group, or shape of the nose. All the cells in the body, except eggs and sperm, contain coded instructions in the genes for the growth and development of a complete human being. Eggs and sperm each contain only half the number of genes.

---

4 a What is studied in genetics? **c** What are inherited characteristics?
  b What is a gene? **d** Give the difference between genotype and phenotype.

What are chromosomes?

5 a What is a chromosome?
  b Where in the resting cell do chromosomes exist?
  c When can chromosomes be seen?

A **chromosome** is a chain of thousands of genes. Most of the time, chromosomes are invisible even with an electron microscope. When cells are in the resting stage (not dividing), chromosomes exist in the nucleus as long, thin threads, and their presence is indicated by granules of DNA.

Chromosomes become visible when the cell is about to divide. They appear as threads which seem to gradually shorten and thicken as they coil up. Each chromosome can then be seen to consist of two strands which are joined together at one point.

6 a How many chromosomes occur in all human cells except eggs and sperm?

b What are the sex chromosomes called?

c Do the chromosomes in the karyotype in the photograph come from a male or a female? Explain your answer.

Each person develops from a single cell – a fertilised egg. This contains 46 chromosomes: 23 were in the unfertilised egg and 23 were added from the sperm. The 46 chromosomes match together in 23 pairs. The fertilised egg divides into two cells, these divide again and again and eventually produce the countless millions of cells that make up a human body.

Every time a cell divides, its chromosomes duplicate, so the number of chromosomes in a human cell (except eggs and sperm) is always 46 (23 pairs). This means that cells, except eggs and sperm, always contain two copies of a gene, one on each chromosome in a pair. In 22 of the 23 pairs, both chromosomes are alike. The 23rd pair are the **sex chromosomes** and they are only alike in females. One sex chromosome is called X, the other is smaller and is called Y. All the cells (except eggs) in a female contain two X chromosomes (XX). All the cells in a male (except sperm) contain one X and one Y chromosome (XY).

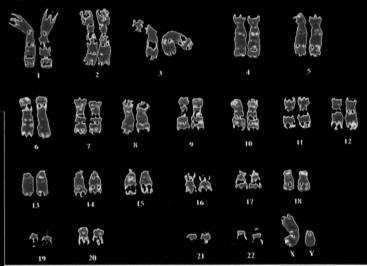

This false-colour transmission electron micrograph shows a full set of male human chromosomes.

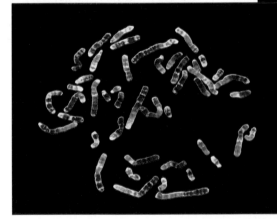

A **karyotype**, like this one of human chromosomes, is made by cutting out the chromosomes from an electron micrograph and arranging them in **homologous** (matching) pairs.

What are alleles?

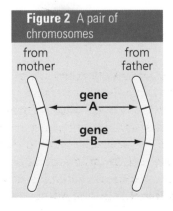

Figure 2 A pair of chromosomes

from mother

from father

gene A

gene B

Two sets of chromosomes are inherited: one from the father and one from the mother. Therefore, two sets of genes are inherited which match together in pairs. Each gene of a pair occupies exactly the same position on its respective chromosome and affects the same characteristic (see Figure 2).

7 a Why do genes always occur in pairs?

b Draw a diagram of a pair chromosomes, marking the position of genes A and B.

8 a What are alleles?

  b Give four alleles for hair colour.

  c Give the difference between homozygous and heterozygous.

Although both genes of a pair affect the same characteristic, they may vary in their effect. For example, the gene for hair colour, may give rise to brown, black, blonde or red hair. Alternative forms of the same gene are called **alleles**. Alleles occupy the same position on each chromosome in a pair and they control the same characteristic.

If both alleles in a pair have the same effect, for example, they both give rise to black hair, they are called **homozygous** for that characteristic. If the alleles have different effects, for example, one is for black hair and one for blonde hair, they are called **heterozygous**.

What are dominant genes?

9 a What is the difference between dominant genes and recessive genes?

  b Describe, using an example, how a dominant gene masks the presence of a recessive gene.

  c When is a person said to be a carrier for a particular gene?

Genes always occur in pairs, but when the genes are different alleles, one of the pair usually dominates the other. Taking a pair of genes for hair colour as an example, if a child inherits a gene for dark hair from one parent and a gene for red hair from the other, the child's hair will be dark because the gene for dark hair is dominant to that for red hair.

Dominant genes produce the same effect whether two are present or only one. They mask the effect of recessive genes. **Recessive genes** are expressed (have an effect) only if there is no dominant gene in the pair. A recessive gene that is not expressed makes a person a **carrier** for that gene. For example, the child mentioned above would be a carrier for red hair even though he or she would have dark hair. The gene for red hair may be passed on to future generations, and will have an effect if it pairs up with another recessive gene for red hair.

Many characteristics are controlled by several pairs of genes, for example height and weight. However, some characteristics result from a single pair of genes (see Table 1).

Table 1 Characteristics controlled by a single pair of genes

Characteristic	Dominant	Recessive
hair type	curly	straight
hair colour	black	blonde
eye colour	brown	blue
blood group	A and B	O
rhesus factor	Rh positive	Rh negative
tongue-rolling ability	roller	non-roller

10 a Write down whether the young man in the photograph possesses dominant or recessive genes for:

  i hair colour

  ii hair type

  iii eye colour

  iv ABO blood group

  v rhesus factor.

  b Now do the same for the young woman in the photograph.

This young man has blood group O Rh positive. This young woman has blood group A Rh negative.

How is tongue-rolling ability inherited?

Not everybody can do this.

The inheritance of characteristics depends on the combined effects of the genes from both parents. The way genes combine to produce characteristics follows certain patterns. This can be shown in its simplest form by the inheritance of the ability to roll the tongue.

The ability to roll the tongue is due to a dominant gene, which can be called T (capital letters are used for dominant genes). The recessive gene for non-rolling can be called t (small letters are used for recessive genes). So the genotype of a roller is either TT (homozygous dominant) or Tt (heterozygous). The genotype of a non-roller is tt (homozygous recessive).

It is not difficult to work out whether the children will be rollers or non-rollers when one parent can roll the tongue and the other cannot. The non-roller parent has the homozygous recessive genotype tt; the roller is either homozygous dominant TT, or heterozygous Tt. There are two methods of working out the genotypes of the children (see Figure 3). It does not matter which method you use.

Figure 3 Working out genotypes

When the tongue-roller is TT

In this method, lines are drawn from each gamete of one parent. They join lines drawn from each gamete of the other parent. Where the lines join, the genes in the gametes are put together.

When the tongue-roller is Tt

In the 'chess-board' method, the gametes from one parent are put at the side of the board, and those from the other at the top. The genes are then put together in the boxes.

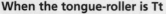

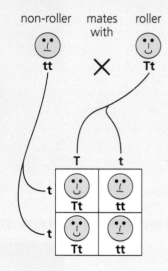

Genotype of parents
Each cell of the parent contains a pair of genes affecting tongue-rolling ability.

Gametes (eggs and sperm)
When eggs or sperm are formed, the genes separate, so each gamete has only one of the genes.

Fertilisation
It is a matter of chance which gametes unite in a fertilised egg.

Children
The four possible ways in which the gametes can unite will, in this case, all have the same result, Tt, which will make all the children of these parents rollers.

Children
The children of these parents could be either rollers or non-rollers; they have a 50% chance of being either.

---

11 Will children inherit the ability to roll the tongue when one parent is a heterozygous roller and the other parent a non-roller? Use diagrams to explain your answer.

How are blood groups inherited?

Usually, the alleles of a gene exist in two contrasting forms, as in tongue rolling and non-rolling. But there might be more alleles than two, for example there are three alleles for blood group: A, B and O. Each individual has only two alleles, which can be the same (for example, OO) or different (for example, AO). A and B are dominant to O. A and B are co-dominant (have equal dominance) when they are together (see Figure 4).

Figure 5 shows how to work out what blood group the children have will when one parent has blood group A and the other has blood group O. The parent with blood group A can have genotype AA or AO. The parent with blood group O has genotype OO. So, two 'chess-boards' are needed to work out the possible genotypes of the children.

Figure 4 Inheritance of blood groups

	A	B	O
A	AA	AB	AO
B	AB	BB	BO
O	AO	BO	OO

Genotype AA or AO will be blood group A.
Genotype AB will be blood group AB.
Genotype BB or BO will be blood group B.
Genotype OO will be blood group O.

Figure 5 An example of blood group inheritance

Parents AA and OO

	O	O
A	AO	AO
A	AO	AO

All the children will have an AO genotype and therefore will be blood group A.

Parents AO and OO

	O	O
A	AO	AO
O	OO	OO

The children will have a 50% (1 in 2) chance of being group A or group O.

12 a List the different alleles for ABO blood groups.
 b How many blood group alleles does each person have?
 c Give the six different ways in which these alleles can be combined in pairs.
 d For each blood group, give the possible genotypes.
 e When the mother has blood group B and the father has blood group O:
  i write down the genotype of the father
  ii write down the two possible genotypes of the mother
  iii work out the genotype and blood group of the children if the mother is genotype BB
  iv work out the percentage chance of the children having group O if the mother is genotype BO.
 f Explain, with diagrams, why a child whose blood group is O:
  i could have parents who both have blood group B
  ii could not have parents who both have blood group AB.

How is gender inherited?

Gender, being male or female, is a complex mix of characteristics. There is no single gene for maleness or femaleness. A package of genes on the sex chromosomes is needed to produce all the physical differences between men and women. Gender is, therefore, an example of inheritance by a package of genes rather than by a single gene. Males have two different sex chromosomes, X and Y. Females have two X chromosomes.

When the sex cells form in the ovaries or testes, a special type of cell division takes place called **meiosis** or **reduction division**. The eggs and sperm produced contain only one chromosome from each pair. This halves the number of chromosomes from 46 to 23. During meiosis, the pair of XX chromosomes in females separates so that the eggs produced each have one X chromosome. Similarly, the XY chromosomes in male cells separate, and sperm with either an X or a Y chromosome are produced.

The number of chromosomes is restored to 46 when an egg is fertilised by a sperm. The fertilised egg contains the instructions needed for the growth and development of a complete human being, either male or female.

13 a What is gender?
 b How do eggs and sperm differ from other cells in the body?
 c How many chromosomes does a fertilised egg contain?

165

The sex of an individual is determined at the moment of fertilisation and depends on whether the egg with its X chromosome is fertilised by a sperm with an X chromosome or one with a Y chromosome. During fertilisation, an egg has the same chance of uniting with either type of sperm. Consequently, roughly equal numbers of boys (XY) and girls (XX) are born (see Figure 6).

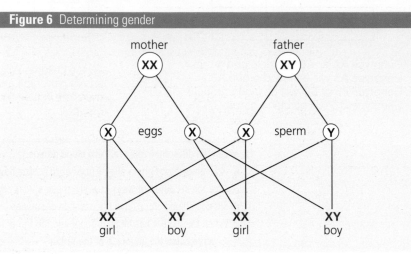

Figure 6 Determining gender

14 **a** When is the sex of an individual determined?

b How do the X and Y chromosomes determine whether a baby will be a boy or a girl?

c Using a diagram, explain why the numbers of boys and girls born are roughly equal.

What is a mutation?

A **mutation** is a random change in the genetic code. If a mutation takes place in a body cell, the change will occur in all the cells that develop from that cell. If the mutation occurs to a gene when eggs or sperm are being formed, it may be transmitted to the offspring.

Mutations are uncommon and the cells or embryos that contain them usually do not survive. If the embryos do survive, the mutations, which are usually harmful, can cause disease or deformity. In rare cases, a mutation can be beneficial and improve the individual's chance of survival. The mutation rate in humans is increased by ionising radiation, such as X-rays, and by some chemicals.

Chromosome disorders occur when the chromosomes fail to divide properly during cell division. If this happens when eggs or sperm are being formed, it can produce an individual with more, or fewer, chromosomes than normal. For example, a person with **Down's syndrome** has three copies of chromosome 21 instead of the normal two; he or she therefore has 47 chromosomes instead of the normal 46. Children with this condition develop slowly and do not reach full adult size or mental ability.

15 **a** What is a mutation?

b What is known to increase the mutation rate in humans?

c What is the difference in the effect of a mutation that occurs during egg or sperm production and one that happens in a body cell?

d When do chromosome disorders occur, and what can the effect be?

Can diseases be inherited?

A few diseases are passed on from one generation to the next by genes (see Table 2).

Table 2 Some inherited diseases

Disease	Cause	Symptoms
cystic fibrosis	recessive gene; the disease develops when two recessive genes are inherited, one from each parent	abnormally thick mucus blocks the air passages in the lungs; it is very difficult to cough up and is easily infected the pancreas is blocked by sticky mucus and fails to produce digestive juices in adequate amounts
Huntington's chorea	dominant gene; only one gene needs to be inherited to cause the disease	the brain gradually loses its ability to function (loss of mental powers and control of movement) symptoms usually first appear between 30 and 50 years of age; by that time patients may already have children
haemophilia	sex-linked recessive gene; this is a recessive gene on the X chromosome	blood cannot clot properly because Factor VIII, one of the factors that is necessary for clotting, is missing severe bleeding can occur from minor injuries; bleeding can be external or internal and can also follow dental and general surgery unless Factor VIII is given beforehand

16 a Name a disease caused by:
  i a dominant gene
  ii a recessive gene
  iii a sex-linked recessive gene.
b Give a brief description of each of the diseases you have just named.
c What is Factor VIII?

How is haemophilia inherited?

The genes controlling haemophilia can be dominant (H) or recessive (h). A dominant gene makes Factor VIII, a recessive gene does not. The genes are carried on the X chromosome, but not on the Y chromosome which, being smaller, lacks a matching position for the gene. For this reason, the chromosome is always included in the genotype (see Table 3).

Table 3 Genotypes and characteristics associated with haemophilia

Genotype	Characteristics
$X^H X^H$	female, can make Factor VIII and does not have haemophilia
$X^H X^h$	female, can make Factor VIII but is a carrier for the ressive gene; her children have a 50% chance of inheriting X^h
$X^h X^h$	female, cannot make Factor VIII and has haemophilia; this genotype is extremely rare
$X^H Y$	male, can make Factor VIII and does not have haemophilia
$X^h Y$	male, cannot make Factor VIII and has haemophilia

The inheritance of haemophilia can be worked out using a 'chessboard' diagram (see Figure 7).

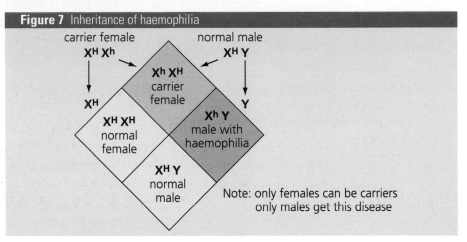

Figure 7 Inheritance of haemophilia

To see how this pattern of inheritance might work out in a family, study the fictional family of Mary and Dennis, three generations of which are shown in Figure 8.

17 a Using a diagram, explain how haemophilia is inherited.

b From Figure 8:

  i name the person with haemophilia

  ii give the genotypes of his parents

  iii Give the sex and genotype of Louise and Tom's child.

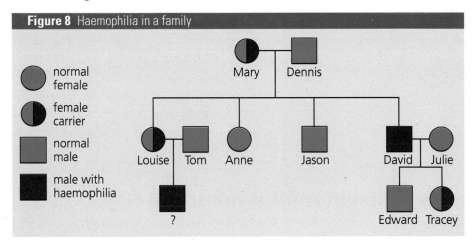

Figure 8 Haemophilia in a family

What is genetic counselling?

Genetic counselling is given to people when there is a chance of their offspring developing a disorder that:

• affects one or both of the parents
• affected an earlier child
• affected the grandparents or near relatives.

Advice is given about the chance of any children being affected. If conception has already taken place, and the unborn child is likely to inherit a particular disease, certain tests may be carried out to determine whether or not the child does have the disease. In some circumstances, termination of the pregnancy may be offered to the parents. It is always up to the parents to consider all the advice and decide what they want to do.

How can diseases be detected in unborn children?

18 a When is genetic counselling given?

b Name two tests that can be carried out to see if an unborn child has an inherited disease.

c Write down when the following are important:
  i number of chromosomes
  ii the sex of the child
  iii AFP level.

When there is a chance that an unborn child may have inherited a disease, a test such as **amniocentesis** (which uses some fetal cells taken from the amniotic fluid) or **chorionic villus sampling** (which uses placental cells) may be offered to the mother. These tests can be used to discover:

- the number of chromosomes in fetal cells, which is important in detecting Down's syndrome
- the sex of the fetus, which is important when there is a risk of muscular dystrophy or haemophilia as these diseases are much more common in males than in females
- the level of alpha-feto-protein (AFP) in the amniotic fluid, a high level indicates spina bifida or other severe defects of the nervous system.

Summary of genetics

- A gene is a part of a chromosome that codes for a particular characteristic, for example eye colour or blood group.

- Genes can have more than one form; the different forms are called alleles. So, the allele for blue eye colour is different from the allele for brown eyes but they are both forms of the gene for eye colour.

- A chromosome is a chain of thousands of genes. Chromosomes only become visible during cell division. Human cells usually have 46 chromosomes (23 pairs). There are only half this number (one chromosome from each pair) in the sperm and egg cells.

- A dominant gene is expressed whenever it is present in a genotype. A recessive gene is expressed only if the pair does not contain a dominant gene.

- The ABO blood groups are inherited as a gene with three alleles, A, B and O. A and B are co-dominant, O is recessive to both.

- A mutation is a random change in the genetic code. Most mutations are disadvantageous.

- Cystic fibrosis, Huntington's chorea and haemophilia are all examples of genetic diseases. The chance of inheriting a disease depends on whether the disease gene is dominant or recessive and whether one or both parents have the defective gene.

- Genetic counselling is offered to parents from families with a history of genetic disease. Genetic counselling offers advice on the probability of children being born with a genetic illness.

8.3 DNA and cell division

How is the genetic information coded?

All cells contain nucleic acids. Deoxyribonucleic acid, usually known as **DNA,** is found in the nucleus. Ribonucleic acid, known as **RNA,** is made by DNA and then moves into the cytoplasm carrying information from the DNA.

Each chromosome contains one long, highly coiled molecule of DNA. When it is uncoiled, the DNA is like a twisted ladder, the sides of which spiral round each other; this structure is called a **double helix**. The rungs of the ladder are formed from four bases: adenine (A), thymine (T), guanine (G) and cytosine (C). These join to form **base pairs**: A and T always join together, and G always joins with C (see Figure 9).

The segment of DNA that makes a gene consists of thousands of base pairs. The order in which the base pairs are arranged forms the code for making a particular protein.

Figure 9 Coding genetic information

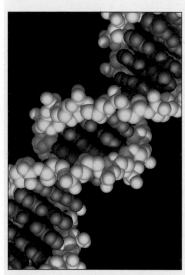

In this computer-generated model of part of a DNA molecule, you can clearly see the twisted double-helix shape. The yellow sides of the ladder are formed from sugar and phosphate molecules. The rungs of the ladder, the base pairs, are blue.

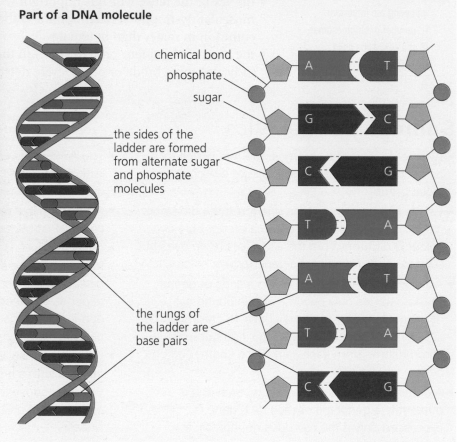

Part of a DNA molecule

chemical bond
phosphate
sugar
the sides of the ladder are formed from alternate sugar and phosphate molecules
the rungs of the ladder are base pairs

19 a What does DNA stand for?

  b Where is DNA usually found?

  c What does RNA stand for?

  d What happens to RNA after it is made in the nucleus?

  e What does a chromosome consist of?

  f What are the sides of the DNA 'ladder' made of?

  g Which bases always join together to form the base pairs?

  h Draw a small part of a DNA molecule showing four base pairs.

DNA can make an exact copy of itself. This happens to the chromosomes before a cell divides. The new cells that are produced then each have an identical set of chromosomes (see Figure 10).

20 Using Figure 10, describe how a DNA molecule makes an exact copy of itself.

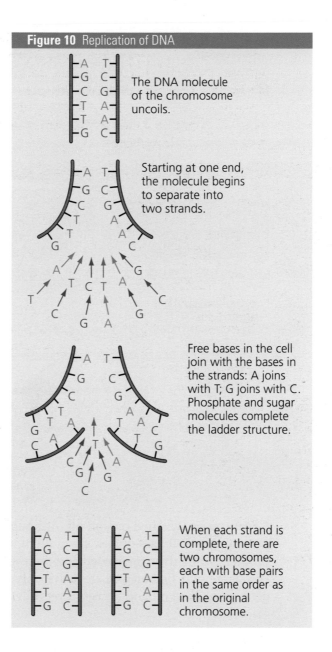

Figure 10 Replication of DNA

The DNA molecule of the chromosome uncoils.

Starting at one end, the molecule begins to separate into two strands.

Free bases in the cell join with the bases in the strands: A joins with T; G joins with C. Phosphate and sugar molecules complete the ladder structure.

When each strand is complete, there are two chromosomes, each with base pairs in the same order as in the original chromosome.

How does a gene produce a characteristic?

Through the genes, parents pass on to their children the ability to make proteins. The physical characteristics of an individual depend on proteins, which depend on the genes the person possesses. Proteins are found in:

- hair, skin, muscle, heart, lungs and all the other parts of the body
- enzymes, of which there are about 2000 in a cell, each with its own effect on the cell's activities; if even one of these is missing or fails to function properly, it can have a dramatic effect on development and health
- hormones
- plasma proteins, fibrinogen and antibodies.

21 a How do parents pass to their children the ability to make proteins?

b List four ways in which the body uses proteins.

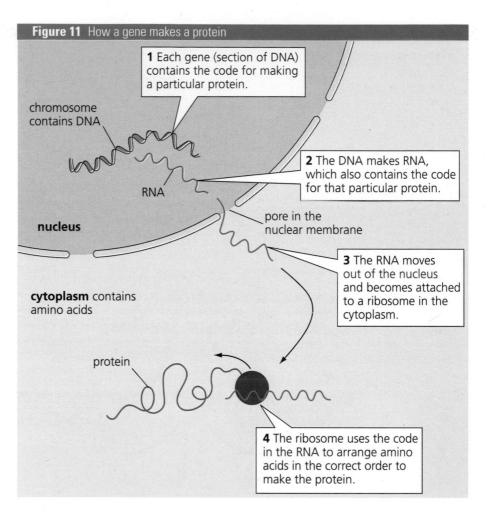

Figure 11 How a gene makes a protein

1 Each gene (section of DNA) contains the code for making a particular protein.

2 The DNA makes RNA, which also contains the code for that particular protein.

3 The RNA moves out of the nucleus and becomes attached to a ribosome in the cytoplasm.

4 The ribosome uses the code in the RNA to arrange amino acids in the correct order to make the protein.

chromosome contains DNA

RNA

nucleus

pore in the nuclear membrane

cytoplasm contains amino acids

protein

22 a Using Figure 11, describe how a gene makes a protein.

b What is meant by the phrase 'genes are switched on and off'?

Genes can be switched on and off. Although each cell possesses all of a person's genes, it uses only some of them. Genes function at the precise moment when they are needed and then stop. For example, genes for eye colour are switched on and are active only in the cells of the iris. How a gene is switched on and off is not yet fully understood.

How do cells divide?

New cells are formed from existing cells by cell division. There are two types of cell division: mitosis and meiosis (see Figure 12).

23 a Using Figure 12 name:
 i the two types of cell division
 ii what type of cell each produces
 b How many chromosomes do cells produced by mitosis contain?
 c How many chromosomes do cells produced by meiosis contain?
 d What is crossing-over?
 e Why do gametes contain a mixture of genes from the original parent cell?
 f Draw up a table of differences between mitosis and meiosis.

Figure 12 Mitosis and meiosis

Mitosis

This type of cell division takes place in all parts of the body and produces new cells that are used for growth and for replacement of worn-out or damaged body cells. Cells produced by mitosis have 46 chromosomes, the same number as in the parent cell. For simplicity only two pairs are shown here.

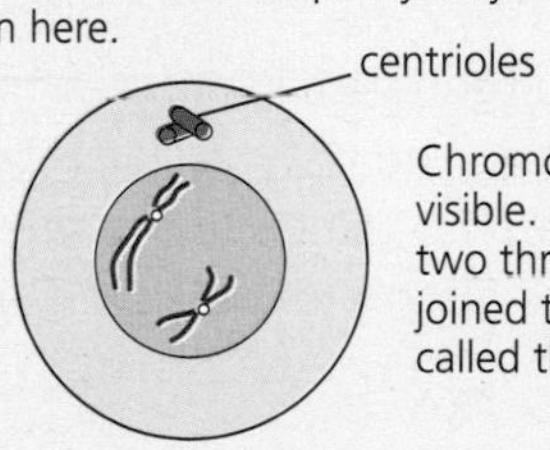

centrioles

Chromosomes become visible. Each consists of two threads (**chromatids**) joined together at a point called the **centromere**.

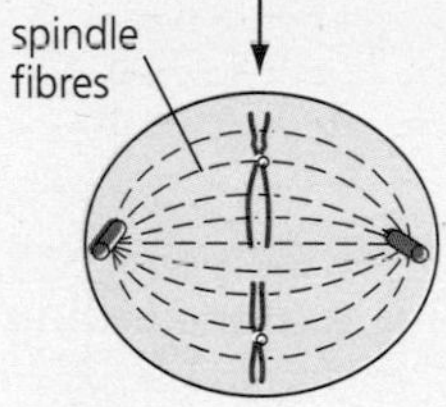

spindle fibres

The nuclear membrane disappears. The chromosomes shorten and thicken and move to the equator of the cell. The **centrioles** separate and go to opposite poles of the cell. **Spindle fibres** appear in the cytoplasm between the centrioles.

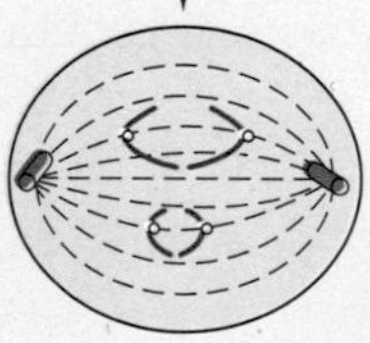

The chromatids separate and move to opposite poles of the cell to become the chromosomes of the new cells.

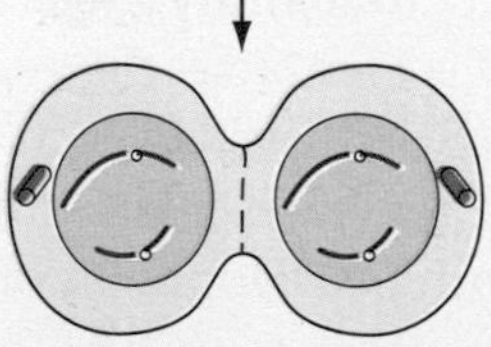

A nuclear membrane forms round each group of chromosomes. The chromosomes lengthen and become invisible. The cell splits across the middle to form two daughter cells.

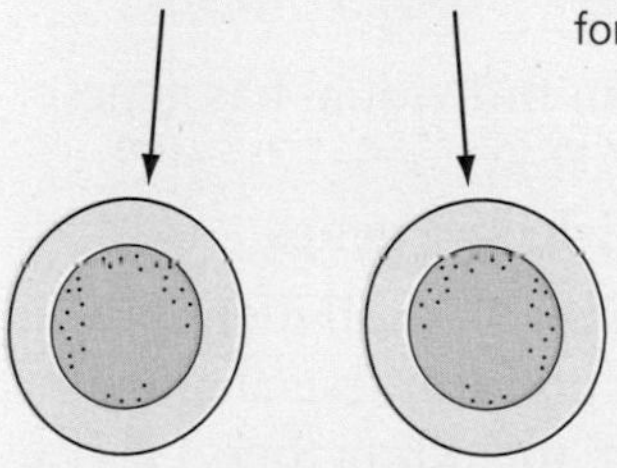

These new cells grow and either divide again or develop into a particular type of cell (e.g. neurone, blood cell).

Meiosis

This type of cell division is often called **reduction division** because the number of chromosomes is halved. It takes place only in ovaries and testes to produce gametes (eggs or sperm) containing chromosomes. For simplicity, just two of the 23 pairs are shown.

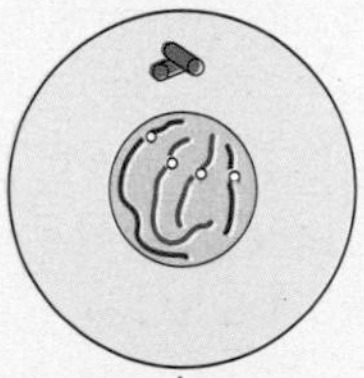

Chromosomes become visible as threads. There are two copies of each chromosome, one from each parent.

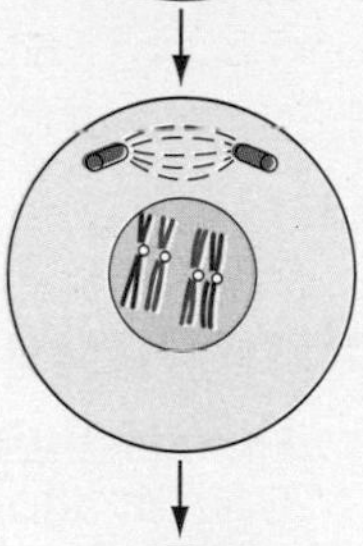

Chromosomes come together in homologous pairs. They shorten and thicken, and each chromosome is now seen to consist of two chromatids.

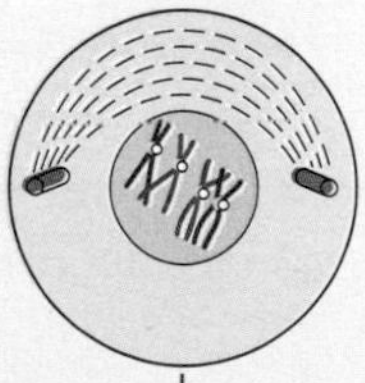

The chromatids coil around each other, and parts may be exchanged. This process is called **crossing-over**. It results in new combinations of genes.

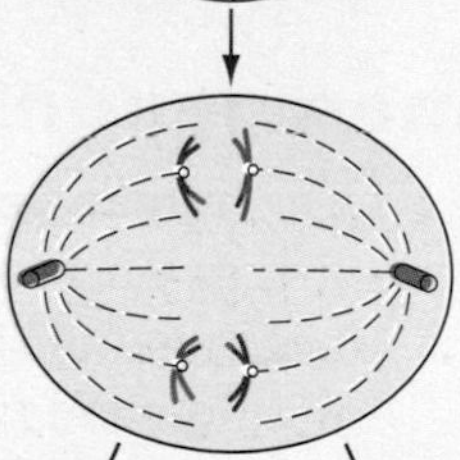

The pairs of chromosomes move to the equator of the cell. They then separate, one chromosome going to each pole, and the cell divides.

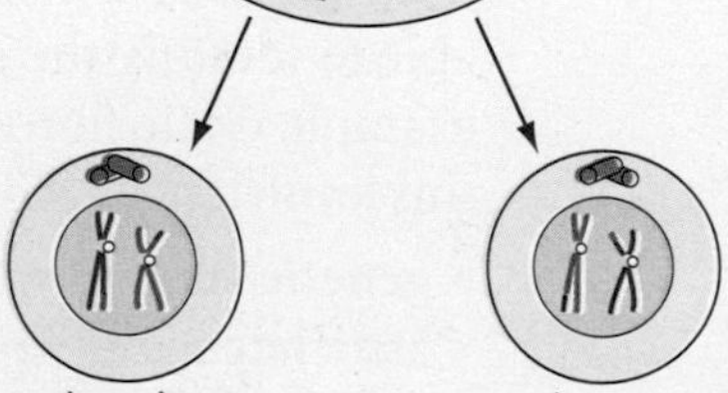

Each daughter cell has one copy of each chromosome, each with two chromatids. The daughter cells divide and this time the chromatids separate.

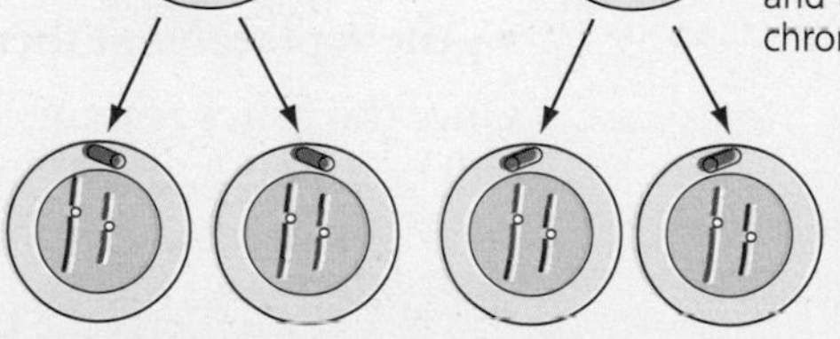

One chromatid from each pair moves into a new cell. The chromatids become the chromosomes of the new cells.

The final cells produced are the gametes and each contains a variable mix of genes from the original cell because of:
• crossing-over
• the random way in which the chromosomes separate as the gametes are formed.

Summary of DNA and cell division

- DNA is a very large molecule consisting of two spirals joined together in a double helix.
- The sequence of base pairs in a DNA molecule acts as a code for the sequence of amino acids in a particular protein. The sequence of bases contains the information to build proteins in the cytoplasm of the cell.
- RNA is another type of nucleic acid that is made from DNA in the nucleus and then moves to the cytoplasm where proteins are made.

- Mitosis produces two genetically identical daughter cells from each division. The daughter cells contain the same number of chromosomes as the parent cell. Mitosis is used for growth and repair of the body.
- Meiosis produces four genetically different new cells from each division. The new cells contain half the number of chromosomes of the parental cell. Meiosis produces sperm in males and eggs in females.

8.4 DNA technology

What is DNA technology?

24 a What is DNA technology?
  b What is genetic screening based on?
  c What is genetic engineering based on?

DNA technology is the practical application of scientific understanding of DNA. It allows us to:

- identify and catalogue the human genome; this is the basis of genetic screening and genetic fingerprinting
- isolate and manipulate individual genes; this is the basis of genetic engineering.

What is the human genome project (HGP)?

The **human genome** is the catalogue of all the genes that make human beings. There are about 100 000 of them. The project to identify each one began in the USA in the late 1980s. When the HGP is complete, the location and function of every gene will be known. Scientists will then be able to identify the genes responsible for over 7000 genetic diseases, for example cystic fibrosis and haemophilia. The on-going development of this knowledge leads to:

- **genetic screening** to discover whether or not an individual has genes associated with specific genetic diseases
- **gene replacement therapy** to alter or replace defective genes.

Once the genes responsible for human characteristics are all identified, it will be possible to take a cell from a person and perform tests that will give considerable information about that person, including their susceptibility to disease, their race, and perhaps even their intelligence. This information could be misused, for example:

25 a What is the human genome?
  b Why might it be desirable to identify people carrying a genetic disease?
  c What is genetic screening?
  d What is gene replacement therapy?

- insurance companies might refuse insurance to anyone who has a genetic condition that might be costly to treat
- employers might refuse to employ people with characteristics the employers consider undesirable.

What are genetic fingerprints?

A **genetic fingerprint** is an analysis of a person's DNA. The DNA in a person's cells is unique to each individual, except in the case of identical twins. So, like a fingerprint, DNA from a body cell can be used to identify people. It can also demonstrate whether or not people are related. Genetic fingerprinting is already used to show if, for example, two or more people have the same father, or if a child is biologically related to someone claiming to be a parent.

26 Why can a person's DNA be used as a genetic fingerprint?

What is genetic engineering?

Genetic engineering is a set of techniques that enables scientists to add genes to, or remove genes from, living cells. The organism's modified DNA then produces more or different chemicals, or performs completely new functions. Genetic engineering can be used to:

- transfer hormone genes into bacteria or yeast so that these microbes can make hormones for human use, for example, human insulin and human growth hormone
- transfer genes between plants, for example an anti-ageing gene can be added to tomatoes to give them a longer shelf-life
- transfer genes between plants and animals, for example, an 'antifreeze' gene from fish can enable crops to grow in a colder climate.

Transgenic organisms are those that have had genes from a different species transferred into their genome, for example the transgenic bacteria containing human genes for producing insulin.

27 a What is genetic engineering?
b Give three examples of genetic engineering.
c What is a transgenic organism?

What is a clone?

A **clone** is a group of organisms that are genetically identical. Identical twins are a naturally occurring clone. In the laboratory, cloning is a method used to produce exact copies of an individual. A sheep called Dolly is famous for being the first cloned mammal.

Dolly was cloned by the following method. All the chromosomes were removed from a sheep's unfertilised egg and replaced with chromosomes taken from a cell of another sheep's udder. The egg developed into Dolly, who is genetically identical to the adult sheep whose udder chromosomes went into the unfertilised egg.

28 a What is a clone?
b How was Dolly the sheep cloned?

How can genetic engineering help people with diabetes?

Most young people with diabetes need to inject themselves with insulin. Insulin used to be obtained from the pancreas of pigs or cattle and then refined. Despite the refining process, the insulin was still neither completely pure nor chemically identical to human insulin, and it sometimes caused local swellings. Pure human insulin is an improvement because it does not cause such reactions. Human insulin for injection by diabetics is made by genetic engineering.

29 In what way is genetically engineered insulin an improvement on insulin obtained from pigs?

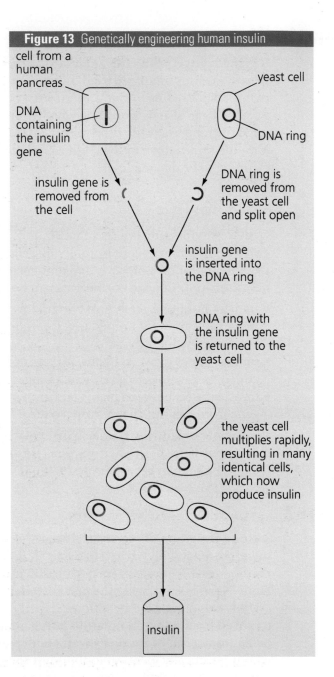

Figure 13 Genetically engineering human insulin

cell from a human pancreas

DNA containing the insulin gene

insulin gene is removed from the cell

yeast cell

DNA ring

DNA ring is removed from the yeast cell and split open

insulin gene is inserted into the DNA ring

DNA ring with the insulin gene is returned to the yeast cell

the yeast cell multiplies rapidly, resulting in many identical cells, which now produce insulin

insulin

30 Use Figure 13 to describe how genetically engineered insulin is made.

What is human growth hormone?

Human growth hormone (HGH) is used to treat children who are growing more slowly than normal due to growth hormone deficiency. It is produced by a technique similar to that used to produce human insulin.

HGH is misused in sport because it increases muscle development and has few side-effects. It is difficult to detect as it is identical to the body's own growth hormone. Those who misuse HGH risk over-development of the heart muscle. Once this has happened, the heart muscle will probably never return to normal and early heart disease may result.

31 a What is HGH?
 b What is HGH used for?
 c What is the danger of faced by sports people who misuse HGH?

What are genetically modified organisms?

Genetically modified organisms (GMOs) are organisms that have had their genetic code changed (modified) by genetic engineering to produce new varieties with particular qualities. This technique has been used to create genetically modified crops.

The traditional way of producing new and improved varieties of crop plants is **selective breeding**. The best individual plants are selected for certain qualities and used to breed future generations. This lengthy process can now be speeded up by selecting the precise gene for the characteristic to incorporate into a new variety (see Table 4).

32 a What are GMOs?

b Describe the traditional way of producing new varieties.

c Give one advantage of producing new varieties by genetic engineering.

d Name the advantage of increasing the resistance of plants to:

  i drought

  ii frost

  iii insect pests

  iv herbicides.

e What is a GM construct? Give an example.

Table 4 Some desirable plant characteristics for GM crops

Characteristic	Advantage
resistance to drought	less water needed for irrigation
resistance to frost	reduces harm done by low temperatures
resistance to insect pests	reduces need for insecticides
resistance to herbicides	weeds are killed but not the crop

GMOs are actually modified by a **construct** (a package of genes) rather that a single gene. The construct used for genetically modified tomatoes contains both a gene to improve the flavour, and a gene for resistance to a particular antibiotic. So, if tomato plants treated with this antibiotic die, they do not contain the construct and therefore cannot contain the gene for flavour. This allows scientists to distinguish GM tomato plants from normal ones while they are still seedlings.

What are genetically modified foods?

Genetically modified foods (GM foods) are foods that contain ingredients from genetically modified crops. One of the most common GM ingredients in food is soya flour made from GM soya beans. These beans have come from plants that have had their genes altered to make them resistant to herbicides. Herbicides can then be used to kill off the weeds in a field of GM soya plants. This allows the GM soya plants to thrive, and greatly increases the yield of the crop. Soya plants are made resistant to herbicide using genes taken from a bacterium.

Soya flour is used in a wide range of convenience foods and ready-made meals. GM and non-GM soya beans are often mixed, so it can be difficult to tell if soya flour was made from a batch of beans containing some GM ones. When a manufacturer knows that food contains GM soya the pack is usually labelled – but not always.

33 a What are GM foods?

b How do GM soya plants differ from other soya plants, and what is the advantage?

c How are soya plants made resistant to herbicide?

d What can GM soya flour be used for?

Are GM foods safe to eat?

Whether you believe GM foods are safe to eat or not, depends on whom you choose to believe. You must consider the speaker's or writer's motives when you hear or read any statement.

GM foods have to pass certain safety tests before they are released for human consumption. These tests can pick up immediately dangerous effects, and foods that fail are not passed. However, some people are worried that there has not been time to investigate long-term effects.

Television and newspapers can promote public debate, but the discussions could be directed more at selling papers and keeping advertisers happy than towards scientific truth. The BSE scare has made some people nervous about reassurances on safety from government, scientists and food manufacturers. Some people feel that assurances are given to protect profits before enough real evidence has been collected.

34 Do you consider that GM foods are safe or unsafe to eat, or don't you know? Give a reason for your answer.

What are the possible advantages and disadvantages of GM crops?

Possible advantages include:

- GM crops could be developed with new tastes and flavours
- crops with increased protein levels and longer shelf-life could help to feed the world
- GM crops designed to be poisonous to insects could reduce the use of pesticides.

Possible disadvantages include:

- pollen from GM crops that are resistant to herbicide could transfer GM genes into weeds; this could lead to superweeds that cannot be killed by herbicides
- if crops are poisonous to insects, the food supply for insects could be reduced and the numbers of insects would fall; the numbers of insect-eating birds would also fall
- GM foods might have long-term effects on health, and perhaps we should not use these new foods until they have been proved safe to eat.

35 List three possible advantages and three possible disadvantages of GM crops.

Summary of DNA technology

- The human genome project aims to identify the location and function of all human genes.
- A genetic fingerprint is an analysis of a person's DNA.
- Genetic engineering is the addition or removal of genes from cells.
- A clone is a group of genetically identical organisms.
- A transgenic organism contains a gene from a different species.
- A genetically modified organism has had its genome changed by genetic engineering.

Reproduction and growth

Learning objectives

By the end of this chapter you should be able to:

- **list** the changes that occur at puberty in males and females
- **describe** the structure of the male reproductive system
- **describe** the structure of the female reproductive system
- **describe** the menstrual cycle and explain how it is controlled
- **describe** the processes of fertilisation and implantation
- **list** common causes of infertility and suggest possible treatments
- **list** the common methods of contraception and assess their reliability
- **describe** the development of the fetus up to birth

- **describe** the structure and functioning of the placenta
- **list** some of the common antenatal tests and explain what they show
- **describe** the process of birth and list some of the pain relief methods available
- **list** some of the common postnatal tests and explain what they show
- **list** the benefits of breast feeding
- **describe** the changes in the circulatory system to support air breathing by the baby at birth
- **describe** the typical developmental and ageing patterns for males and females.

9.1 The male reproductive system

What does the male reproductive system do?

The **male reproductive system** has three functions:

- to make hormones
- to make sperm (spermatozoa)
- to eject sperm into the female vagina.

Puberty is the stage during which the sex organs mature. In males, this usually takes place between the ages of 11 and 15. The two testes grow and start to produce male sex hormones that cause:

- sperm production in the testes and growth of the penis
- development of **male secondary sexual characteristics**
  - muscle development and broadening of the shoulders
  - growth of facial and pubic hair, hair in the armpits and sometimes on the chest
  - deepening of the voice
- increased oiliness of the skin, which may lead to acne
- changes in behaviour and attitudes.

1 a Give three functions of the male reproductive system.

b At what age does puberty usually occur in boys?

c Where are male sex hormones produced?

d List four effects of male sex hormones.

e List seven male secondary sexual characteristics.

Most of the time, the penis is soft and hangs downwards. It can also enlarge, become stiff, and stand out from the body. This is called an erection. The penis becomes erect when the three columns of erectile tissue within it fill with blood (see Figure 2). All boys, even babies, have erections, but they become more frequent during puberty.

Figure 1 Male reproductive system

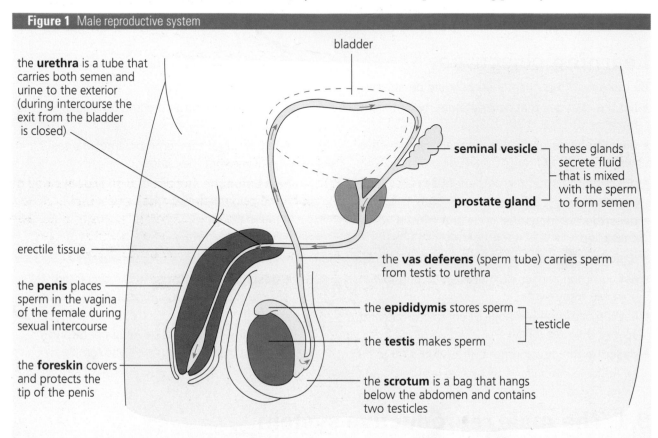

the **urethra** is a tube that carries both semen and urine to the exterior (during intercourse the exit from the bladder is closed)

bladder

seminal vesicle — these glands secrete fluid that is mixed with the sperm to form semen

prostate gland

erectile tissue

the **vas deferens** (sperm tube) carries sperm from testis to urethra

the **penis** places sperm in the vagina of the female during sexual intercourse

the **epididymis** stores sperm — testicle

the **testis** makes sperm

the **foreskin** covers and protects the tip of the penis

the **scrotum** is a bag that hangs below the abdomen and contains two testicles

→ path of sperm from epididymis to exterior

Circumcision is the removal of the foreskin by surgery. It is rarely necessary for medical reasons, although it is widely carried out among some religious groups. The foreskin is absent in males who have been circumcised.

The prostate gland surrounds the urethra at the outlet from the bladder. From middle age onwards, the prostate gland enlarges. This may cause a frequent desire to urinate, delay in urinating, a thin stream of urine, and dribbling. Treatment to correct this condition is by an operation to remove part of the prostate gland, or by medicines that shrink it.

2 a Using Figure 1, place the following in order to show the pathway along which sperm travel:
  • urethra • epididymis • vas deferens • testis.
  b Name the two glands that produce fluid which mixes with the sperm.
  c Give the reproductive function of the penis.

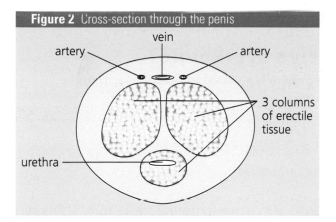

Figure 2 Cross-section through the penis

vein

artery

artery

3 columns of erectile tissue

urethra

3 a Draw and label a cross-section through the penis, giving a function for each part.

b What is circumcision?

c Describe the position of the prostate gland.

d The prostate gland can become enlarged. Write down:

   i at what age this may happen

  ii what this enlargement may cause

 iii how the condition can be treated.

Where are sperm produced and stored?

The two testes begin to produce sperm during puberty and continue to do so throughout life. The sperm are stored in the epididymis. Each testicle includes one testis and an epididymis (see Figure 3). The testicles are held in the scrotum outside the body. Sperm are therefore stored at a cooler and more suitable temperature than if they were inside the body.

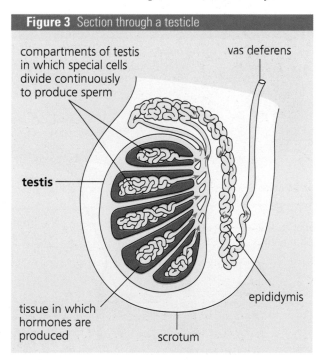

Figure 3 Section through a testicle

compartments of testis in which special cells divide continuously to produce sperm

vas deferens

testis

tissue in which hormones are produced

epididymis

scrotum

4 a Of the words 'testes' and 'testis', which is singular and which is plural?

b Where are sperm produced?

c Where are sperm stored?

d Where are the testicles situated and why?

e What is semen?

Sperm cannot be stored indefinitely, and after a while they *either*:

• disintegrate and the particles are removed in the bloodstream, *or*

• are pushed down the erect penis and out of the body in fluid called semen (this may happen during sleep and is often called a 'wet dream').

Semen is the thick, milky-white fluid that is released from the penis. It contains sperm and fluid from the seminal vesicles and prostate gland.

9.2 The female reproductive system

What does the female reproductive system do?

The **female reproductive system** is situated in the lower part of the abdominal cavity. Its functions are:

- to make hormones
- to develop eggs
- to receive sperm
- to protect and feed an unborn child
- to give birth.

Puberty usually takes place in girls between the ages of 11 and 15. During this time the two ovaries start to produce female sex hormones that cause:

- egg development in the ovaries, enlargement of the uterus and vagina, and the onset of periods
- development of **female secondary sexual characteristics**
  – breast development and broadening of hips
  – growth of pubic hair and hair in the armpits
- increased oiliness of the skin, which may lead to acne
- changes in behaviour and attitudes.

5 a Give five functions of the female reproductive system.

b At what age does puberty usually occur in girls?

c Where are female sex hormones produced?

d List four effects of the female sex hormones.

e List four female secondary sexual characteristics.

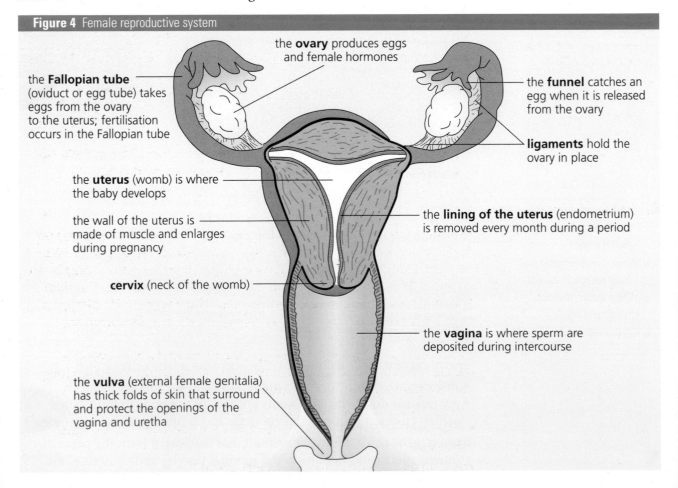

Figure 4 Female reproductive system

the **ovary** produces eggs and female hormones

the **Fallopian tube** (oviduct or egg tube) takes eggs from the ovary to the uterus; fertilisation occurs in the Fallopian tube

the **funnel** catches an egg when it is released from the ovary

ligaments hold the ovary in place

the **uterus** (womb) is where the baby develops

the wall of the uterus is made of muscle and enlarges during pregnancy

the **lining of the uterus** (endometrium) is removed every month during a period

cervix (neck of the womb)

the **vagina** is where sperm are deposited during intercourse

the **vulva** (external female genitalia) has thick folds of skin that surround and protect the openings of the vagina and uretha

Hysterectomy is an operation to remove the uterus. It may be carried out when:

- very heavy or painful periods are caused by **fibroids** (lumps of fibrous and muscular tissue) in the uterus
- the patient has a cancer that is too advanced for treatment in other ways.

Cervical cancer is a common type of cancer in women. It can be prevented by regular **cervical smear** tests. A small amount of tissue (called a smear) is scraped from the surface of the cervix and examined for abnormal cells. If pre-cancerous cells are found, they can be removed, so a hysterectomy will not be needed later.

6 a Using Figure 4, write down:
  i where fertilisation takes place
  ii which part is removed every month
  iii where sperm are deposited during intercourse
  iv the other name for the neck of the womb.
 b What is a hysterectomy and why might it be carried out?
 c What is the purpose of regular cervical smear tests?
 d Describe in your own words what you can see in the micrograph.

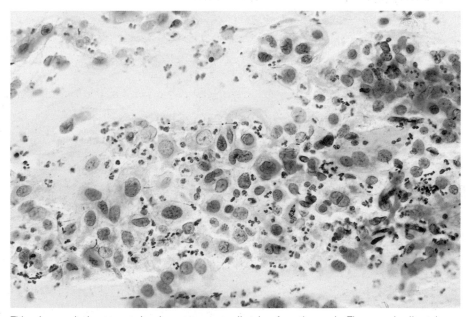

This micrograph shows normal and pre-cancerous cells taken from the cervix. The normal cells stain blue, but potentially cancerous cells stain orange and have large nuclei that stain red.

Where do eggs develop?

At birth, a female has about a million immature eggs in her ovaries, and no more are produced. From puberty to the menopause, a span of 30 to 40 years, some eggs complete their development at the rate of roughly one egg every 28 days (see Figure 5 on page 184). This means that less than 500 of the million immature eggs develop. The rest gradually disappear from birth onwards. The ovaries also produce the female hormones, oestrogen and progesterone.

Ovulation is the release of an egg from an ovary. An egg (ovum) is released each month from one of the ovaries and it moves slowly along the Fallopian tube towards the uterus due to:

- **peristalsis**, rhythmic squeezing movements of the Fallopian tube
- **cilia**, tiny 'hairs' that line the tube and move the ovum in the right direction.

The journey from ovary to uterus takes about 7 days.

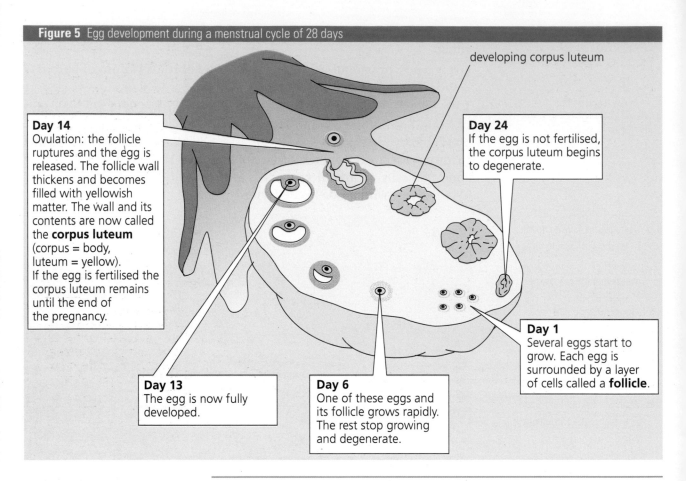

Figure 5 Egg development during a menstrual cycle of 28 days

developing corpus luteum

Day 14
Ovulation: the follicle ruptures and the egg is released. The follicle wall thickens and becomes filled with yellowish matter. The wall and its contents are now called the **corpus luteum** (corpus = body, luteum = yellow). If the egg is fertilised the corpus luteum remains until the end of the pregnancy.

Day 24
If the egg is not fertilised, the corpus luteum begins to degenerate.

Day 1
Several eggs start to grow. Each egg is surrounded by a layer of cells called a **follicle**.

Day 13
The egg is now fully developed.

Day 6
One of these eggs and its follicle grows rapidly. The rest stop growing and degenerate.

7 a Where do eggs develop?

b Draw and label a section through an ovary to show the following stages of egg development in a 28-day cycle:

  i an egg at day 1   **ii** an egg at day 6   **iii** release of an egg at day 14.

c What is ovulation and how often does it occur?

d What does the corpus luteum develop from?

e Draw and label diagrams to show:

  i a developing corpus luteum   **ii** a fully developed corpus luteum

  iii a degenerating corpus luteum.

f What would prevent the corpus luteum from degenerating?

9.3 The menstrual cycle

What is the menstrual cycle?

The **menstrual cycle** is a regular series of changes that take place in the female reproductive system to prepare for fertilisation and pregnancy. The cycle takes, on average, about 28 days to complete and is controlled by hormones from the hypothalamus, pituitary gland and ovaries. During the menstrual cycle, the uterus lining goes through four stages (see Figure 6).

Figure 6 A typical menstrual cycle

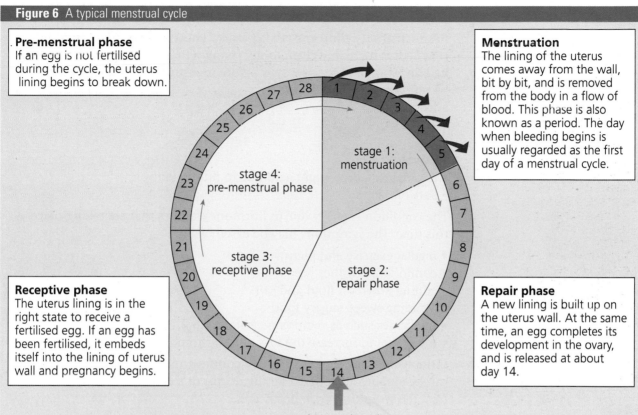

. Pre-menstrual phase
If an egg is not fertilised during the cycle, the uterus lining begins to break down.

Menstruation
The lining of the uterus comes away from the wall, bit by bit, and is removed from the body in a flow of blood. This phase is also known as a period. The day when bleeding begins is usually regarded as the first day of a menstrual cycle.

Receptive phase
The uterus lining is in the right state to receive a fertilised egg. If an egg has been fertilised, it embeds itself into the lining of uterus wall and pregnancy begins.

Repair phase
A new lining is built up on the uterus wall. At the same time, an egg completes its development in the ovary, and is released at about day 14.

stage 1: menstruation
stage 4: pre-menstrual phase
stage 3: receptive phase
stage 2: repair phase

ovulation takes place at about day 14

8 a What is the menstrual cycle?

b What controls the menstrual cycle?

c How long is the average menstrual cycle?

d What happens during menstruation?

e On which day of the cycle does menstruation begin?

f What happens during the repair phase?

g On which day of the cycle is an egg released from the ovary?

h What happens to the uterus lining if the egg is not fertilised?

i What name is given to the last stage of the menstrual cycle?

Girls usually begin to **menstruate**, have periods, between the ages of 11 and 15. The periods are likely to be irregular and slight at first. The second period can be as long as a year after the first. After puberty, the cycles gradually become more or less regular, but they can vary considerably. A period can last from 3 to 7 days, and there can be from 21 to 35 days between periods.

The amount of blood lost during a period is usually about 30 cm^3, but it can be as much as 180 cm^3. Excessively heavy menstrual bleeding is called **menorrhagia** and requires medical advice.

Periods stop during pregnancy and for several months afterwards. Absence of periods in women of child-bearing age who are not pregnant is called **amenorrhoea**. This may be due to illness, poor feeding or emotional upset. Medical advice is needed if more than two periods are missed. At some time, generally between the ages of 45 and 55, the menstrual cycle ceases and periods stop permanently. The time when this is happening is called the **menopause**.

9 a Between what ages does menstruation begin?

b Describe three ways in which cycles can vary.

c List four reasons why periods might stop in a woman of child-bearing age.

d What is the menopause?

What is pre-menstrual syndrome?

Pre-menstrual syndrome (PMS) is also known as **pre-menstrual tension (PMT)**. It is the name given to the changes that occur regularly in many healthy women in the few days before menstruation. The symptoms can be mild or severe and include:

- irritability
- tiredness
- depression
- headache
- bloatedness and weight gain due to fluid retention
- sore breasts.

The condition is partly due to hormone changes that are taking place at this time. The symptoms may be eased by:

- regular exercise and plenty of sleep
- comfortable clothes
- cutting down on fluid and salt
- avoiding sweet, sugary food
- medicines such as pyridoxine (vitamin B_6)
- medicines to increase the loss of fluid from the body via the kidneys.

If the symptoms are very severe or continue to be a problem, expert help can be obtained through a family doctor or a clinic. It may be possible to treat the symptoms with hormones.

10 a What is pre-menstrual syndrome?
   b What are the symptoms of PMS?
   c How may the symptoms of PMS be eased?

How is the menstrual cycle controlled?

The menstrual cycle is controlled by the hypothalamus, which is in the brain and acts as a 'menstrual clock'. The hypothalamus receives information about conditions in all parts of the body from the nervous system, and from the blood flowing through the brain. When the conditions are right, the hypothalamus releases hormones that control the production, by the pituitary gland, of **follicle-stimulating hormone (FSH)** and **luteinising hormone (LH)**. FSH and LH act on the ovaries, which in turn, produce oestrogen and progesterone. Oestrogen and progesterone act on the uterus (see Figure 7).

11 a Name two hormones produced by the pituitary gland and name the organ they act on.
   b Name two hormones produced by the ovaries and give the effect of each on the uterus.
   c In a typical 28-day cycle, describe what happens to:
     i the level of oestrogen in the blood
     ii the level of progesterone in the blood
     iii body temperature.

Figure 7 Control of the menstrual cycle

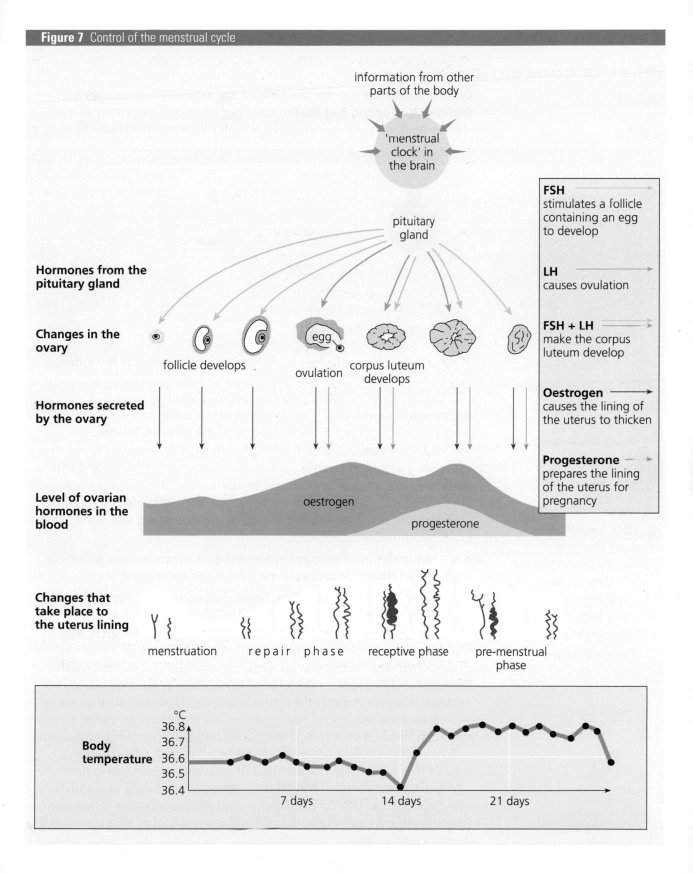

information from other
parts of the body

'menstrual
clock' in
the brain

pituitary
gland

**Hormones from the
pituitary gland**

**Changes in the
ovary**

follicle develops

ovulation

corpus luteum
develops

egg

FSH
stimulates a follicle
containing an egg
to develop

LH
causes ovulation

FSH + LH
make the corpus
luteum develop

Oestrogen
causes the lining of
the uterus to thicken

Progesterone
prepares the lining
of the uterus for
pregnancy

**Hormones secreted
by the ovary**

**Level of ovarian
hormones in the
blood**

oestrogen

progesterone

**Changes that
take place to
the uterus lining**

menstruation   r e p a i r   p h a s e   receptive phase   pre-menstrual
phase

**Body
temperature**

°C
36.8
36.7
36.6
36.5
36.4

7 days   14 days   21 days

9.4 Conception

What is conception?

Conception is the process in which an egg in the Fallopian tube is fertilised by a sperm and the fertilised egg later implants in the uterus wall. A human egg is very much larger than a sperm (see Figure 8).

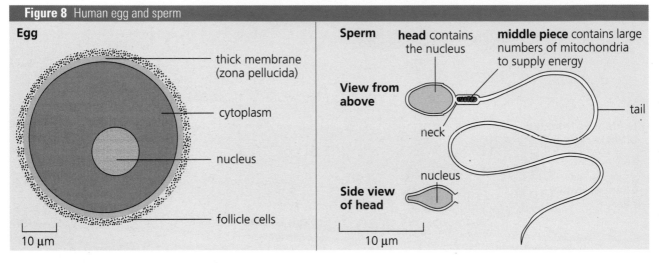

Figure 8 Human egg and sperm

Egg
- thick membrane (zona pellucida)
- cytoplasm
- nucleus
- follicle cells

10 µm

Sperm
head contains the nucleus
middle piece contains large numbers of mitochondria to supply energy
View from above
neck
tail
nucleus
Side view of head

10 µm

12 a What is conception?

b Draw and label a diagram of:
  i an egg
  ii a sperm.

c About how many sperm are placed inside the vagina during intercourse?

d How are sperm in the vagina able to become active, and where do they get their energy from?

e How do sperm get from the vagina to the Fallopian tubes?

Before sexual intercourse (coitus) takes place, the man's penis becomes erect and is able to penetrate the vagina of the woman. During intercourse, sperm stored in the testicles are rapidly squeezed along the vas deferens and through the urethra. On the way, they are mixed with fluid from the seminal vesicles and prostate gland to make the thick sticky fluid called semen, which is ejaculated from the penis into the vagina.

About 300 million sperm are placed inside the vagina and are then able to swim around because:

- fluid from the prostate gland enables the sperm to become active
- fluid from the seminal vesicles provides food for energy.

The sperm swim in all directions. Some find their way through the cervix, into the uterus and along the Fallopian tubes (see Figure 9).

Fertilisation is the fusion of a sperm with an egg. Although several sperm may reach the egg, only one will penetrate the thick membrane that surrounds it. The membrane immediately changes and forms a barrier to the entry of other sperm. The head of the sperm contains the male nucleus. It moves through the cytoplasm towards the female nucleus in the egg and the two nuclei join together. The fertilised egg, called a **zygote**, now starts to divide. It first forms two cells, then four, and so on, as it continues on its journey along the Fallopian tube. By the time it reaches the uterus, it is a hollow ball of cells and is called an **embryo**.

Implantation is embedding of the embryo in the lining of the uterus wall. This process takes place about 6 days after fertilisation. The mother then supplies the embryo with food and oxygen so that it can grow and develop into a baby.

13 **a** What is fertilisation?

b Where does fertilisation take place?

c What happens to the egg soon after it has been fertilised?

d At what stage does a fertilised egg become called an embryo?

e What is implantation and how long after fertilisation does it take place?

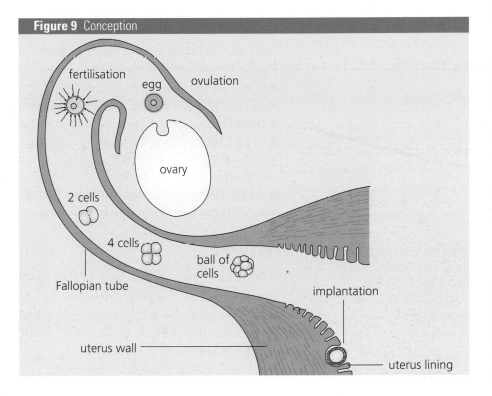

Figure 9 Conception

Why do twins develop?

There are two types of twins (see Figure 10).

Identical twins develop when a fertilised egg splits into two at an early stage of development and each develops into an individual. The twins are of the same sex and, as they have the same genes, they are very similar in appearance and behaviour.

Non-identical twins result when two eggs are released at the same time, and each egg is fertilised by a different sperm. The eggs could be both from the same ovary or one from each. The twins may or may not be of the same sex, and are no more alike than any other brothers or sisters.

Siamese twins are identical twins who failed to separate completely.

14 **a** Use diagrams to explain why twins can be identical or non-identical.

b Which type of twins are always of the same sex?

c What is the cause of Siamese twins?

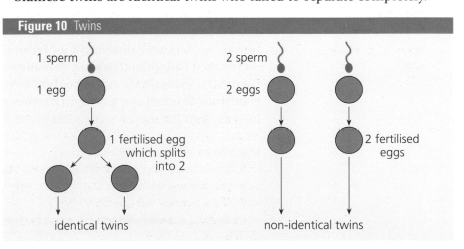

Figure 10 Twins

What is pre-conception care?

Because the first few weeks after conception are most important for the health of the developing baby, a woman who is hoping to conceive is advised:

- to keep in good health and free from infection
- not to be overweight
- to give up smoking and drinking alcohol
- to have a good, nutritious diet; in particular, to eat plenty of foods containing folic acid
- avoid taking medicines except on the advice of a doctor, or those needed for chronic conditions such as diabetes, epilepsy, or asthma.

15 a What advice is given to a woman who is hoping to conceive?

b Why is this advice given?

What causes infertility?

16 a What is infertility?

b Give two causes of infertility in men.

c Give three causes of infertility in women.

d What is impotence?

Infertility is the inability to conceive. Some of the causes are:

- the ovaries are not producing eggs
- the Fallopian tubes are closed or blocked
- mucus in the cervix is abnormal and stops the sperm from entering
- too few sperm are produced
- the sperm are not sufficiently active.

Impotence is the inability to sustain an erection adequate for sexual intercourse. Temporary impotence is common among all age groups of men due to excess alcohol. It also commonly occurs at times of emotional stress or depression regardless of age.

How can infertility be treated?

Women who are infertile because they do not ovulate may be given **fertility drugs**. These drugs contain hormones, and it can be difficult to adjust the dose to suit a particular person. This sometimes causes several eggs to be released at once, and can result in multiple births.

In vitro **fertilisation** is a technique in which fertilisation takes place outside the mother's body, using the couple's own egg and sperm. When the fertilised egg is a few days old, it is implanted into the mother's uterus and development proceeds in the normal way. Babies conceived in this way are sometimes called 'test-tube babies'.

Damaged Fallopian tubes can sometimes be repaired by surgery.

Artificial insemination is a method of treating infertility when the man is infertile. Semen from a donor (another male) is collected, and then inserted into the uterus at the time of ovulation.

17 a What do fertility drugs contain?

b Why do fertility drugs sometimes lead to multiple births?

c What is *in vitro* fertilisation?

d What is meant by 'test-tube baby'?

e When may artificial insemination be used to treat infertility?

9.5 Contraception

What is contraception?

Contraception is the deliberate prevention of pregnancy (contra = against, ception = conceiving). It is natural for two people who love each other to want to have intercourse, more commonly referred to as 'making love' or 'having sex'. If they do not want a baby, they need to know how to prevent conception. All methods of contraception aim to prevent an egg being fertilised by a sperm and implanting in the wall of the uterus.

Deciding on which method of contraception to use depends on a number of factors including:

- individual preference
- religious beliefs
- age
- whether a short-term or long-term method is required.

Abstention means 'not doing something'. Abstention from sexual intercourse and 'heavy petting' are a completely reliable ways of not starting a baby because there is no possibility of a sperm being able to fertilise an egg.

Family planning and contraception are worldwide issues. In some countries there are government policies to restrict the size of families, for example the one-child policy in China.

18 a What is contraception?

b What factors might govern the choice of contraceptive method?

c Why is abstention a completely reliable way of not starting a baby?

What forms of contraception are available?

Figure 11 Methods of contraception for men

Withdrawal ('being careful', coitus interruptus)
The penis is withdrawn from the vagina before semen is ejaculated.
- A very unreliable method of birth control because a little semen can leak from the erect penis before the main amount is released.

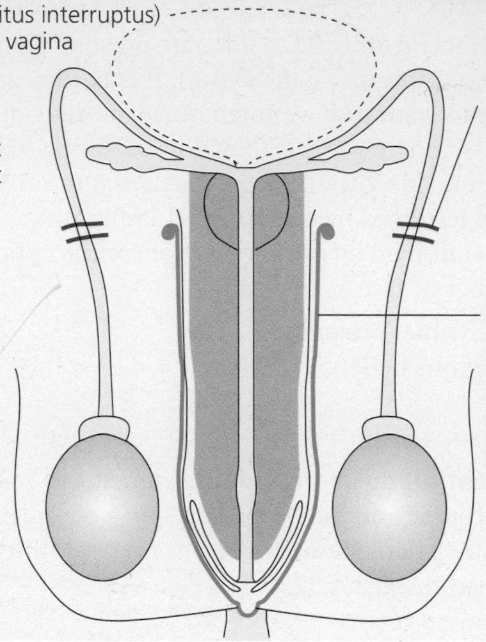

Male sterilisation (vasectomy)*
A simple operation following medical advice in which the vas deferens (sperm duct) on each side is cut to prevent semen from containing sperm.
- A permanent method of birth control which is almost 100 % reliable. It does not affect the hormone function of the testes.

Condom, sheath
A thin rubber covering fitted over the erect penis before intercourse prevents sperm from being deposited in the vagina.
- Very reliable if properly used so that no semen comes into contact with the vaginal area. Spermicide placed in the vagina gives extra protection.
- Using a condom also helps to protect against sexually transmitted diseases including AIDS.

* This method requires medical advice or treatment from a doctor or family planning clinic.

19 a Copy and complete Table 1 using Figures 11 and 13 for information.
   b Which of these methods require advice or treatment from a doctor or family planning clinic?
   c Draw and label a diagram to show the fertile period and the safe period in a 28-day cycle.

Table 1 Methods of contraception

Method	Description	Reliability
For men		
For women		

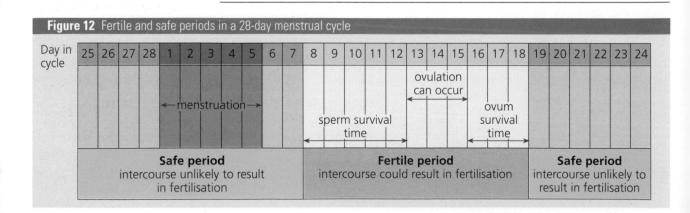

Figure 12 Fertile and safe periods in a 28-day menstrual cycle

Day in cycle	25	26	27	28	1	2	3	4	5	6	7	8	9	10	11	12	13	14	15	16	17	18	19	20	21	22	23	24

←menstruation→

ovulation can occur

sperm survival time

ovum survival time

Safe period
intercourse unlikely to result in fertilisation

Fertile period
intercourse could result in fertilisation

Safe period
intercourse unlikely to result in fertilisation

Figure 13 Methods of contraception for women

Female condom
A soft polyurethane sheath that lines the vagina and covers the area just outside. It stops sperm from entering the vagina.
• Reliable if properly used.
• Also helps to protect against sexually transmitted diseases including AIDS.

Intra-uterine device (IUD)*
A small plastic and copper device that is placed in the uterus, and can be left there for at least 5 years. It stops sperm from reaching an egg, and can prevent a fertilised egg from settling in the uterus.
• Almost 100% reliable.

Intra-uterine system (IUS): Mirena*
A small T-shaped plastic device that is placed in the uterus. It contains progestogen (synthetic progesterone), which is slowly released. The IUS stops sperm from meeting an egg, and can be left in place for 5 years.
• Almost 100% reliable.

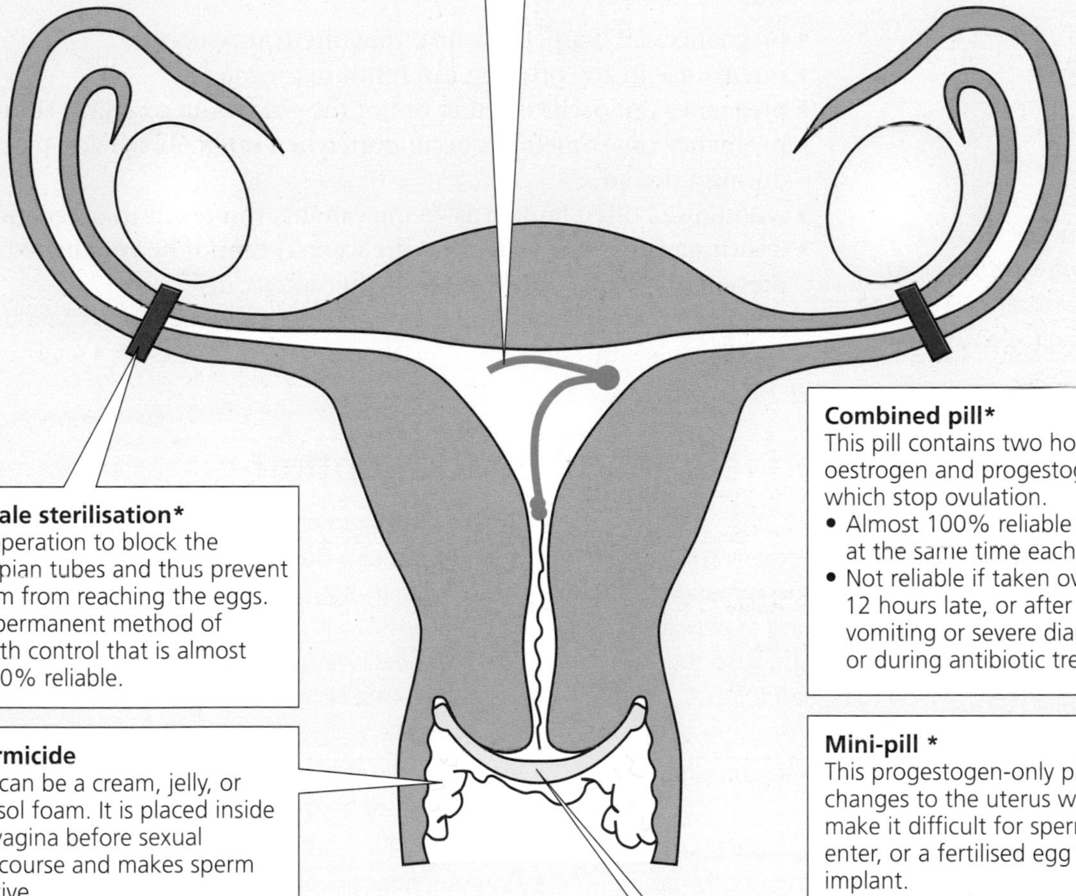

Female sterilisation*
An operation to block the Fallopian tubes and thus prevent sperm from reaching the eggs.
• A permanent method of birth control that is almost 100% reliable.

Spermicide
This can be a cream, jelly, or aerosol foam. It is placed inside the vagina before sexual intercourse and makes sperm inactive.
• Very unreliable on its own.
• Helps to make a cap or condom more reliable.

Combined pill*
This pill contains two hormones, oestrogen and progestogen, which stop ovulation.
• Almost 100% reliable if taken at the same time each day.
• Not reliable if taken over 12 hours late, or after vomiting or severe diarrhoea, or during antibiotic treatment.

Mini-pill *
This progestogen-only pill causes changes to the uterus which make it difficult for sperm to enter, or a fertilised egg to implant.
• Almost 100% reliable if taken at the same time each day.
• Not reliable if taken over 3 hours late, or after vomiting or severe diarrhoea.

Natural methods
These methods rely on calculating the fertile and infertile (safe) periods of the menstrual cycle (see Figure 12).
• Unreliable unless carried out very carefully because it can be difficult to be sure of the date of ovulation.

Diaphragm or cap*
A flexible rubber device that is put into the vagina to cover the cervix before sexual intercourse, and which must stay in place for at least 6 hours afterwards.
• Very reliable if properly fitted and used with a spermicide.

* These methods require medical advice or treatment from a doctor or family planning clinic.

What is emergency contraception?

This is a method of contraception for emergency use, after sexual intercourse has taken place and there is the risk of an unwanted pregnancy. There are two types of emergency contraception:

- **emergency pills** containing hormones, taken within 3 days
- a **copper IUD**, fitted within 5 days.

Emergency contraception may be needed when girls do not realise how easy it is to get pregnant. A girl who does not which to become pregnant should remember:

- pregnancy can happen the first time intercourse occurs
- intercourse in any position can result in pregnancy
- pregnancy can occur whether or not the girl has an orgasm ('comes')
- pregnancy can sometimes occur even when intercourse takes place during a period
- withdrawal, often known as 'being careful', can result in pregnancy
- douching (squirting water into the vagina) cannot be guaranteed to prevent pregnancy, however soon after intercourse
- pregnancy can occur even if the penis does not enter the vagina because sperm can swim.

20 a What is emergency contraception?

b What are the two types of emergency contraception?

c List seven things that should be remembered about how easy it is to get pregnant.

Summary of reproduction and contraception

- At puberty, changes in males include: development of penis, testes beginning to produce sperm, deepening of the voice, growth of facial and body hair, broadening of shoulders and general muscle development. Also the skin becomes greasy, which may lead to acne.

- The testes produce sperm which is stored in the epididymis until it is ejaculated through the erect penis.

- At puberty, changes in females include: development of breasts, growth of body hair, broadening of the hips, enlargement of the uterus and vagina, and the start of periods. The skin becomes greasy, which may lead to acne.

- Ovaries have a store of eggs. One egg matures and is released roughly every month between puberty and the menopause. The development of the egg is controlled by hormones from the pituitary gland.

- The regular cycle of egg production, thickening of the uterus wall, and breakdown and release of blood in a period, is called the menstrual cycle.

- Sexual intercourse involves transfer of sperm from male to female. Conception occurs when a sperm fuses with an egg in the Fallopian tube and implants in the uterus wall. If more than one egg is fertilised non-identical twins can form. Identical twins are formed from a single fertilised egg.

- Infertility can be caused by a lack of active sperm, a lack of eggs, or blockages in the Fallopian tubes. Infertility may be treatable by drugs, artificial insemination, or surgery.

- Contraception involves methods to keep eggs and sperm separate (withdrawal, male and female condoms, diaphragm or cap, spermicides and IUS); devices that prevent implantation of fertilised eggs (IUD); and systems that prevent the production of eggs (the contraceptive pill). Sterilisation permanently cuts the connection between the sperm-producing or egg-producing organs and the rest of the reproductive system.

9.6 After conception

How does a fertilised egg develop into a baby?

21 a Name two structures, other than the baby, that are produced from a fertilised egg and say happens to them after the baby is born.

b While in the baby is in the uterus, what functions does the mother carry out for it?

It takes about 9 months for a fertilised egg to grow and develop into a fully formed baby (see Figure 14). During this time, the mother provides it with food, breathes for it, excretes its waste materials, keeps it warm at a constant temperature of about 37 °C, and protects it from damage and disease.

The fertilised egg not only produces the embryo, it also gives rise to structures for the support of the baby: the placenta, umbilical cord and amnion. After the baby has been born, these structures leave the uterus as the **afterbirth**.

Figure 14 Growth and development of the baby

One month
A human embryo looks rather like the embryo of a fish or frog. It is possible to see a tail and parts that look as though they might develop into gills.

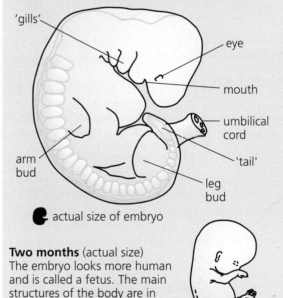

'gills'
eye
mouth
umbilical cord
'tail'
arm bud
leg bud

● actual size of embryo

Two months (actual size)
The embryo looks more human and is called a fetus. The main structures of the body are in place and the heart is beating.

Three months (actual size)
The nerves and muscles are developing rapidly. The fetus can swallow, frown, clench its fists, turn its head, and kick. It weighs about 50 g.

Five months
The mother can feel movements made by the baby. Very fine hairs cover its skin and the sex organs have developed enough to tell, from an ultrasound scan, whether it is a boy or a girl. At this stage the foetus weighs about 350 g.

Seven months
Development is almost complete. The baby will spend the next two months growing larger and stronger: the weight will double, and the length increase three times. Fat is stored under the skin and makes the baby look plump.

---

22 a How long does it take for a fertilised egg to develop into fully-formed baby?

b Using Figure 14 for as a guide, draw and label an embryo 2 months after conception.

c When does an embryo become called a fetus?

d By what age is the heart beating?

e Draw a 3-month old fetus and label the parts you can identify.

f How heavy is a 3-month old fetus and what is it able to do?

g How old is the fetus when:

   i the mother can feel its movements   **ii** a scan can reveal its sex   **ii** development is almost complete?

h What changes take place to the fetus during the last two months in the uterus?

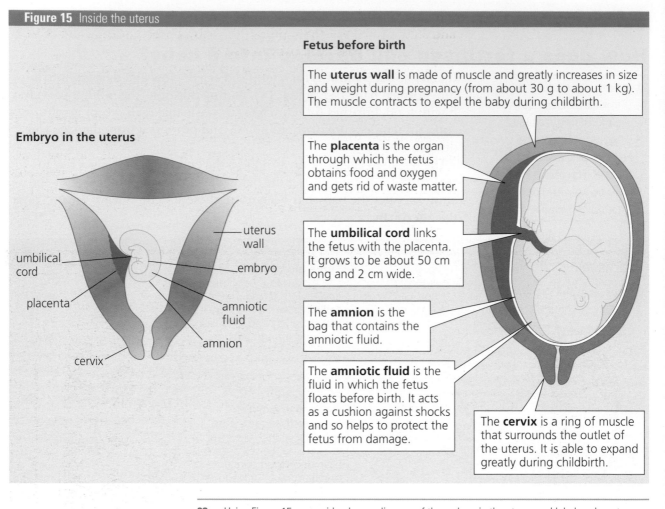

Figure 15 Inside the uterus

Embryo in the uterus

uterus wall

umbilical cord

embryo

placenta

amniotic fluid

amnion

cervix

Fetus before birth

The **uterus wall** is made of muscle and greatly increases in size and weight during pregnancy (from about 30 g to about 1 kg). The muscle contracts to expel the baby during childbirth.

The **placenta** is the organ through which the fetus obtains food and oxygen and gets rid of waste matter.

The **umbilical cord** links the fetus with the placenta. It grows to be about 50 cm long and 2 cm wide.

The **amnion** is the bag that contains the amniotic fluid.

The **amniotic fluid** is the fluid in which the fetus floats before birth. It acts as a cushion against shocks and so helps to protect the fetus from damage.

The **cervix** is a ring of muscle that surrounds the outlet of the uterus. It is able to expand greatly during childbirth.

23 a Using Figure 15 as a guide, draw a diagram of the embryo in the uterus and label each part.

  b Describe the changes that take place in the uterus as the embryo develops into a fetus ready for birth.

What does the placenta do?

As soon as an embryo implants in the uterus, some of its cells start to develop into a placenta. Identical twins share the same placenta, but non-identical twins each develop their own placenta. After about 12 weeks, the placenta is a thick, disc-like structure firmly attached to the uterus wall. As the baby develops, the placenta grows to about 15 centimetres across and about 500 grams in weight. It is the organ through which the baby both obtains the materials it needs and eliminates its waste. The placenta also produces hormones that help to maintain pregnancy.

Blood from the baby flows continuously to and from the placenta through the umbilical cord. In the placenta, the baby's blood and the mother's blood do not mix (see Figure 16). However, they are close enough for dissolved substances to be exchanged by diffusion through the capillary walls.

Useful substances that pass from mother to baby are food and oxygen, and antibodies that help to protect the baby. Carbon dioxide and other waste products pass from baby to mother.

Other substances can also cross from the mother's blood to the baby's blood, for example, medicines, alcohol, chemicals from cigarette smoke, and viruses. This is why pregnant women are advised not to take medicines without medical supervision, to drink only small quantities of alcohol, not to smoke, and to avoid contact with rubella (German measles), an illness caused by a virus that can damage a developing fetus.

The red blood cells made by a fetus contain a fetal form of haemoglobin that allows the fetus to obtain oxygen readily from the mother's blood. During the first few months after birth, fetal haemoglobin is replaced by the adult type.

Figure 16 Mother's and baby's blood in the placenta

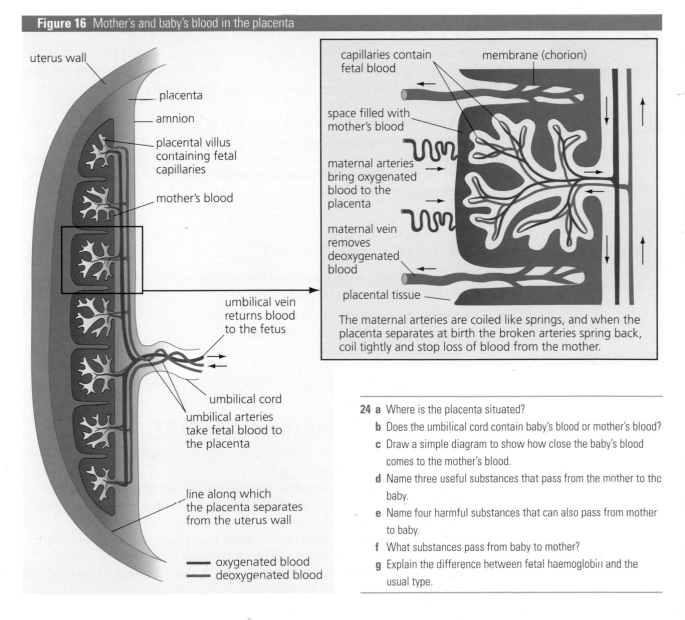

The maternal arteries are coiled like springs, and when the placenta separates at birth the broken arteries spring back, coil tightly and stop loss of blood from the mother.

24 **a** Where is the placenta situated?

  b Does the umbilical cord contain baby's blood or mother's blood?

  c Draw a simple diagram to show how close the baby's blood comes to the mother's blood.

  d Name three useful substances that pass from the mother to the baby.

  e Name four harmful substances that can also pass from mother to baby.

  f What substances pass from baby to mother?

  g Explain the difference between fetal haemoglobin and the usual type.

What is a miscarriage?

25 a What is a miscarriage?
  b What can be the first sign of miscarriage?

A **miscarriage**, also called a spontaneous abortion, occurs when the baby comes out of the uterus naturally but too early to survive on its own. It is estimated that between 10% and 20% of all pregnancies end in miscarriage.

The first sign of a miscarriage is bleeding from the vagina, sometimes with pain. However, slight bleeding or spotting does not always lead to a miscarriage.

9.7 Pregnancy

What are the first symptoms of pregnancy?

For a woman whose periods are regular and who has had sexual intercourse recently, the first symptom is usually a missed period. By the time a second period has been missed, other symptoms of pregnancy may be noticeable: feelings of nausea, enlarged and tender breasts, and more frequent passing of urine.

A **pregnancy test** measures the amount of a hormone called HCG. This hormone is present in the urine of pregnant women, and can usually be detected 10 days after conception. It is best to wait at least 2 weeks after the first missed period because a pregnancy test before this time may give a false negative result. Like every other test, a pregnancy test is not 100% reliable.

What happens in an antenatal clinic?

26 a Give four symptoms of pregnancy.
  b What does a pregnancy test measure?
  c Give four reasons why a mother should visit an antenatal clinic.

Pregnant women are advised to make regular visits to an antenatal clinic (ante = before, natal = birth) to have:

- the mother's health checked
- the baby's development monitored
- early medical treatment if necessary
- the opportunity to obtain parenting advice and the chance to ask questions.

What checks are made on the mother's health?

Weight checks

27 a Describe the average weight gain in pregnancy.
  b Give five causes of increase in weight in pregnancy.

Apart from the first few months, a pregnant woman gains, on average, about 500 grams in weight per week. In total, over the whole pregnancy, she puts on about 12 kilograms.

The increased weight is due to the baby plus the greatly enlarged uterus, the placenta, umbilical cord and amniotic fluid. Extra fat may also be stored in the layer under the mother's skin. If the mother puts on too much weight, she will be advised to diet.

Urine tests

At every visit to the antenatal clinic, a sample of the mother's urine is tested for glucose and albumin. If glucose is present, it may indicate diabetes; if albumin is present, it may indicate infection of the kidneys or bladder, or a condition called pre-eclampsia (see 'Blood pressure' below). If either is found, further tests will be made so that early treatment can be given if needed.

Blood tests

A blood sample is taken from the mother to test for haemoglobin, blood group and rubella antibodies.

Haemoglobin is the pigment in red blood cells. A shortage of haemoglobin is called **anaemia**, and it reduces the amount of oxygen the blood can carry. This leads to tiredness and weakness. Iron and folic acid are essential for the production of haemoglobin, so the usual treatment is to take iron–folate tablets. During pregnancy, the demand for iron and folic acid increases as the fetus grows.

Information about the mother's blood group is essential to prevent a rhesus-damaged baby (see page 42), and in case an emergency blood transfusion is needed.

If the mother has rubella antibodies, she is immune to the disease; without the antibodies she is not. If she catches rubella in the early months of pregnancy, the virus may kill the baby or leave it deaf, blind, mentally handicapped, or with heart disease.

Vaginal examination

On the first visit to the antenatal clinic, the mother's vagina is examined to check that there is no infection such as thrush, and to obtain a cervical smear to check for pre-cancerous cells (see page 183). Towards the end of pregnancy, the pelvis is checked to make sure that the opening is big enough for the baby's head to pass through.

Blood pressure

The mother's blood pressure is checked at every visit to the clinic, because high blood pressure may be a sign of pre-eclampsia.

Pre-eclampsia, also called toxaemia of pregnancy, occurs only during late pregnancy. It disappears as soon as the pregnancy is over. The signs are high blood pressure, protein in the urine, and swollen ankles. If the mother develops this condition, the growth of the baby is slowed. A patient with pre-eclampsia requires rest, often in hospital. If the condition is neglected, it may lead to a type of epilepsy called **eclampsia**, which can be fatal to both the baby and the mother. Fortunately, with modern antenatal care, eclampsia now occurs only rarely in the UK.

28 a Give two substances that the mother's urine is tested for, and say why each is important.

b List three things that the mother's blood is tested for, and say why each is important.

c Why is the vagina examined:

  i on the first visit to the clinic

  ii towards the end of pregnancy?

d Why is blood pressure checked regularly?

e When does pre-eclampsia occur and what are the signs?

f Why should pre-eclampsia not be neglected?

Placental hormones

The placenta produces hormones that can be detected in the mother's blood. In the last 8 weeks of pregnancy, her blood may be tested for oestrogen to check that the placenta is functioning normally and can keep the baby well supplied with food and oxygen.

29 When and why is the mother's blood tested for oestrogen?

What checks are made on the baby?

Position in the uterus

By gently pressing the outside of the abdomen, it is possible for the doctor to get some idea of the baby's size and position in the uterus. Towards the end of pregnancy, it is important to know if the baby is in the best position to be born (see page 201). If it is not, the doctor will try to move the baby into the proper position.

The baby's heartbeat

In the second half of pregnancy, the baby's heartbeat can be heard through a stethoscope placed on the mother's abdomen. It will be beating between 120 and 160 times per minute, which is much faster than the mother's heart rate.

Ultrasound scanning

Ultrasound is sound at a higher frequency than can be heard by the human ear. It is used to produce pictures of the baby in the uterus. Ultrasound scans give information about the baby's size, age, sex, and position. They also show the position of the placenta and whether or not twins are present.

30 a What information about the baby can be gained by pressing on the outside of the abdomen?

b What distinguishes the baby's heartbeat from the mother's?

c Why can't we hear ultrasound?

d Why is ultrasound used in pregnancy?

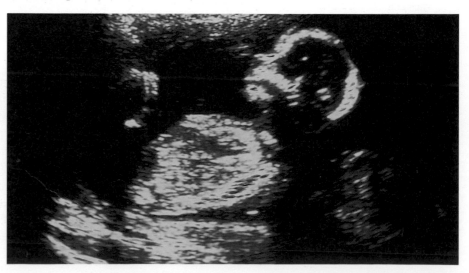

This ultrasound scan shows a 16-week-old fetus in side view. The head is at the upper right with the face pointing towards the left. Thre trunk is in the middle and a limb can be seen on the left.

9.8 Birth

What is the estimated date of delivery?

31 a What does EDD stand for, and what does it mean?

b How is EDD calculated?

c If a mother's last period started on March 1, when is the EDD?

d Describe the birth position.

The estimated date of delivery (EDD) is the date on which the child is most likely to be born. It is calculated by adding 40 weeks to the first day of the mother's last period. Pregnancy lasts, on average, about 38 weeks from the date of fertilisation and this is most likely to have happened about 2 weeks after the last period began. Towards the end of the pregnancy, the baby moves down and into the correct position to be born, that is, with the head downwards and facing the mother's back (see Figure 17).

What does 'being in labour' mean?

As the mother goes through the process of giving birth she is said to be 'in labour'. She is usually assisted by a midwife.

First stage: dilatation

One or more of the following signs indicates that labour has started:

32 a When a mother is 'in labour', what does this mean?

b Give three signs that indicate labour has started.

c What is the purpose of the contractions during the first stage of labour?

d How long does the first stage of labour take and when does it end?

e Which parts make the birth canal?

- a small discharge of blood and mucus comes away from the cervix where it formed a plug; this is called '**a show**'
- **contractions** of the muscles in the uterus wall are felt as pains in the abdomen occurring perhaps once every 20 to 30 minutes; contractions then become stronger, regular and more frequent
- the amnion breaks and the amniotic fluid is released; this is called '**breaking of the waters**'.

During the first stage of labour, the contractions gradually dilate the cervix. This means that the opening from the uterus into the vagina widens. The amnion may burst when labour first starts, or some time later. Dilatation is the longest stage of labour, usually taking between 4 and 12 hours. It comes to an end when the cervix is wide enough for the baby's head to pass through. The uterus, cervix and vagina are now one continuous **birth canal** (see Figure 18).

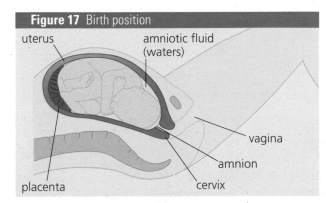

Figure 17 Birth position

uterus
amniotic fluid (waters)
vagina
amnion
placenta
cervix

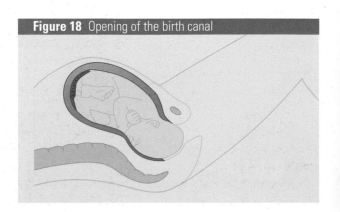

Figure 18 Opening of the birth canal

Second stage: delivery

During this stage, the uterus wall is contracting strongly and pushing the baby head first through the birth canal. The moment when the baby's head emerges from the vagina is called **crowning**. The midwife can now clear mucus from the baby's nose and mouth and the baby may start to breathe, and even cry. Next, the midwife eases the shoulders through the birth canal and the baby slides out into the world.

When the baby first appears, the skin is a bluish colour. As soon as breathing starts, the skin quickly turns pink as increased supplies of oxygen are collected from the baby's lungs by the haemoglobin in the red blood cells. The haemoglobin (dark red) becomes oxyhaemoglobin (bright red). Once the baby is breathing, the umbilical cord is clamped in two places, to prevent bleeding, and then cut between the clamps. There are no nerves in the cord, so there is no pain to the baby. The baby is now separated from the mother (see Figure 19).

Figure 19 From crowning to cutting the cord

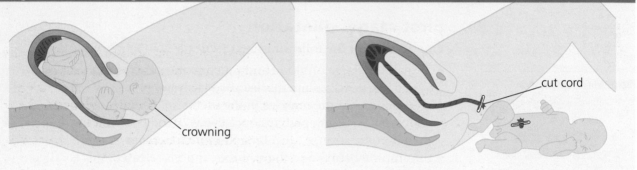

crowning

cut cord

Third stage: afterbirth

Contractions of the uterus continue until the placenta has become separated from the wall of the uterus and has been pushed out through the vagina (see Figure 20). Labour is now completed.

Figure 20 The afterbirth

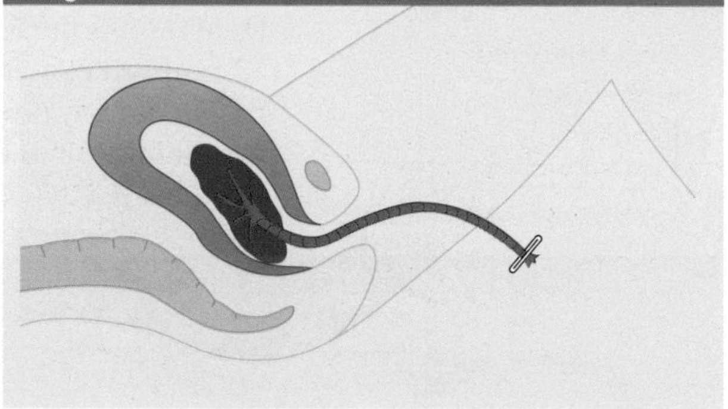

---

33 a What is the purpose of the contractions in the second stage of labour?

b What is meant by crowning?

c What action might the midwife take at crowning?

d How is the baby separated from the mother?

e Explain the change in colour of the baby from blue to pink.

f What is the purpose of contractions in the third stage of labour?

What pain relief is available?

Labour is usually painful, but there are a number of ways in which the pain can be relieved.

Relaxation and breathing exercises help relax the mother's muscles and this makes labour easier. The exercises are taught in antenatal classes and work well for many women, especially during the first stage of labour.

A **gas-and-oxygen mixture** may be offered to the mother during the second stage of labour. The mother inhales a gas such as nitrous oxide mixed with oxygen through a mouthpiece when she feels that the contractions are very strong and uncomfortable.

Pethidine is a powerful pain reliever. An injection of pethidine may be given if the contractions become very painful.

An **epidural anaesthetic** is an anaesthetic injected into the space around the lower part of the spinal cord. It blocks the sensory nerves that relay pain from the lower abdomen. No labour pains can now be felt, but the mother remains fully conscious.

34 Describe four ways in which the pain of childbirth can be relieved.

What complications can occur during birth?

A **breech birth** occurs when the baby comes out bottom first. It is usually much more difficult than a birth in which the head comes out first.

In **vacuum extraction**, a vacuum cup device is placed by the doctor on the baby's head to ease the baby gently through the birth canal. This may be necessary when the contractions are not strong enough to push the baby out, or when the baby is lying in an awkward position. Forceps are less commonly used for this purpose.

Caesarean section is a surgical operation to remove the baby from the uterus. It is carried out when the birth canal is too narrow, or when the health of the mother or baby makes immediate delivery necessary. The mother is given a general anaesthetic or epidural anaesthetic and a cut is made through the abdominal wall and into the uterus so that the baby can be removed. The umbilical cord is cut, the placenta is then removed, and the uterus and abdominal wall are stitched up.

Induction is the starting of labour by artificial means. It may be used when the baby is overdue, or when the health of the mother or baby is at risk. It may be possible to induce birth by breaking the waters. Sometimes, the mother might be given prostaglandin hormones through a 'drip' in her arm or applied to the cervix. These hormones stimulate the uterus to start contracting.

35 a What is a breech birth?
b When might a vacuum cup device be used?
c What is a Caesarean section and when is it carried out?
d When might birth be induced?
e Give two ways of inducing a birth.

9.9 Postnatal care

What care is given after the birth?

Postnatal care is the care given to the baby and the mother after the birth has taken place (post = after, natal = birth).

All newborn babies are given a routine examination in which the doctor or midwife examines the skin, listens to the heart, checks the mouth for cleft palate, and counts the fingers and toes to see if an extra one is present. Other checks include testing the movement of the hip joints for congenital dislocation of the hip. If a dislocated hip is discovered, the baby will require hospital treatment to prevent the development of a permanent limp.

When the baby is a few days old, a few drops of blood from its heel are tested for:

• phenylketonuria (PKU)
• thyroid hormone levels.

Phenylketonuria is an inherited condition that affects about one child in 15 000. It is due to the absence of the enzyme that deals with the amino acid phenylalanine, an amino acid found in the protein in milk and other foods. Without the enzyme, phenylalanine accumulates to toxic levels, and this damages the brain. The child will then have learning difficulties and reduced growth. If this condition is discovered early enough and the child is given a special diet lacking phenylalanine, he or she will develop normally.

The thyroid gland produces thyroid hormone, which is needed for normal growth and development. A baby with **thyroid hormone deficiency**, that is one who lacks thyroid hormone, would develop into a **cretin**: undersized and mentally handicapped. Cretinism can be completely prevented by giving the child doses of thyroid hormone immediately.

The stump of the umbilical cord attached to the baby dries, shrivels and drops off after about a week; this leaves the umbilicus, often called the **navel** or belly button.

36 a Why is movement of the hip joints of newborn babies checked by a doctor?

b What is phenylketonuria?

c How can PKU be treated?

d What would happen to a baby who lacked thyroid hormone?

e How can cretinism be prevented?

f How is the navel formed?

What changes take place in the mother after birth?

The enlarged uterus shrinks rapidly in the days following the birth, and this is speeded up by breast-feeding. Eventually the uterus will be almost as small as it was before the baby was conceived. A little bleeding continues from the place in the uterus where the placenta was attached until the wound is healed. Healing of this wound may take up to a month.

Pregnancy greatly stretches the muscles of the abdomen and afterwards they are very loose and floppy. The muscles of the pelvic floor (between the tops of the legs) are also stretched and weakened during delivery. All these muscles will gradually improve and tighten. Special postnatal exercises help them to regain their shape and tone.

The time at which periods start again varies considerably; it may be 6 months or longer after the birth. It is possible to become pregnant again before periods return. It is also possible to become pregnant while still breast-feeding, although breast-feeding makes conception less likely.

37 a After the baby is born, what happens to the mother's uterus?

b Which two sets of muscles are stretched during pregnancy?

c What helps the stretched muscles to regain their shape?

d When does the menstrual cycle start again?

What causes 'baby blues'?

During the week following the birth, commonly between the third and fifth day, it is quite usual for the mother to feel miserable and depressed without knowing why. This period of mild depression is often called the 'baby blues'. Reasons for it include:

- the hormones that controlled pregnancy and childbirth have not yet settled back into their normal pattern of activity – this makes the mother feel 'out of sorts'
- tiredness due to disturbed nights and busy days looking after the baby
- reaction to the excitement of the birth – now it is all over, life seems to be nothing but a constant round of feeding, changing nappies and washing.

It can help the mother to know that these feelings are quite common and normal in new mothers. If her family know how she feels, they can help out and be supportive. She can also ask the midwife for advice.

More severe cases of 'baby blues' are often called **postnatal depression**. Mothers with this condition usually need medical advice.

38 Give three reasons why a mother might suffer from mild depression after the baby is born.

When do the breasts produce milk?

During pregnancy, the breasts (**mammary glands**) enlarge as the glandular tissue within them develops so that it is ready to supply food for the baby (see Figure 21). The size of the breasts before pregnancy depends on the amount of fat tissue present, not on the amount of milk-producing tissue.

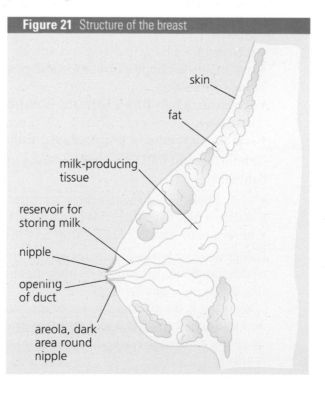

Figure 21 Structure of the breast

skin

fat

milk-producing tissue

reservoir for storing milk

nipple

opening of duct

areola, dark area round nipple

39 Draw and label a diagram to show the structure of the breast.

40 a When do the breasts start to secrete colostrum?

b What does colostrum contain?

c Which hormone stimulates the breasts to produce milk?

d When do the breasts start producing milk?

e How does a baby's feeding pattern change during the first 3 months?

Women with small breasts should be able to breast-feed just as well as those with larger breasts.

Each breast contains about 15 to 20 ducts that open on the surface of the nipple; the milk therefore comes from a number of tiny openings.

Towards the end of pregnancy, the breasts start to secrete small amounts of a yellow, watery fluid called **colostrum** and the baby feeds on this for the first few days. Besides containing water, colostrum is rich in protein, and it also contains antibodies which give the baby protection against some diseases.

After the baby has been born, the pituitary hormone prolactin stimulates milk production, and about 3 days later milk is produced. The baby is now ready for much larger quantities of food and may want to feed ten or twelve times in 24 hours. This helps to establish a good supply of milk, because the more the baby sucks, the more the breasts are stimulated to produce milk.

The baby soon settles into a pattern of wanting to be fed about six times a day. Gradually, the interval between the feeds in the night gets longer and longer so that by the age of 3 months, the night feed is usually given up altogether.

Why are young babies fed on milk?

Babies are fed entirely on milk for the first few months of life, either from the breast or bottle. Milk is about 90% water and 10% nutrients. It contains all the substances that a young baby needs. Breast milk is the natural food for a baby and is ideal because:

- it contains all the necessary ingredients in the right amounts for healthy growth
- it is easy for a baby to digest and absorb
- it contains antibodies from the mother, which help to protect the baby against infections
- it is clean; a fully breast-fed baby is much less likely to get gastro-enteritis
- it is safe; it cannot be prepared incorrectly and does not cause allergies.

Although breast milk is a complete food for a young baby, it does not contain:

- iron; a baby is born with several months' supply stored in the liver
- starch; a new baby does not possess the right enzymes to digest starch
- fibre; a baby has no need for fibre in the first few months.

Babies who are bottle-fed are usually given 'infant formula'. This is a type of dried milk made from cow's milk that has been altered to make it more like breast milk (see Table 2).

Weaning is the gradual change of diet from milk to a mixture of foods, and it usually begins at 3 to 4 months. By the age of 1 year, the child will be eating a mixed diet which is similar to that eaten by the rest of the family.

Table 2 Nutrients in breast milk and cow's milk in grams per 100 cm^3

Nutrient	Breast milk	Cow's milk
sugar	6.6	4.4
protein	1.2	3.0
fat	3.8	3.8
minerals	0.4	0.8
vitamins	traces	traces

41 a List five reasons why breast milk is an ideal food for a baby.

   b Name three substances that are not present in breast milk, and explain why a baby does not need them.

   c What type of milk is usually given to a baby who is bottle-fed?

   d Give three ways in which the nutrients in breast milk and cow's milk differ.

   e What is meant by weaning?

Summary of pregnancy, birth and postnatal care

- Pregnancy usually lasts 9 months in humans. Pregnancy test kits use the rise in a hormone called HCG to detect pregnancy.
- The placenta develops with the baby to supply food and oxygen and take away waste products. In the placenta, blood from the mother comes very close to blood from the fetus but the two bloodstreams do not mix.
- Antenatal clinics check the mother's weight, urine, blood and the state of the vagina to ensure a healthy pregnancy.
- The baby's health can be assessed by listening to the heart beat, feeling the shape of the uterus and by ultrasound examinations.
- Labour has three stages: in the first, the cervix dilates to open up the birth canal; in the second, the baby is delivered from the mother's body; in the third, the placenta is delivered as the afterbirth.

- In a breech birth, the baby is born bottom first. In a Caesarean section, a surgeon cuts through the abdomen into the uterus to remove the baby.
- A routine check on the baby after birth includes counting the number of fingers and toes and looking for hip dislocation. Blood tests to check for phenylketonuria and thyroid deficiency are usually given a few days after birth.
- Changes in the mother after the birth include contraction of the uterus and the production of milk in the breasts. Emotional upsets and mild depression can occur at this point.
- Colostrum is produced by the mother to feed the baby for the first few days. It is rich in protein and in antibodies to protect the baby against disease. Breast milk contains a higher concentration of sugar, and less protein and minerals than cow's milk.

9.10 Newborn babies

What changes happen at birth?

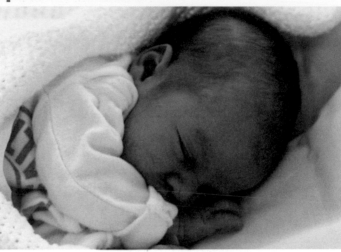

When this tiny baby emerged from the uterus, changes rapidly took place to enable it to live a separate existence from its mother.

---

42 Describe five changes that take place at birth to enable a baby to live separately from its mother.

Changes at birth that enable the baby to live a separate existence include the following:

- breathing starts almost immediately
- the kidneys begin to function on their own
- the digestive system starts to function on its own
- changes in circulation take place because oxygen arrives from the lungs and not the placenta
- the baby can stretch and move unhindered.

How does breathing start?

At birth, the baby has to get its oxygen from the air by breathing, and no longer from the mother's blood. This change involves re-routing the blood from the placenta to the lungs (see Figure 22).

---

43 Using Figure 22, describe in your own words the changes involved in switching from obtaining oxygen through the umbilical cord to breathing air.

What can newborn babies do?

Most newborn babies sleep for much of the time, but they are able to do many other things. For example, they:

- feed by sucking
- express their feelings by crying when hungry, in pain or lonely
- can see, although not clearly – they blink at nearby movements and shut their eyes when a bright light is suddenly turned on
- can hear and are startled by loud noises
- are sensitive to smell – they turn the head away from an unpleasant smell

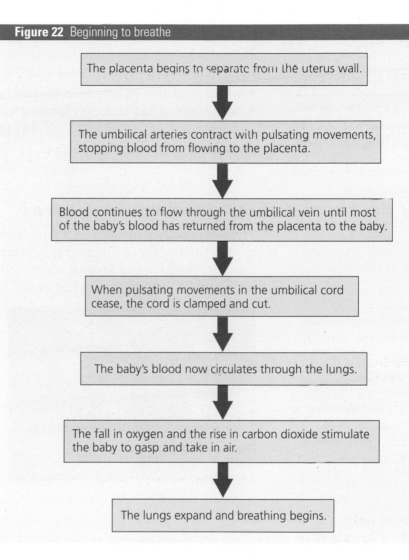

Figure 22 Beginning to breathe

The placenta begins to separate from the uterus wall.

↓

The umbilical arteries contract with pulsating movements, stopping blood from flowing to the placenta.

↓

Blood continues to flow through the umbilical vein until most of the baby's blood has returned from the placenta to the baby.

↓

When pulsating movements in the umbilical cord cease, the cord is clamped and cut.

↓

The baby's blood now circulates through the lungs.

↓

The fall in oxygen and the rise in carbon dioxide stimulate the baby to gasp and take in air.

↓

The lungs expand and breathing begins.

44 a How do newborn babies express their feelings?

b Do newborn babies have control over their muscles?

c In what three ways are the sense organs working?

45 a What is a reflex action? (see pages 137 and 138)

b Give some examples of reflex actions shown by newborn babies.

c When do these reflexes disappear?

- have a certain amount of muscle control and can make jerky movements
- have a certain amount of coordination between the senses and can turn their eyes towards the source of a noise
- have started to learn.

A young baby displays a number of automatic movements called reflex actions that help them survive. Four examples are:

- when anything is put into a baby's mouth, the baby immediately sucks and swallows
- when gently touched on the cheek, a baby turns its head as if in search of the nipple; this is called the rooting reflex
- when an object is put into a baby's hand, it is firmly grasped
- when held upright with the feet touching a firm surface, a baby makes walking movements.

These reflexes mainly disappear within 3 months and are replaced by actions the baby has to learn.

How do young babies keep warm?

Full-term babies, babies that have completed 9 months in the uterus, are born with a store of fat under the skin. This fat layer:

- acts as insulation to help keep the baby warm
- can be used as fuel to supply extra heat when necessary.

Nevertheless, newborn babies have difficulty in keeping warm and, for the first month of life, should be kept at a room temperature of around 20 °C day and night.

46 Why are mothers advised to keep newborn babies at a constant temperature of about 20 °C?

Why do some babies need special care?

Premature babies are babies who are born before 37 weeks. They tend to be small and weak, and to need special care. They often have difficulty breathing, sucking and keeping warm, and may need to be kept in an incubator for the first few days or weeks.

47 a What is a premature baby?
b Why do premature babies often need special care?
c List two ways in which the conditions in an incubator:
i resemble conditions in the uterus
ii differ from conditions in the uterus.

An incubator acts as halfway house between the uterus and the outside world. The baby is kept isolated, protected, and in a controlled environment where temperature and humidity are constant. Food is supplied through a tube or dropper until the baby has the strength to suck. If necessary, extra oxygen can be supplied to help with breathing.

9.11 Growth

How is growth measured?

48 What is the difference between the growth curve for a boy and the growth curve for a girl?

Growth can be measured as increase in height and weight. Generally, as children grow taller they also becomes heavier, but not always, because weight also depends on how fat or thin the child is. On average, full height is reached at about age 16 in females and 18 in males (see Figure 23).

How does body shape change with growth?

49 a Why do body proportions change with growth?
b Use Figure 24 to describe the change in proportions:
i between birth and age 7
ii between ages 7 and 18.

As a child grows, the different parts of the body increase in size and alter in shape. This has the effect of changing the proportions of the body as the child gets older (see Figure 24). For example, at birth, the legs are about three-eighths of the total length of the body, but by the age of 16, they are about half of total body length. However, children do not all grow at the same rate.

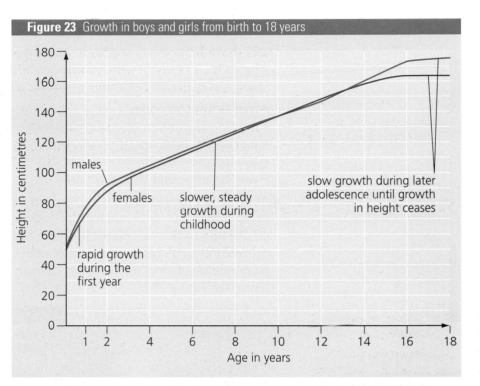

Figure 23 Growth in boys and girls from birth to 18 years

Height in centimetres

males

females

rapid growth during the first year

slower, steady growth during childhood

slow growth during later adolescence until growth in height ceases

Age in years

Even in the same school class, children of the same age vary noticeably in shape and size.

Figure 24 Body proportions change with growth

newborn   2 years   7 years   18 years

Why do children vary in size?

The height and weight measurements of children of the same age can vary greatly and are spread over a wide range on either side of the average. Four factors are responsible for this variation:

- genetic differences
- sex differences
- food supply
- severe illness.

50 List four factors that influence growth.

211

What changes take place in the skeleton?

The shape of the body is governed by the shape of the skeleton. As the various bones change with growth, so the different parts of the body change in shape. For example:

- babies have bow-legs
- 3-year-old children often develop knock-knees
- 6-year-olds have usually developed straight legs
- the feet grow rapidly in early puberty
- the legs grow rapidly later in puberty.

At birth, the skeleton consists mainly of cartilage. As growth proceeds, most of the cartilage is replaced by bone, a process known as **ossification**. Ossification is not completed until the late teens. Because ossification proceeds in a regular pattern, it is possible to estimate the age of a child from examination of the skeleton, or even just the bones of the wrist and hand (see Figure 25).

51 Describe the changes to the legs as a child grows.

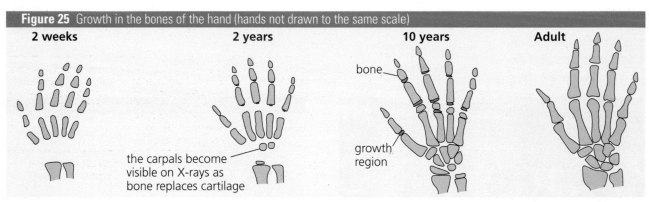

Figure 25 Growth in the bones of the hand (hands not drawn to the same scale)

2 weeks   2 years   10 years   Adult

the carpals become visible on X-rays as bone replaces cartilage

bone

growth region

Fontanelles are the 'soft spots' on a baby's head. They are gaps between the bones of the skull that are covered by a tough, flexible membrane (see Figure 26). Fontanelles allow the skull to alter shape slightly during childbirth as the head is pushed through the birth canal. The fontanelles disappear as the skull bones enlarge and join together. The posterior fontanelle has disappeared by the age of 2 months, and the anterior fontanelle by about the age of 18 months.

52 a Using Figure 25, describe the changes that take place in the bones of the hand as it grows.

  b What is the purpose of the fontanelles in the skull?

  c Could the skull in Figure 26 belong to a baby aged 1 month or 1 year? Give a reason.

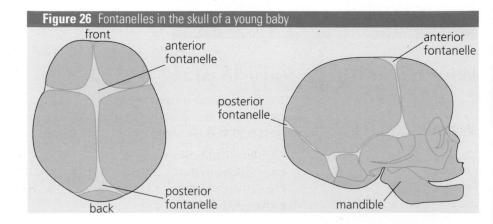

Figure 26 Fontanelles in the skull of a young baby

front

anterior fontanelle

anterior fontanelle

posterior fontanelle

posterior fontanelle

back

mandible

9.12 Development

How do growing children change?

The first few years of life see great changes in a child as it grows and develops. The speed at which any of these changes occur varies between children. Table 3 gives the average age at which some stages of development occur, but remember that the age at which normal babies and children do any of these things varies greatly on either side of the average.

Table 3 Five aspects of development from birth to 3 years old

Age	Body movements	Hands	Eyes	Communication and speech	Behaviour
newborn	kicks, stretches, moves arms and turns head	hands usually closed with thumbs turned in	aware of light and movement but very short-sighted	cries when hungry, lonely or in pain	comforted by being held close and cuddled
3 months	lifts head when lying face downwards	hands usually open	very interested in things nearby, especially faces	gurgles and babbles and holds 'conversations' with people	smiles with pleasure at people
6 months	sits with support	grasps toys and can pass them from hand to hand	eyes work together and are rarely crossed	makes a variety of sounds and spends time practising them	laughs and chuckles with delight when getting attention
9 months	tries to crawl	drops things on the floor	shows interest in things up to 4 metres away	makes the sounds 'dad-dad', 'mum-mum' and 'bab-bab'	shy with strangers
1 year	begins to walk	points to things	recognises known people at a distance	says a few words with meaning, such as 'bye-bye'	understands the meaning of 'no'
2 years	climbs onto furniture	holds pencil and scribbles	can see as far as an adult can see	makes simple sentences of 2 to 3 words	may have temper tantrums
3 years	stands on one leg	uses scissors	begins to recognise colours	talks ceaselessly	understands sharing

53 a Give the average age by which children:

    i begin to walk   **iv** begin to recognise colours

    ii say 'dad-dad'   **v** are very interested in people's faces

    iii have temper tantrums   **vi** can pass things from hand to hand.

  b Make a table to compare a newborn baby and a 1-year-old in each of the five aspects of development.

What changes take place at puberty?

During childhood, there is little difference in strength between boys and girls. But at puberty, physical changes occur that result in males becoming generally stronger than females, whereas females tend to be lighter and more supple than males.

For example, there is a tendency for:

- males to develop larger muscles than females
- males to develop a larger heart than females, so they can pump more blood with each heartbeat
- males to develop more red cells and a greater haemoglobin content per unit of blood than females
- males to develop larger lungs than females, so greater quantities of oxygen can be obtained and carbon dioxide excreted
- males to develop a higher metabolic rate than females and need more food to supply their increased energy needs
- males to develop greater arm length than females, which helps them to throw objects harder and further, or hit them with greater force
- females to develop a wider pelvis than males so they have a more acute angle at the joint between pelvis and femur; this is a disadvantage when running
- females to develop more flexible muscles and joints than males
- females to develop more body fat than males so they have greater insulation from heat loss and added buoyancy when swimming.

54 a List four differences in body structure that explain why males tend to be stronger than females.

b Suggest a reason why females tend to do better than males in the forms of gymnastics that do not require strength.

Shot-putting tends to be a male sport while gymnastics tends to be a sport for very young women. However, there are female shot-putters and male gymnasts.

What is the advantage of a long childhood?

Humans have a very long childhood, a much longer period of dependency on parents than is found in any other animal. This gives time for learning the skills needed for survival in highly complex human societies. These skills include: language, use of tools and technical skills, social skills necessary for group living, and the ability to acquire knowledge continually.

55 List four skills that a long childhood gives time to learn.

The period of dependence has become longer during this century partly because of the increased amount of knowledge and skills required for living in a technological society. In Britain, the age at which children could legally leave school was raised from 12 to 14 years in 1918, from 14 to 15 years in 1944, and from 15 to 16 years in 1972. It is now common for young people to be educated until the age of 18 or older. Children now spend up to 6 years longer at school than in 1918.

9.13 Ageing

How old is 'old'?

Generally, in our society, people are not considered elderly until they reach the age of 75 or more. Ageing is not the same as getting older: all people get older at the same rate, but the rate at which they age varies greatly. Some very old people remain energetic, mentally active and enjoy life, while some much younger people are 'old for their years'.

Why do people age?

Ageing is a natural process and results from gradual changes in the various tissues and organs that prevent them from functioning as efficiently as they once did. The causes of these changes include:

- loss of cells which, when damaged or worn out, are not renewed (for example, nerve cells, teeth)
- inaccurate repair of tissues
- accumulation of unwanted matter in the tissues (for example, cholesterol in blood vessels)
- reduced immunity to fight disease.

The rate at which people age depends on many factors including:

- inherited genes
- attitude to life
- state of health
- money – on average, rich people live longer than poor people and age more slowly.

Different tissues and organs age at different rates, for example:

- arteries begin to clog up from childhood onwards, a process that is encouraged by lack of exercise, over-eating and smoking
- the skin begins to lose elasticity in early adult life
- eyesight and hearing become less efficient from the mid-forties
- the number of brain cells decreases throughout life (although there are many millions of brain cells left, it becomes more difficult to remember recent events than to recall those which happened many years ago)
- the liver and kidneys are usually healthy throughout life and rarely cause problems.

56 a Why do tissues and organs become less efficient as people grow older?

b Give four reasons why people age at different rates.

c When do arteries begin to clog up?

d When does skin begin to lose elasticity?

e When do eyesight and hearing become less efficient?

What happens as you age?

Almost all aspects of your body change with age (see Figure 27).

Figure 27 Body changes that happen as you age

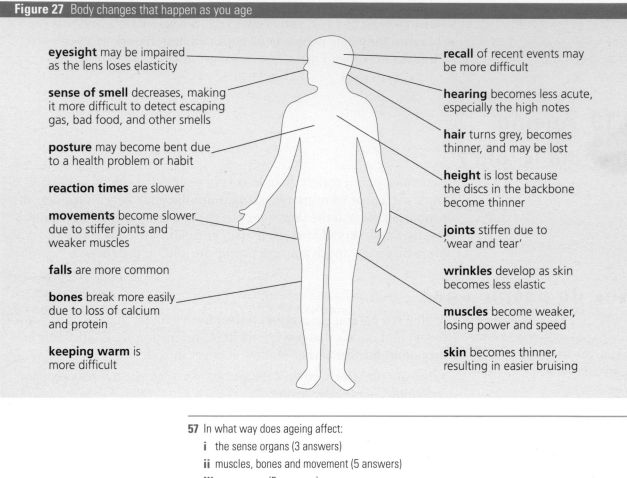

eyesight may be impaired as the lens loses elasticity

sense of smell decreases, making it more difficult to detect escaping gas, bad food, and other smells

posture may become bent due to a health problem or habit

reaction times are slower

movements become slower due to stiffer joints and weaker muscles

falls are more common

bones break more easily due to loss of calcium and protein

keeping warm is more difficult

recall of recent events may be more difficult

hearing becomes less acute, especially the high notes

hair turns grey, becomes thinner, and may be lost

height is lost because the discs in the backbone become thinner

joints stiffen due to 'wear and tear'

wrinkles develop as skin becomes less elastic

muscles become weaker, losing power and speed

skin becomes thinner, resulting in easier bruising

---

57 In what way does ageing affect:

i the sense organs (3 answers)

ii muscles, bones and movement (5 answers)

iii appearance (5 answers)

iv ability to keep warm (1 answer)

v recall (1 answer).

Why 'use it or lose it'?

If the body and brain are not used, the ability to use them will decline. To help delay the effects of ageing:

- take regular exercise because muscles that are not used weaken
- take care of the feet because painful feet make walking difficult
- avoid becoming overweight because it puts strain on the heart and joints, and makes diabetes and high blood pressure more likely
- keep mentally active because a brain that is not used deteriorates
- keep interested in other people and events because it helps to prevent boredom and loneliness
- have a well balanced diet to keep healthy.

58 Give six actions that help to delay the effects of ageing.

Summary of newborn babies, growth, development and ageing

- Changes are necessary at birth to enable a baby to live separately from it's mother. These changes involve the lungs, the kidneys, the digestive system and the circulation.
- Significant changes to the circulation are needed at birth to ensure that the baby switches from obtaining oxygen through the umbilical cord to breathing air.
- Newborn babies possess a number of reflexes that ensure they are able to survive, for example the sucking reflex.
- Premature babies often need special care and may require an incubator for a while.
- Growth involves an increase in total body length and a change in the proportions of various body parts.
- Males and females develop at slightly different rates with females reaching their full adult height slightly sooner than males.
- Changes to the skeleton include ossification of cartilage in the bones, and closure of the fontanelles.

- The average age at which certain development changes occur can be charted. However, people develop at different rates and the age at which normal babies and children reach any particular stage varies greatly.
- At puberty, physical changes result in males becoming generally stronger than females by developing larger muscles, a larger heart, and larger lungs. Females tend to develop more flexible joints, a wider pelvis and more body fat than males.
- A long childhood helps children to learn and prepare for adult life in a complex, technological world.
- Ageing is a natural process affecting all parts of the body, but to different extents. The rate and effects of ageing vary considerably from person to person. Looking after the body and remaining mentally active may help delay the effects of ageing.

Health and lifestyle

Learning objectives

By the end of this chapter you should be able to:

- **define** health and lifestyle
- **describe** the part played by individuals and medical staff in the promotion of health
- **recognise** the risks and benefits of medicines
- **describe** the main forms of complementary medicine
- **describe** the health implications of tobacco smoking, alcohol consumption and illegal drug use

- **review** some illegal drugs
- **describe** appetite control and its disorders
- **describe** the health implications of good posture and plenty of exercise
- **distinguish** between stress and tension
- **describe** the development of communication skills in human beings.

10. 1 Health and medicine

What is health?

The World Health Organisation (WHO) defines health as a state of complete mental, physical and social well-being. It is not merely the absence of disease or infirmity.

In the developed world, mental, physical, and social well-being are inter-related:

- happy and contented people are less likely to be ill
- people in jobs they enjoy are less likely to have days off sick
- bored or discontented people are more likely to complain of ill-health or to have accidents
- poor people tend to have more health problems than rich people.

In the developing world, health issues are dominated by:

- food shortages and crop failures
- inadequate water supplies and sanitation
- diseases such as cholera and malaria
- inadequate medical services.

---

1 a Give a definition of health.

  b Say who, in the developed world, are:

    i less likely to be ill

    ii more likely to be ill.

  c In the developing world, what is ill-health likely to be due to?

What does an individual's health depend on?

Health depends on many factors:

- personal choices, such as whether or not to smoke or to take regular exercise
- choices made by your parents, such as whether or not you were taken to the dentist for regular check-ups or immunised against common illnesses
- the area where you live; for example pollution may come from a local factory, and many diseases are prevented by clean water and food
- national political decisions; for example a decision might be made on whether to build a new hospital or a city bypass
- safety standards for domestic equipment such as washing machines, safety at work regulations, and road safety rules
- global factors; for example increasing atmospheric pollution is slowly thinning the ozone layer which gives protection against the ultra-violet rays that cause skin cancer.

2 From your general knowledge, give two examples of ill-health that can be prevented by five of the items listed.

This is Kraków (Poland), where many years of acid air pollution have damaged buildings and health. The building on the right shows the results of this. The restored yellow building will not suffer this damage as air quality has now improved considerably. However, lung cancer, asthma and chronic bronchitis are still more frequent than elsewhere in Poland and this difference will take years to clear.

How does lifestyle affect health?

Nowadays, people know quite a lot about their own bodies, and how to improve their health and avoid risks. People have choices about their **lifestyle**, that is, the way they live. Lifestyle decisions concern issues such as:

- smoking, drinking alcohol, and taking drugs
- diet, exercise, and posture
- work, leisure, and sleep
- living conditions and personal cleanliness
- friendships.

3 a What is meant by lifestyle?
  b Choose three items in the list and say how a change in lifestyle could improve your health.

Who is responsible for our health?

Doctors pay much attention to maintaining health by providing health checks, and by offering advice about lifestyle issues such as diet, obesity, smoking, alcohol, exposure to sun, exercise, and sexually transmitted diseases. Maintaining health is a partnership between the individual and his or her doctor. The chief responsibility is usually with the individual: lifestyle changes can only happen when the individual takes action. Doctor and patient need to understand what each other can and cannot achieve. **Disease** is present when all or part of the body does not function properly.

4 Who is responsible for your health?

What is modern medicine?

Modern conventional medicine is based on scientific research. This means that it depends on testing ideas about the prevention and treatment of disease by experiment. Modern medicine tries to assess the balance between the benefits and risks of treatment. Modern diagnosis and treatment of disease can involve special procedures such as:

- blood transfusion
- dialysis for kidney failure
- radiotherapy
- transplant surgery.

Modern medicine demands specially trained and registered people, for example:

- doctors with various skills such as general practitioners, hospital specialists, surgeons, radiologists, microbiologists
- general and specialist nurses, midwives
- rehabilitation experts such as physiotherapists, occupational therapists, speech therapists
- diagnosis experts such as laboratory, cardiac and measurement technicians
- treatment experts such as radiotherapists, pharmacists, chiropodists.

Modern medicine demands special technologies in diagnosis and treatment, for example:

- computerised tomography (CT) scanners, magnetic resonance imaging (MRI) scanners, linear accelerators, isotope gamma cameras
- powerful and often specially designed medicines and anti-cancer treatments
- keyhole surgery, microsurgery with microscopes, laser surgery
- general anaesthetics and heart bypass surgery.

5 a What is modern medicine based on?

  b Name four procedures used in modern medicine.

  c Choose eight from the list of specially trained people and say what you think each does.

  d List six examples of technology used in diagnosis and treatment.

What are medicines?

Medicines are drugs that are used to treat or prevent disease. They may be taken to:

- treat disease, for example chemotherapy for cancer
- prevent disease, for example a low dosage of aspirin to prevent strokes and heart attacks
- destroy **pathogens** (sometimes called '**germs**'), the harmful microorganisms that cause disease, for example antibiotics to destroy bacteria
- supply hormones in which the body is deficient, for example insulin
- correct body processes when they are not functioning properly, for example laxatives to relieve constipation
- relieve symptoms such as pain
- prevent pregnancy, as with the contraceptive pill.

Over-the-counter medicines, for example paracetamol and cough mixture, can be bought from a pharmacy or other shop. **Prescription-only medicines** are available only from a pharmacy with a doctor's prescription because medical knowledge is required for their safe use.

All medicines can have harmful side-effects. They may:

- interact with other drugs or with food that the patient is taking
- have different effects on different people
- be dangerous if taken in the wrong doses
- be addictive if taken repeatedly.

6 a What are medicines?
b What can medicines do?
c Why are some medicines obtainable only by prescription?
d List four possible side-effects of medicines.

How do medicines enter the body?

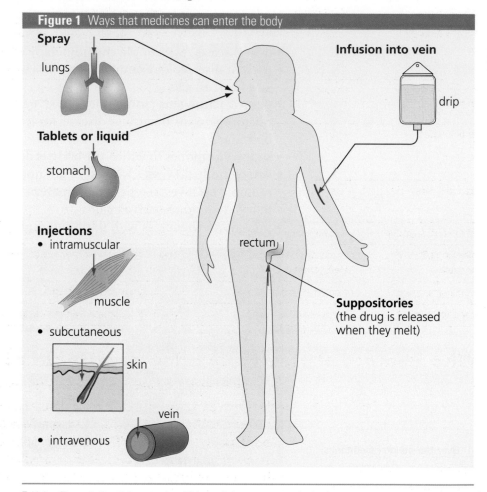

Figure 1 Ways that medicines can enter the body

Spray
lungs

Infusion into vein
drip

Tablets or liquid
stomach

Injections
• intramuscular
muscle

• subcutaneous
skin

• intravenous
vein

rectum

Suppositories
(the drug is released
when they melt)

---

7 Using Figure 1, list eight ways in which medicines can enter the body.

Do all medicines have risks?

All medicines can have side-effects, depending on factors such as:

• the individual's reaction to a particular medicine
• the dose taken
• whether or not the medicine is taken with food
• whether or not the medicine is taken with alcohol or other drugs.

Before taking medicine of any kind, it is sensible to weigh the benefit against the risk (see Table 1).

---

8 a What can side-effects of medicines depend on?

 b Name six medicines that can cause drowsiness.

 c Name two activities in which drowsiness could be dangerous.

 d What is the risk of taking antibiotics too often?

 e Why do women on the contraceptive pill need regular medical check-ups?

Table 1 Medicines and side-effects

Medicine	Why taken	Possible side-effects
pain relievers	to numb pain	some pain relievers cause drowsiness and are dangerous if taken before driving or using machinery
		others, for example aspirin, can irritate the stomach lining
cough medicines	to stop a dry cough	drowsiness, nausea, constipation
laxatives	to relieve constipation	if taken too often, they stop the gut muscles from working normally
antibiotics	to treat bacterial infection	rashes, diarrhoea
		if taken too often, they increase the risk of bacteria arising that are resistant to antibiotics
tranquillisers	to reduce tension	drowsiness, lack of concentration
		anxiety when stopped
some anti-depressants	to ease severe depression	drowsiness, dry mouth, blurred vision
sleeping pills and sedatives	to restore disrupted sleep patterns	drowsiness, lack of concentration, 'hungover' feeling
travel sickness pills	to relieve motion sickness	drowsiness, dry mouth, blurred vision
contraceptive pill	to prevent pregnancy	slight risk of increased blood pressure and thrombosis

Who is most at risk from adverse effects of medicines?

The following groups are most at risk from the effects of medicines:

- the very young because they react differently from adults
- the very old because they are more sensitive to many medicines and, as they tend to take many different kinds of medicine, there is an increased chance of drug interaction and unwanted effects
- the fetus and breast-fed babies when the mother takes medicine
- those who are taking other medicines because of possible drug interactions
- drivers and machinery operators who take medicines that may cause drowsiness, lack of concentration, blurred vision and slow reactions; these side-effects are increased if taken with even a little alcohol.

9 Explain why extra care is needed when giving medicines to:
  i very young children
  ii very old people
  iii pregnant women.

Do we need medicines for all illnesses?

Most minor ailments such as colds, coughs, headaches or diarrhoea will get better without medicines. The body just needs time to heal itself. Medicines are needed only when they are likely to benefit an individual patient.

A **placebo** (pronounced pla-sea-bo) is a harmless substance that can be given in place of active medicine. For instance, about one-third of the population will go to sleep more easily if told they have been given a 'sleeping pill', or will gain some pain relief after taking a 'pain reliever' that contains only sugar or starch.

10 What is a placebo?

What is complementary medicine?

For most illnesses, it seems sensible for an ill person to seek advice first from a doctor. If the advice or treatment does not appear to help, the patient may then decide to try complementary medicine, often with their doctor's agreement. **Complementary medicine** provides treatment, or prevention of illness, without using modern drugs or surgery. It consists of a number of therapies that have little in common, but many have roots in the past and in Eastern patterns of thought and tradition. Each therapy has its own way of explaining the origin of a patient's symptoms (see Table 2).

11 a What is complementary medicine?

b What can be the chief problem?

c When does complementary medicine usually work best?

Table 2 Summary of some common forms of complementary medicine

Name of therapy	Brief notes	What it is used for
Alexander technique	posture training when standing, walking, sitting or lying	muscle and joint pain
aromatherapy	aromatic 'essential oils' are inhaled or absorbed through the skin during massage; lavender oil is the most frequently used for general purposes	physical and emotional stress depression
chiropractic	manipulation of the spine to relieve pressure on nerves caused by problems with the joints of the vertebral column	back pain
healing: 'laying on of hands'	the healer's touch transmits healing influences to the troubled person or the damaged part	all types of illness
herbalism	plant preparations are used to prevent or treat disease; many modern medicines contain the same ingredients in a purified form	all types of illness
homeopathy	the theory is that if a particular substance causes particular symptoms, it will cure the same symptoms when given as very diluted dose e.g. belladonna poisoning makes the patient hot and dry, so greatly diluted belladonna is used to treat fevers	all types of illness
hypnotherapy hypnosis	a state of deep trance now also used in modern medicine	asthma and pain relief some emotional problems
osteopathy	the theory is that abnormal tensions in the joints, especially in the spine, cause symptoms that can be relieved by skilled manipulation	muscle and joint pain
reflexology	the theory is that certain points in one or other foot represent other body parts and that massage of these points results in healing of the part	all types of illness
yoga	ancient Hindu exercises intended to reunite a person with the universal spirit through muscle and breathing control	stress relief
transcendental meditation (TM)	a westernised form of yoga	stress relief
Chinese herbal therapy	a combination of flowers, seeds and roots selected for the individual patient are used to make an infusion like tea	all types of illness
acupuncture	needles are inserted at specific points in the skin and rotated	pain relief
shia-tsu	acupressure using finger pressure rather than needles	stress relief

These homeopathic remedies were devised in the 1930s by Edward Bach.

The chief problem with complementary medicine is that a serious condition could be missed or not treated early and effectively enough. So, most complementary therapists ask an ill patient to see a doctor first. They also do not treat dangerous diseases and refer patients to doctors for conditions such as AIDS/HIV, cancerous lumps, pneumonia, heart attacks and coughing up blood. Another problem is that few complementary medicines are monitored for effectiveness, quality, labelling or purity. Complementary medicine is usually at its best when dealing with long-term, often painful conditions that have not responded to modern medical treatment, or when there are unacceptable side-effects.

Summary of health and medicine

- Health is not simply an absence of disease. The World Health Organisation defines it as 'a state of complete mental, physical and social well-being'.
- Food supplies, basic sanitation and clean water supplies are the dominant issues in the developing world. The developed world tends to suffer from lifestyle diseases and diseases of old age.
- Personal health depends on decisions made by the individual, parents, medical staff, and decision-makers at national and international levels.
- Lifestyle choices that affect health involve decisions about drug use, diet, exercise, work and leisure, personal hygiene and use of medical services.
- Modern medicine requires trained staff, technology, medicines and surgery to diagnose and treat illness.

- Medicines include chemotherapy for cancer, preventive medicines, antibiotics, pain relievers, and hormone treatments including the contraceptive pill.
- Medicines can enter the body by injection into muscles, under the skin or into blood vessels; through drips into a vein; by the mouth or rectum; or through the lungs. All medicines can have side-effects.
- Complementary medicine includes a wide range of different therapies that are not based on modern scientific trials.
- Complementary medicine can offer relief for a range of long-term conditions and is often used when conventional medicine has failed to improve the patient's health.

10. 2 Smoking

Why is smoking dangerous to health?

Tobacco smoke is a harmful mixture of gases, tar droplets and particles of ash. It contains, for example:

- **nicotine**, a fast-acting drug to which many people become addicted
- **tar**, the sticky brown substance that stains fingers and teeth and produces cancer when applied to the skin and lungs of animals
- **carbon monoxide**, a gas that is readily absorbed into the blood and takes the place of oxygen.

Every time a smoker sucks at a lighted cigarette, smoke is drawn through it. Some of the substances smoke contains are trapped in the unburnt tobacco and the filter tip. But the further down a cigarette is smoked, the greater the amount of the substances in the smoke that reaches the smoker's lungs. So, the last third or 'fag-end' of a cigarette produces more tar and nicotine than the other two-thirds put together.

12 a Name three substances in tobacco smoke and give one effect of each on the body.

b Why is there more tar and nicotine in the 'fag end' of a cigarette than in the first two-thirds?

How does smoke affect the body?

Smoke passes through the mouth and into the lungs (see Figure 2).

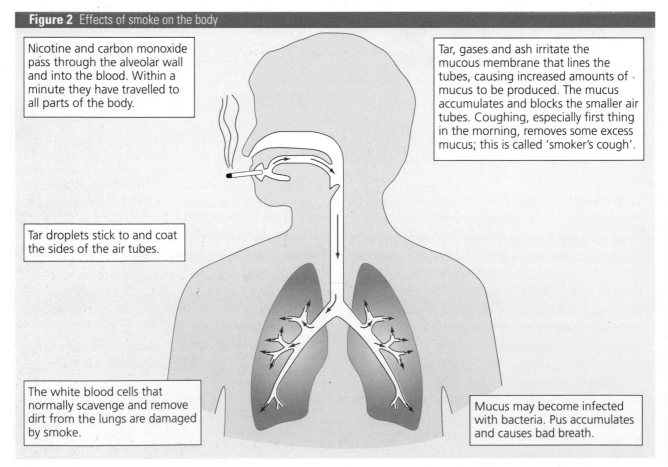

Figure 2 Effects of smoke on the body

Nicotine and carbon monoxide pass through the alveolar wall and into the blood. Within a minute they have travelled to all parts of the body.

Tar, gases and ash irritate the mucous membrane that lines the tubes, causing increased amounts of mucus to be produced. The mucus accumulates and blocks the smaller air tubes. Coughing, especially first thing in the morning, removes some excess mucus; this is called 'smoker's cough'.

Tar droplets stick to and coat the sides of the air tubes.

The white blood cells that normally scavenge and remove dirt from the lungs are damaged by smoke.

Mucus may become infected with bacteria. Pus accumulates and causes bad breath.

13 **a** What effect does smoking have on the mucous membrane of the lungs?

  b Explain why smokers are liable to:

    i shortness of breath

    ii bad breath

    iii smoker's cough.

  c What effect does smoke have on the white cells in the lungs?

Which diseases are linked with smoking?

The earlier a child starts smoking, the greater the damage to health in later years. Smoking day after day, year after year, puts increasing strain on certain tissues and makes them more prone to diseases such as:

- cancer of the mouth, larynx, oesophagus, lung and bladder
- lung diseases such as bronchitis, emphysema, pneumonia
- atheroma, which blocks arteries and can lead to heart attack, stroke, gangrene and amputation of the legs.

Non-smokers also suffer from these diseases, but their chances of illness are very much less than those of smokers. For those who smoke 25 or more cigarettes a day, the risk of death from lung cancer is 25 times that of non-smokers. In the UK in 1995 there were:

- 36 459 deaths from lung cancer of which at least 80% were due to smoking
- 29 790 deaths from bronchitis and emphysema of which at least 80% were due to smoking.

14 a Give one reason for not encouraging young people to smoke.

  b Which diseases are linked with smoking?

  c Calculate the number of deaths per week in 1995 in the UK from:

    i lung cancer

    ii bronchitis and emphysema.

Young people who smoke suffer more frequently than their non-smoking friends from coughs and colds, and are also more likely to be short of breath after exercise.

What is passive smoking?

Passive smoking is breathing in the smoke from other people's cigarettes. Non-smokers who have lived or worked with smokers for a long time have an increased risk of lung cancer. The children of smokers are more likely to get asthma, bronchitis, pneumonia and other chest infections.

15 a What is passive smoking?
  b What effects does passive smoking have?

Why are pregnant mothers advised not to smoke?

16 a How can substances from smoke reach an unborn baby?
  b Give four possible effects of heavy smoking during pregnancy.

When a pregnant woman smokes, substances in the smoke, such as carbon monoxide and nicotine, cross the placenta and enter her unborn baby's bloodstream. Pregnant women who smoke more than 20 cigarettes a day, are more likely to have:

- a miscarriage
- a still-born baby or one who dies in the first week after birth
- a smaller, weaker baby
- a baby who suffers from lung infections.

Why do some people smoke?

17 a When does smoking usually start?
  b Why do some people continue to smoke?
  c List the reasons for starting to smoke in the order that you consider to be important. Can you add at least one more item to your list?
  d Repeat (**c**) for the reasons for not smoking.

The smoking habit usually begins in childhood or adolescence and anyone who reaches the age of 20 without smoking is unlikely to start. The addiction created by nicotine is the main reason people continue to smoke, even when they know it is doing them harm.

Reasons for starting to smoke:

- wanting to be like friends who smoke
- following parents' example
- reaction against being told not to smoke
- curiosity
- wishing to appear 'grown up'.

Reasons for not smoking:

- wishing not to be addicted to nicotine
- being aware of the health risks
- finding it an unpleasant and antisocial habit that makes you smell of stale tobacco
- it is too expensive
- it can be easier to get a job, rent accommodation, buy life assurance.

Why do people give up smoking?

Reasons for giving up smoking include:

- becoming pregnant
- to prevent passive smoking by young children
- wishing to set an example to children
- getting breathless or having chest pains
- having a heart attack or stroke
- fear of an early death.

18 a List the reasons for giving up smoking. Can you add any more reasons?

b What suggestions would you make to help a person stop smoking?

c Calculate the cost per week of smoking 10 cigarettes a day at current prices.

d Calculate the cost per year of smoking 20 cigarettes a day at current prices.

Giving up smoking requires a strong desire to break the habit and the will-power to do so. Because people smoke for different reasons, there is no one method of stopping the habit. The following can help:

• dummy cigarettes
• tablets that give cigarettes a nasty taste
• nicotine patches and chewing gum
• eating mints or apples instead
• hypnosis
• counselling or attending a clinic for advice and support.

When a heavy smoker gives up the habit, his or her body will recover from many of the effects of smoking within a year.

10.3 Drinking alcohol

What is sensible drinking?

Many people enjoy drinking alcohol from time to time. They feel it helps them to relax or overcomes shyness; it also relieves worry, eases mild pain and generally makes them feel better.

1 unit (10 cm^3) of alcohol is found in half a pint of beer, 1 glass of wine or sherry, or a single measure of spirits (whisky, brandy, rum, vodka, gin). The guidelines for sensible drinking are up to 21 units per week for adult males, and up to 14 units per week for adult females. The difference is due to the differences in size and metabolism between males and females. Alcohol-related illnesses are likely to develop with the regular drinking of over 56 units per week for adult males, and over 35 units per week for adult females.

19 a How much alcohol does 1 unit represent?

b How many pints of beer per week is regarded as a sensible drinking limit for adult males, and for adult females?

c How many glasses of wine per week is regarded as a sensible drinking limit for adult males, and for adult females?

What are the effects of alcohol on the body?

The effects of alcohol can vary from person to person and with the same person on different occasions. Factors causing these differences include:

• the amount that is drunk in a certain time
• whether or not the drinker is used to alcohol
• whether or not the drinker has eaten recently
• the size of the person; alcohol is more diluted in a larger body
• whether the drinker is male or female; they have different metabolisms
• whether or not certain medicines or drugs have also been taken
• the mood of the drinker at the time
• how alert or tired the drinker is.

20 List eight reasons why people can react differently to the same amount of alcohol.

21 Use Figure 3 to describe what happens to alcohol in the body.

When alcohol is drunk, it is quickly absorbed into the blood from the stomach and small intestine (see Figure 3). Alcohol is absorbed more quickly from an empty stomach than one containing food. Alcohol rapidly affects the brain in a number of ways (see Figure 4).

22 a Why is alcohol a sedative?

   b Why is a drinker less aware of discomfort?

   c Describe the effect of alcohol on:

     i behaviour

     ii judgement

     iii muscle coordination.

   d If a footballer 'had a few beers' before playing, how might his game be affected?

A person who is drunk has little control over his or her actions. When sufficient alcohol has been taken to slow down all parts of the brain, the person falls into a drunken stupor (deep sleep). A person can be so drunk that afterwards he or she remembers nothing about it.

An inexperienced drinker can easily get drunk on small quantities of alcohol; heavy drinkers need more alcohol to get the same effect. Neither strong coffee nor a cold shower will reduce the level of alcohol in the blood, or speed up the rate at which the liver destroys it.

Alcohol causes the small blood vessels in the skin to dilate (widen), which brings blood to the surface of the body. This makes the skin look flushed and gives the person a false feeling of 'being hot' as the body loses heat. This is why it is a mistake to give alcohol to people suffering from the cold, or to take an alcoholic drink before going out into severe cold.

23 a When is a person considered to be drunk?

   b Does strong coffee help a person to sober up?

   c Why is it a mistake to give alcohol to someone suffering from the cold?

What is a hangover?

Heavy drinking may be followed the next day by a **hangover**: feelings of headache, weakness, nausea and tiredness. The hangover may be worse if the drinker has had a mixture of drinks, a late night, or a combination of alcohol and medicines or illegal drugs.

A hangover is partly caused by the **dehydrating effect** of alcohol; that is, alcohol causes the body to lose water. Non-alcoholic liquid, such as water or a soft drink, taken after heavy drinking helps to reduce the following hangover. 'Hair of the dog' or 'livener' is an alcoholic drink taken to relieve the feelings of a hangover; it puts more alcohol into the body and numbs the senses again.

24 a What is a hangover?

   b What can cause a worse hangover than simply drinking too much alcohol?

   c What can help to reduce a hangover?

Figure 3 What happens to alcohol in the body

When alcohol is drunk

The brain continues to be affected by alcohol as long as there is any in the blood.

4 A little alcohol is lost in breath.

The alcohol circulates around the body in the bloodstream until the liver has had time to destroy it.

3 A little alcohol is lost in urine.

1 Absorption is more rapid when the stomach is empty or if the drink contains bubbles of carbon dioxide (like champagne).

2 The liver destroys alcohol at the rate of about 10 cm³ (10 ml) per hour.

Figure 4 Effects of alcohol on the brain

The pain centre of the brain is numbed and the drinker is less aware of discomfort.

Restraints in behaviour are removed, which might result in easy chatter and loud laughter, or sometimes cause a person to become sentimental or aggressive.

Judgement is affected, making it impossible to see straight or to judge distances.

Alcohol is a sedative: it slows down the activity of the brain.

Muscle coordination is reduced, which can lead to clumsiness, staggering, and slurred speech.

People who take their sport seriously do not drink alcohol before playing. They know it leads to slower reactions, lack of concentration, and poorer judgement.

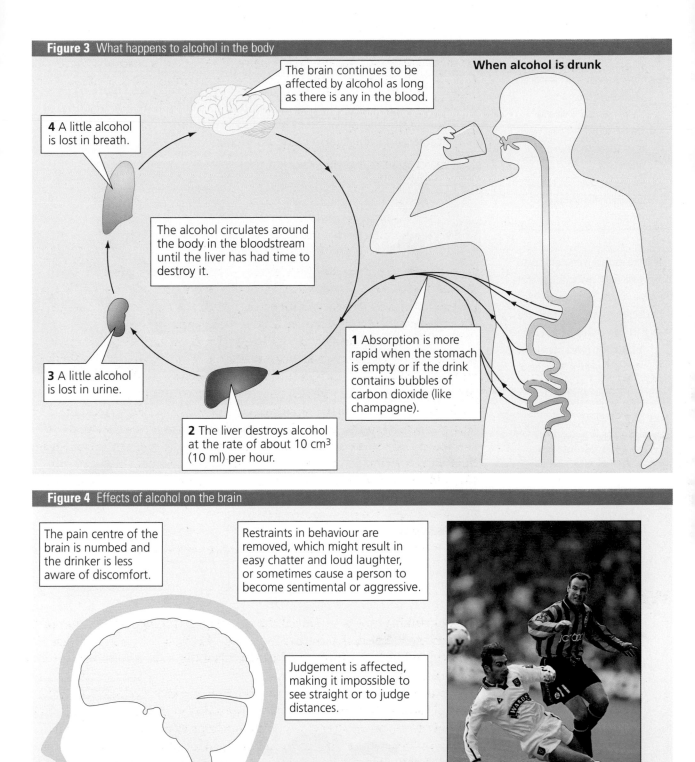

231

Why is it dangerous to drink and drive?

25 a Why do even small amounts of alcohol increase the danger of road accidents?
b From Figure 5, list nine ways in which alcohol can affect driving.
c What penalties can follow a conviction for drunken driving?

The police can ask a driver to take a breath test. If the test indicates that the driver is likely to have more than the legal amount of alcohol in the blood (is 'over the limit'), he or she is taken to a police station for further breath or blood tests.

Even small amounts of alcohol increase the danger of accidents because judgement is impaired and reaction times are slowed (see Figure 5). A conviction for drunken driving can lead to a driving ban, a heavy fine, or imprisonment. Insurance cover becomes much more expensive. Drunken pedestrians and cyclists also cause accidents.

Figure 5 How driving is affected by alcohol

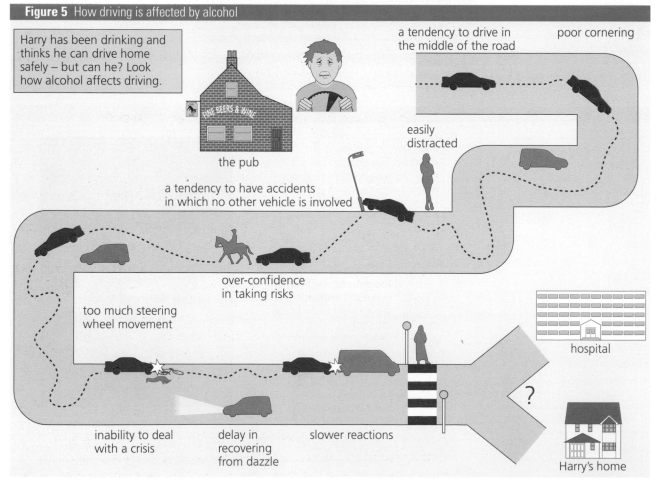

Harry has been drinking and thinks he can drive home safely – but can he? Look how alcohol affects driving.

the pub

a tendency to drive in the middle of the road

poor cornering

easily distracted

a tendency to have accidents in which no other vehicle is involved

over-confidence in taking risks

too much steering wheel movement

hospital

inability to deal with a crisis

delay in recovering from dazzle

slower reactions

Harry's home

What social problems are caused by alcohol?

Regular heavy drinking can cause social problems such as the following.

- **Antisocial behaviour**

  Alcohol reduces the control that people have over their behaviour. For example, a person may become aggressive and more likely to fight or bully. Brawls, wife-beating and baby-battering often follow drinking. Alcohol may give someone the 'courage' to steal. A drunken person may have no consideration for others, or for their safety, or may vandalise property.

- **Self-neglect**

  Persistent heavy drinkers may fail to eat properly or keep clean.

- **Absenteeism**

  A heavy drinker may be too ill to go to work, or persistently be late for work, or be inefficient at work. It is easy for such a person to lose his or her job.

- **Unwanted pregnancy**

  A girl who has had too much to drink may become more easily sexually aroused and may forget or not care about contraception.

- **Spread of sexually transmitted diseases**

  Drunkenness that leads to casual sex can also lead to the spread of sexual infections such as thrush, gonorrhoea, or AIDS.

26 List six problems that can result from regular heavy drinking.

- **Unhappy home**

  One person with an alcohol problem affects the whole family in one or more of the ways mentioned above.

What are the long-term effects of heavy drinking?

Alcohol-related illnesses include the following.

- **Gastritis**

  Alcohol irritates the lining of the stomach, which can then become inflamed and cause **nausea** (feeling sick), **vomiting** (being sick), and loss of appetite.

- **Malnutrition**

  Because large quantities of alcohol affect the stomach and appetite, heavy drinkers tend not to have a full and balanced diet. Although they can get enough calories from alcohol, they may suffer from lack of vitamins, particularly the B vitamins.

- **Cirrhosis of the liver**

  Large amounts of alcohol damage the liver, causing it to shrink and distort (see pages 92 and 93). A woman's liver is more easily damaged by alcohol than that of a man due to their different metabolism.

27 Describe the link between alcohol and:

  i gastritis

  ii malnutrition

  iii cirrhosis of the liver

  iv dementia

  v obesity.

- **Dementia**

  Alcohol destroys nerve cells and may permanently reduce mental ability.

- **Obesity**

  Alcoholic drinks have a high energy content: a pint of strong beer contains nearly as much energy as a pint of milk. Excess alcohol can make a person fat in the same way as too many cakes, biscuits or chips.

What is an alcoholic?

An **alcoholic** is a person who cannot control his or her drinking. Once alcoholics start to drink, they cannot be certain of being able to stop. Some alcoholics do not care what they drink so long as it contains alcohol, and may turn to methylated spirits ('meths') as a quick, cheap way to get drunk. Meths is a poison that destroys various organs in the body, and eventually causes blindness and death.

Any of the following may be evidence of alcoholism:

- frequent heavy drinking
- craving a drink in the morning
- missing time from work because of drinking
- needing a drink to face difficult situations
- blackouts (unconsciousness) due to drinking.

Delirium tremens (the DTs) is a condition that occurs when alcoholics are suddenly deprived of alcohol, for example on being confined to bed following an accident. They become very ill and, among other symptoms, develop the shakes, and have hallucinations. A **hallucination** is 'seeing' things that are not there, such as big black spiders on the walls or ants crawling on the skin.

28 a Describe an alcoholic.
  b Give five warning signs of alcoholism.
  c What is meant by the DTs, and when do they occur?
  d Why might some alcoholics drink meths?

10. 4 Illegal drugs

What is a drug?

A **drug** is a substance taken to alter the physical, mental or emotional state of the body. Drugs can be used as medicines to prevent or treat many physical and mental illness. They may also be used recreationally to alter the mental or emotional state of the drug user. This is called **drug abuse** or **drug misuse**. Using drugs in this way can be harmful, may lead to addiction, and can reduce the overall quality of life as well as shorten it.

Illegal drugs, sometimes called street drugs, are obtained from drug dealers, or from friends or acquaintances who obtained them from drug dealers. Those who possess illegal drugs and those who supply or deal in them are criminals. Illegal drugs are often linked with other crimes.

29 What is drug abuse?

Why do people misuse drugs?

People misuse drugs for all sorts of reasons which might include:

- their friends do
- they think that it might be fun or interesting
- they think that drugs can make them forget their worries
- their parents disapprove
- they have become addicted.

30 Why do people misuse drugs?

Which drugs are misused?

Figure 6 Some illegal drugs

Opiates

Opium, morphine, heroin, codeine, methadone and pethidine make the drug-user feel drowsy and relaxed. They are produced from the seeds of the opium poppy or are manufactured from chemically related substances. Opiates are addictive.

Cannabis

Cannabis has a number of names: grass, dope, hash, blow, marijuana. Cannabis usually relaxes people, but some users get very anxious. It is smoked on its own or with tobacco. It is regarded as a **soft drug** because there is only a little evidence that it is harmful in itself. However, it is illegal and has links with crime and the dealers of **hard drugs** (drugs of addiction). Cannabis can also be dangerous for those with schizophrenic tendencies. **Being stoned** is being under the influence of cannabis: there is reduced concentration, some loss of memory, and slowed reaction times. It therefore increases the chance of an accident while driving a car or motorbike, or operating machinery.

Hypnotics

Temazepam and other hypnotics are used to promote sleep. They are sometimes called jellies because they can make the user feel wobbly. If taken regularly, these drugs are addictive.

Stimulants

Cocaine, also called coke or powder, is an addictive white powder made from the leaves of the coca shrub. Crack, also called crack cocaine is derived from cocaine and is rapidly addictive. These stimulants make the user feel exited and energetic for a short while, but later feel very tired.

Amphetamines, such as speed, are also addictive. E is short for ecstasy, a type of amphetamine that is one of the drugs misused in the club scene.

Hallucinogens

LSD ('acid') and magic mushrooms make people see and hear things that are not there. The user 'trips' to a different world where everything seems more intense. Light, sound, space and distance appear different. A bad trip can be very frightening and can lead to mental illness.

Solvents

Lighter fuel, aerosols and some glues produce fumes which, when inhaled through the nose or mouth, depress the activity of the nervous system and relieve anxiety. They can make the user feel light-headed and dizzy, or drowsy and sick. Solvents can damage the liver and brain, and can lead to death.

31 a Using Figure 6, briefly give the effects of taking:

    i cannabis

    ii stimulants

    iii solvents

    iv hallucinogens

    v opiates

    vi hypnotics.

  b What is meant by 'being stoned', and what effects does it have?

  c Describe an LSD trip.

  d What are jellies?

  e What is the difference between a soft drug and a hard drug?

  f Name some drugs of addiction.

  g Name one drug that is rapidly addictive.

Why do illegal drugs affect people in different ways?

The effect of illegal drugs on the drug user depends on:

- whether the drug is being taken for the first time or is used regularly
- the amount of the drug taken (rarely known)
- the side-effects of any impurities
- interaction with any other drugs taken (including alcohol)
- the mood of the user at the time
- the health of the user
- what the user expects to happen
- the atmosphere of the place the user is in
- the company.

32 Why do illegal drugs affect people in different ways?

What are the dangers of taking illegal drugs?

Illegal drugs may have been stolen from a legal source, or they may have been manufactured illegally. There is no quality control for illegal laboratories, so it is difficult for users or dealers to know how strong a particular dose is. Whatever the source, drugs such as cocaine, LSD and heroine may be cut (mixed) with other substances, often a white powder. This powder could be anything: baking powder, domestic cleaning powder, even the poison strychnine has been used. When a drug is taken, even as a tablet, there is no way to know for certain what it contains, or the size of the dose.

An **overdose** occurs when someone takes more of a drug than their body can cope with. Sometimes this can happen accidentally when a particularly pure preparation of the drug is used instead of the usual low-quality version. The result of overdose can be collapse and death. Death from taking drugs is usually due to either an accidental overdose or a reduced ability to fight infection such as pneumonia.

Often, when a drug is taken regularly, the body may develop **tolerance**, that is, adapt to its presence. Larger quantities are then required to produce the same effect. With certain drugs, the more that is taken, the greater the risk of addiction. Some drugs can quickly become addictive, particularly crack.

Amphetamine, ecstasy and cocaine, are sometimes called **uppers**; they speed the body up and can be particularly dangerous for people who have heart or blood pressure problems. Heroin, hypnotics and solvents are sometimes called **downers**; they slow the body down and can be very dangerous if mixed or taken with alcohol because the body may stop altogether.

Injecting is the most dangerous way to use drugs because the body is affected immediately by the whole dose. Sharing the needles used for injections spreads diseases such as hepatitis and AIDS.

Mood swings are common among drug users. They are liable to become withdrawn, devious and lazy. These signs may be noted by parents, friends, teachers, employers. Drug users may be unable to work normally, or even at all.

33 a Say what risk is involved in taking:
- **i** a white powder
- **ii** a tablet
- **iii** uppers
- **iv** downers
- **v** a new drug.

b What is an overdose?

c What are the two usual causes of death from taking drugs?

d What is meant by tolerance to a drug?

e What are the risks of injecting drugs?

f In what ways do drugs affect behaviour of drug users?

g Is possessing street drugs a crime?

New illegal drugs are coming into use all the time. The range of the effects, purity and dangers of these are not known, and research cannot be done legally.

What to do in some drug-related emergencies

Always try to discover what drugs have been taken. In addition, the following specific circumstances require particular action.

- **Panic attacks**
  Remove the patient from bright lights and loud noises. Talk quietly to him or her and explain that any panicky feeling and over-breathing or panting will gradually go away.
- **Drowsiness**
  Call an ambulance. Keep talking to the patient to prevent unconsciousness.
- **Dehydration**
  Call an ambulance. Take the patient to a cool area and splash him or her with water. Remove any heavy clothing so that he or she can cool down.
- **Water-logged state**
  Call an ambulance. (This condition arises from drinking too much water, such as when taking ecstasy.)
- **Unconsciousness**
  Place the patient in the recovery position (see page 144). Call an ambulance.

34 a What can be done for a panic attack?

b Give four drug related conditions for which an ambulance should be called.

c What information does the hospital need?

d When and why is it desirable to keep talking to the patient?

e When is the patient placed in the recovery position?

f What emergency treatment is given to a person who is dehydratyed?

What happens in addiction?

Addiction is a kind of illness caused by repeated doses of certain drugs, in particular crack and heroin. The body becomes dependent on the drug, which the user feels a compulsive urge to keep taking. When the drug supply is cut off, the person becomes very ill, both physically and emotionally.

Withdrawal symptoms are the body's reaction to the sudden absence of a drug to which it has become addicted. These symptoms can include depression, sweating, restlessness, vomiting, abdominal cramps and weakness. It may take weeks or months for withdrawal symptoms to disappear because the body has to get used to being without the drug.

How can a drug user 'kick the habit'?

35 a What is addiction?

b What are withdrawal symptoms? List six.

c How can a drug user 'kick the habit'?

The user must:

- want to come off drugs.
- keep away from his or her drug-using friends, often easier said than done unless the person moves away from the area
- get help from a drug clinic, family doctor, priest, parents or other relatives, or the National Drugs Helpline 0800 77 66 00.

Summary of smoking, alcohol and illegal drugs

- Tobacco smoke contains a harmful mixture of nicotine, tar and carbon monoxide. Smokers are many times more likely to suffer from cancer, lung disease and heart disease than non-smokers.
- Passive smoking occurs when non-smokers inhale smoke from smokers. Passive smoking carries a significant health risk.
- Alcohol has a range of effects on different people but generally leads to slower reactions, reduced thinking ability and poor muscle control. Alcohol makes driving more dangerous.
- Alcohol dehydrates the body leading to a hangover after heavy drinking. A hangover can be eased by drinking non-alcoholic fluids.
- Heavy drinkers have to cope with repeated hangovers and potential damage to the brain and liver. Alcoholics have no control over their drinking.
- The commonest illegal drugs are: cannabis, cocaine and amphetamines, heroin and morphine, hallucinogens like LSD, and hypnotics like temazepam.

- Lack of quality control for illegally produced drugs means that dosage and strength can vary considerably. Overdoses are common when a particularly pure sample of one of these drugs is used. Substances mixed with the drug to make it go further can also be dangerous.
- Drugs such as uppers are dangerous for people with heart or blood pressure problems. Downers are very dangerous when mixed because the body might cease to function at all. Injecting drugs is dangerous because the whole dose is immediately effective, and because sharing needles spreads a number of dangerous diseases.
- Addiction occurs when a person has become so used to the drug that he or she cannot function normally without it. Withdrawal symptoms can last for weeks or months as the person adjusts to life without the drug.

10. 5 Diet

What is meant by diet?

Diet means the kind and amount of food that a person regularly consumes; it depends on:

- personal preference, which includes the cultural preferences that depend on where a person grew up
- the type of food that is available
- the amount of money available for food
- the level of physical activity.

A **balanced diet** is one that contains the necessary amounts of carbohydrates, fats, proteins, vitamins, minerals and fibre required by the body to stay healthy.

If a person 'goes on a diet', he or she makes deliberate changes in the kind or amount of foods that are regularly eaten. This is normally done in order to slim for medical or other reasons. People lose weight when they take in less energy than they use. Metabolism in the cells requires energy, as does exercise taken by the body. Two rules for slimmers are:

- eat less to reduce energy intake
- exercise more to increase energy use.

36 a What is meant by diet?

b What does a person's diet depend on?

c What is a balanced diet?

d Do you consider that you have a balanced diet? If not, why not?

e Why do people 'go on a diet'?

f Give two rules for slimmers.

How does food contain energy?

The energy in food is locked up in the bonds that hold the molecules together. It is released when enzymes split the molecules into smaller parts. Energy is now measured in units called **kilojoules** (kJ). However, you will often still see the older unit, calories; a **calorie** is really short for a **kilocalorie** (kcal).

1 kJ = 0.24 kcal (approx.)   1 kcal = 4.2 kJ (approx.).

The energy a person requires varies greatly from one person to another and from day to day, depending on age, physical activity, and whether the person is male or female (see Figure 7). The energy requirements for women who are pregnant or breast-feeding are slightly higher than other women of the same age and activity level.

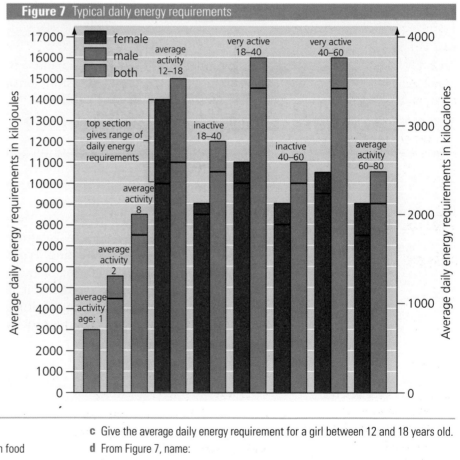

Figure 7 Typical daily energy requirements

37 a Name the unit that:

  i   is now used to measure energy in food

  ii used to be common and is still seen.

b What does a person's energy requirement depend on?

c Give the average daily energy requirement for a girl between 12 and 18 years old.

d From Figure 7, name:

  i   the two male groups with the highest energy requirement

  ii a male group and a female group with the same energy requirement.

What controls appetite?

Appetite is the desire to eat and is controlled by the appetite centre in the hypothalamus of the brain. **Hunger** is a feeling of emptiness; it is one of a number of factors that can stimulate the appetite centre and result in a desire to eat (see Figure 8).

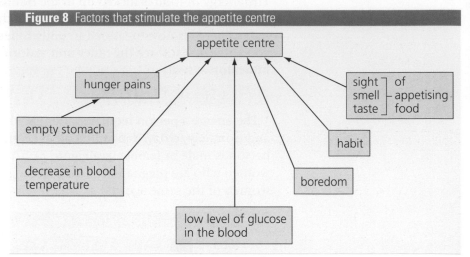

Figure 8 Factors that stimulate the appetite centre

38 a Give the difference between appetite and hunger.

b From Figure 8, list the factors that can cause a desire to eat.

c What is loss of appetite called?

d What can anorexia be due to?

Loss of appetite is called **anorexia** and can be due to to physical illness or emotional illness such as depression, tension and anorexia nervosa.

What are anorexia nervosa and bulimia?

39 a Compare anorexia nervosa with bulimia by saying in which:

  i over-eating occurs

  ii food is refused

  ii vomiting may occur.

b Which is more likely to occur in older people?

Anorexia nervosa is a serious emotional illness in which the patient either refuses food, or eats under protest and then secretly vomits. It occurs most often in teenage girls who think they are too fat even though they may be very thin. This illness leads to such severe loss of weight that the bones stick out, and periods stop. The patient may become too weak to stand, and needs hospital care. Treatment includes skilled counselling.

Bulimia is compulsive over-eating. Typically, a binge on food is followed by self-induced vomiting or excessive use of laxatives. Bulimia may accompany anorexia nervosa, but it also occurs in older women and occasionally in men. People with this illness are worried about putting on weight, but they cannot control their eating.

10. 6 Water

Where does drinking water come from?

40 a Where does our water originally come from?

b Name some naturally occurring chemicals in water and give an effect of each.

Water can be collected from rivers and streams, lakes and reservoirs. It is also obtained from natural underground reservoirs, through natural springs or artificial boreholes. Chemicals in these water sources may be beneficial, harmless or harmful; it often depends on the amount present. Chemicals naturally found in water include:

• magnesium and calcium compounds, which cause 'hardness' in water
• iodine, which prevents **goitre** (enlargement of the thyroid gland)
• iron, which can stain clothes washed in water containing it.

How is water treated?

41 a Name six processes that may take place in a water treatment plant, and give a reason for each.

b What does screening remove from water?

Water treatment aims to supply water that is suitable for drinking. Drinking water must be free from pathogens, and harmful chemicals. If possible, it should also be colourless, tasteless, have no smell and be free from suspended particles. Small amounts of beneficial chemicals are desirable; for example fluoride helps prevent tooth decay. Water treatment includes some or all of the processes in Figure 9, depending on how clean and pure the water is when it enters the plant.

Figure 9 Water treatment plant

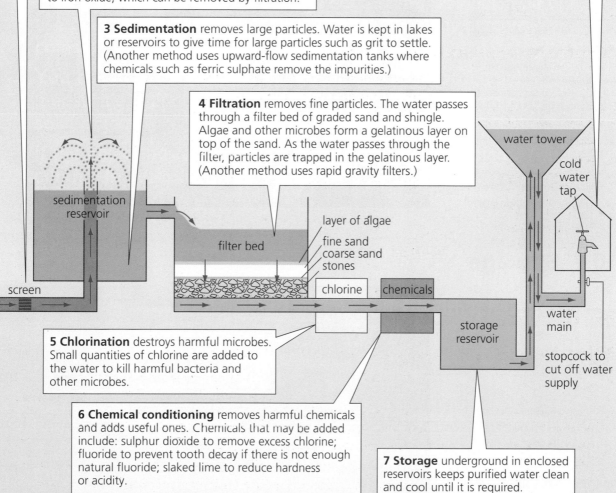

1 Screening removes large objects. The water passes through a mesh to remove fish, worms, insects, leaves, water-weed and other floating objects.

2 Aeration removes smells and tastes. Smelly gases escape as the water is sprayed into the air. At the same time, oxygen is absorbed and oxidises unwanted chemicals; for example, iron is oxidised to iron oxide, which can be removed by filtration.

3 Sedimentation removes large particles. Water is kept in lakes or reservoirs to give time for large particles such as grit to settle. (Another method uses upward-flow sedimentation tanks where chemicals such as ferric sulphate remove the impurities.)

4 Filtration removes fine particles. The water passes through a filter bed of graded sand and shingle. Algae and other microbes form a gelatinous layer on top of the sand. As the water passes through the filter, particles are trapped in the gelatinous layer. (Another method uses rapid gravity filters.)

5 Chlorination destroys harmful microbes. Small quantities of chlorine are added to the water to kill harmful bacteria and other microbes.

6 Chemical conditioning removes harmful chemicals and adds useful ones. Chemicals that may be added include: sulphur dioxide to remove excess chlorine; fluoride to prevent tooth decay if there is not enough natural fluoride; slaked lime to reduce hardness or acidity.

7 Storage underground in enclosed reservoirs keeps purified water clean and cool until it is required.

8 Distribution ensures that when a tap is turned on, water is forced out. If the storage reservoir is not at a level higher than the buildings it supplies, the water is pumped to a higher level, for example, to a water tower, to provide a head of pressure. Gravity causes water to flow through the pipes and into houses and other buildings.

sedimentation reservoir

screen

filter bed

layer of algae
fine sand
coarse sand
stones

chlorine

chemicals

storage reservoir

water tower

cold water tap

water main

stopcock to cut off water supply

241

How is the water supply safeguarded?

42 Use Figure 9 to answer these questions.

  a How can tastes and smells be removed from water?

  b What happens in sedimentation?

  c Draw a diagram of a filter bed and describe how it works.

  d Why is chlorine added to water?

  e Name three chemicals besides chlorine that may be added to water.

  f What is the purpose of a water tower?

43 a Give four ways safeguarding the water supply.

  b Why is water tested for E. coli?

A clean water supply is always essential to health.

Regulations exist in many countries to prevent contamination of the water supply by water-borne diseases such as typhoid, cholera, and dysentery:

- in areas where water is collected, called catchment areas, rules prevent people and animals from polluting the land and the water
- pipes must be carefully maintained because cracks could allow sewage to leak in and contaminate the water
- people employed at water treatment plants must observe strict rules of hygiene; they are tested regularly to check that they are not carriers of disease such as typhoid
- samples of treated water are regularly tested to check that the water is free from E. coli and other pathogens and chemicals.

E. coli bacteria live in the large intestine of humans and are found in large numbers in faeces. Their presence in the water supply indicates contamination by sewage. Such water ceases to be supplied while the source of contamination is investigated and removed.

10.7 Sewage

These tanks are the filter beds of a sewage treatment plant.

44 a Give the meaning of:

  i sewage

  ii a sewerage system

  iii a septic tank

  iv effluent.

b What makes sewage dangerous to health?

c Name three types of organic matter in sewage.

d In the treatment of sewage, describe the action of:

  i aerobic bacteria

  ii anaerobic bacteria.

e What is produced when organic matter is broken down by aerobic bacteria?

f Describe what happens to sewage as it passes through a sewage treatment plant.

Sewage is more than 99% water and comprises all the waste removed from lavatories, baths, washbasins and kitchen sinks together with industrial and agricultural waste. It is dangerous to health as it provides a breeding ground for the pathogens it contains.

Sewage usually flows through a **sewerage system**. This is a network of pipes called sewers, and treatment plants that collect, process and dispose of large quantities of sewage. Small quantities of sewage can be dealt with in a septic tank. A **septic tank** is a tank in which the solid matter in sewage is broken down by bacteria.

A sewage treatment plant extracts the water from sewage and breaks down much of the organic matter (see Figure 10). Bacteria break down faeces, paper and leaves in the filter beds and sludge tanks. Two groups of bacteria are involved:

- aerobic bacteria
- anaerobic bacteria.

Aerobic bacteria, which need oxygen, are active in the filter beds. These are tanks filled with lumps of a hard material called clinker. Clinker is porous and allows air and liquid to pass though it. The bacteria form a slimy film around the clinker. As the **effluent** (liquid waste) filters through, the organic matter it contains is used as food by the bacteria. Worms and insects move around inside the filter bed feeding on the bacteria to prevent the filter from becoming clogged.

$$\text{organic matter} + \underset{\text{oxygen}}{O_2} \xrightarrow{\text{aerobic bacteria}} \underset{\text{carbon dioxide}}{CO_2} + \underset{\text{water}}{H_2O} + \text{nitrogen compounds}$$

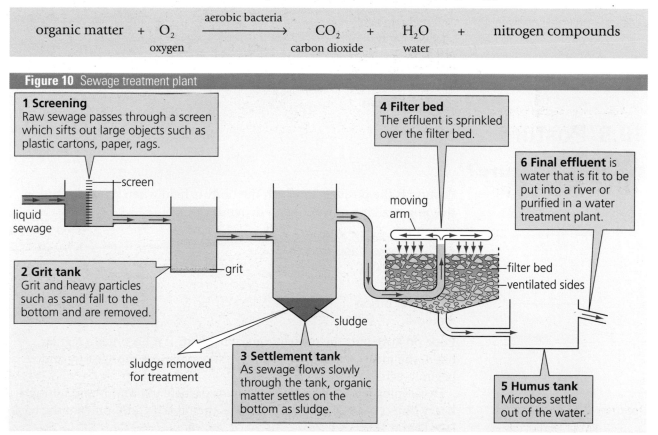

Figure 10 Sewage treatment plant

1 Screening
Raw sewage passes through a screen which sifts out large objects such as plastic cartons, paper, rags.

4 Filter bed
The effluent is sprinkled over the filter bed.

6 Final effluent is water that is fit to be put into a river or purified in a water treatment plant.

screen

liquid sewage

moving arm

filter bed

ventilated sides

2 Grit tank
Grit and heavy particles such as sand fall to the bottom and are removed.

grit

sludge removed for treatment

sludge

3 Settlement tank
As sewage flows slowly through the tank, organic matter settles on the bottom as sludge.

5 Humus tank
Microbes settle out of the water.

45 What is produced when organic matter is broken down by anaerobic bacteria?

Anaerobic bacteria do not need oxygen; they live in the sludge and break it down. This reduces the quantity of sludge, can turn sludge into fertiliser, and produces methane gas, which is a useful fuel.

$$\text{organic matter} \xrightarrow{\text{anaerobic bacteria}} \underset{\text{methane}}{CH_4} + \text{solid waste}$$

Summary of diet, water and sewage

- Diet is the amount and type of food that a person regularly eats. Food contains energy, which is measured in kilojoules. The amount of energy a person needs every day depends on age, sex and level of activity.

- Appetite is controlled by a centre in the brain. It responds to signals from the stomach, low blood temperature or glucose levels, the sight of food, boredom and habit.

- Anorexia nervosa is an illness that particularly affects teenage girls and leads to a refusal to eat, despite a very low body weight. A related illness, bulimia, involves compulsive eating and then vomiting, again to keep body weight low.

- In order to avoid certain water-borne diseases, human societies need a supply of clean drinking water and a way to remove wastes for safe disposal. Water comes from natural sources and is treated to remove pathogens and harmful chemicals.

- The presence of *E. coli* is a good indicator of contamination of water by sewage.

- Sewage is the waste from domestic and industrial sources. It is treated at sewage plants, which use bacteria to convert the organic matter into simpler, safer chemicals.

10.8 Posture

What is posture?

Posture is the position in which the body is held when standing, sitting, sleeping, walking or working. It depends on:

- flexibility of the joints
- muscle power and muscle tone
- state of health
- weight
- physical fitness
- mood.

Poor posture puts the muscles out of balance. If it becomes a regular habit, the muscles that are put under extra strain tire more easily and begin to ache.

Developing a good standing posture is particularly important. Lifting a heavy object in the correct way protects the muscles and joints of the back (see Figure 11).

Figure 11 Standing and lifting postures

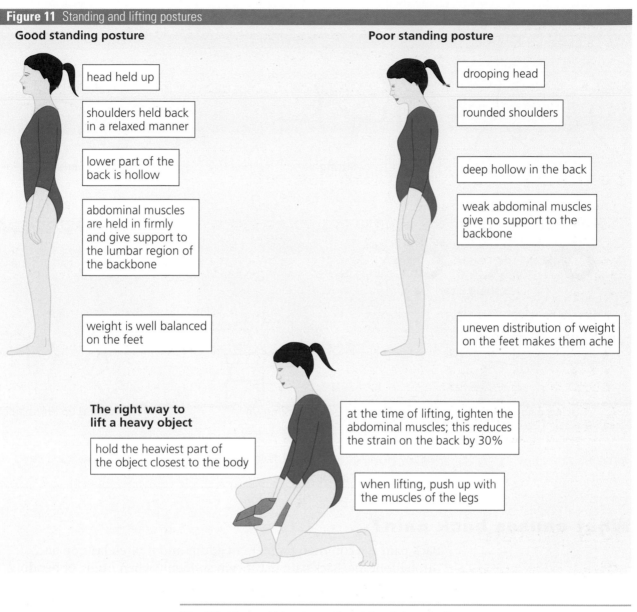

Good standing posture

head held up

shoulders held back in a relaxed manner

lower part of the back is hollow

abdominal muscles are held in firmly and give support to the lumbar region of the backbone

weight is well balanced on the feet

Poor standing posture

drooping head

rounded shoulders

deep hollow in the back

weak abdominal muscles give no support to the backbone

uneven distribution of weight on the feet makes them ache

The right way to lift a heavy object

hold the heaviest part of the object closest to the body

at the time of lifting, tighten the abdominal muscles; this reduces the strain on the back by 30%

when lifting, push up with the muscles of the legs

46 a What is meant by posture, and what does it depend on?

 b Copy and complete Table 3.

 c Describe the right way to lift a heavy object.

Table 3 Comparing good and bad posture when standing

Body part	Good posture	Poor posture
head		
shoulders		
back		
abdominal muscles		
weight on feet		

Posture is important in all sorts of activity (see Figure 12).

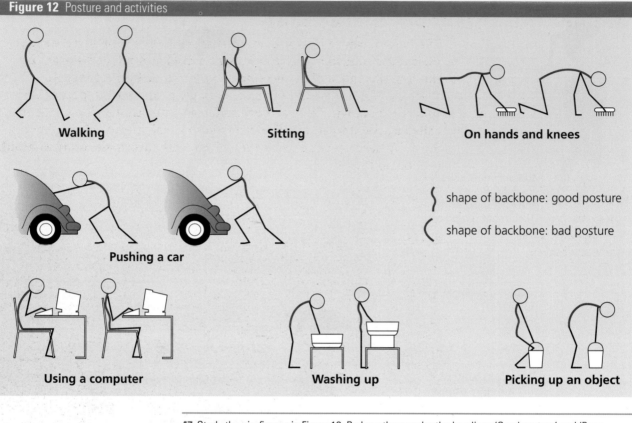

Figure 12 Posture and activities

Walking

Sitting

On hands and knees

Pushing a car

shape of backbone: good posture

shape of backbone: bad posture

Using a computer

Washing up

Picking up an object

47 Study the pin-figures in Figure 12. Redraw them under the headings 'Good posture' and 'Poor posture' for each activity.

What causes back pain?

Back pain is a common problem in adults and it often lasts on and off throughout life. Back pain may begin suddenly when lifting or bending, or may develop gradually and get worse over months or years. The most likely cause is poor posture, which puts a strain on the back and then results in:

• over-stretching of the muscles of the back
• tearing the ligaments that bind the vertebrae firmly together
• a 'slipped disc' (see page 24).

Whenever possible, people with back pain are encouraged to continue with their daily activities. When the pain is severe, pain relievers help. If back pain lasts for more than 48 hours, medical advice should be sought.

48 a How might back pain begin?

b Give three results of poor posture that can cause back pain.

c What treatment helps if back pain is severe?

10.9 Exercise

Are you getting enough exercise?

The natural way of life for humans is an active one. Our ancestors used their muscles as they worked to provide food, warmth and shelter. In modern life, much of the necessary work is done by machines. As machines replace the use of muscles, many people spend most of their time sitting down, either at work, at home, or when travelling. This is called a **sedentary way of life**. Many leisure activities are also sedentary. So, daily life may not provide enough exercise to keep the body as healthy as it could be.

49 a How did our ancestors get exercise?

b Why has modern life become sedentary?

Not everybody has an office job; some ways of life are very active.

What are the benefits of exercise?

People who exercise regularly usually feel fitter and have fewer days off sick than people who take no exercise. Regular exercise helps to:

- keep muscles, including the heart muscle, strong and in good condition
- keep joints free-moving and supple
- prevent excess body weight by burning up fat
- induce sound sleep
- maintain good health
- develop **stamina**, that is, the power to keep going.

The amount and type of exercise suitable for each individual depends on age, physical fitness and state of training. Unsuitable exercise can cause damage of muscles, tendons, joints and ligaments.

During gentle exercise, muscles use aerobic respiration to obtain sufficient energy from glucose, which is delivered by the bloodstream. **Aerobic respiration** uses oxygen, which is also supplied by the bloodstream. During strenuous exercise, oxygen cannot be supplied to the

50 a Give six benefits of regular exercise.

b List three factors that suitable exercise for each individual depends on.

c How might the body be harmed by unsuitable exercise?

muscles fast enough, so energy is obtained by **anaerobic respiration** (respiration without oxygen) for a short time. Lactic acid is a by-product of anaerobic respiration.

Lactic acid diffuses from muscles into the bloodstream. On reaching the liver, some lactic acid is converted back to glucose, and the rest is oxidised to carbon dioxide and water. However, during strenuous exercise there is a shortage of oxygen, and lactic acid is produced faster than it can be removed. The lactic acid builds up in the muscles and makes them slow down and start to ache. This is called **muscle fatigue**. When the muscles rest, oxygen becomes available to break down the lactic acid. The extra oxygen needed to clear the lactic acid is called the **oxygen debt**.

Cramp may also result from a build-up of lactic acid. **Cramp** is painful spasm of a muscle or group of muscles; **spasm** is a prolonged muscle contraction. Cramp can be relieved by gently stretching the muscle, for example by bending the foot upward at the ankle if the calf muscle is affected. A '**stitch**' is a sharp pain in the side of the abdomen that can occur during strenuous physical activity such as running. It is not known why this occurs or how to prevent it. It seems not to be dangerous and disappears with rest or continued exercise. Trained athletes are less prone to it.

Fitness is having suppleness, strength and stamina and can be achieved by exercise (see Figure 13).

51 a Name the type of respiration used during:
   i gentle exercise
   ii strenuous exercise.
  b When is lactic acid produced?
  c How is lactic acid removed from the body?
  d When does an oxygen debt occur?
  e What effect does a build-up of lactic acid have on muscles?
  f What is cramp?
  g What is a 'stitch'?

Exercise like this improves breathing and circulation.

52 a What is meant by fitness?
   b Describe an exercise that keeps:
     i the shoulders supple
     ii the hips mobile
     iii strengthens the abdominal muscles.

Figure 13 Exercising to keep fit

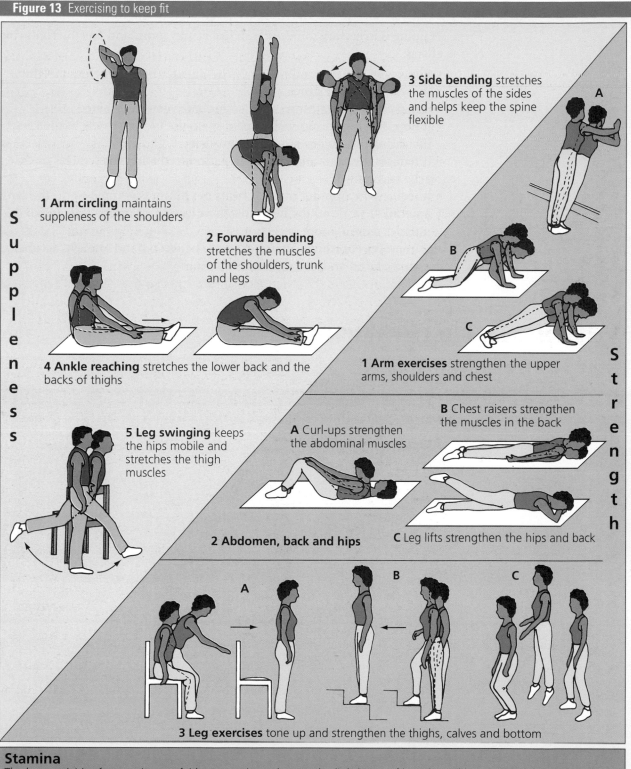

S u p p l e n e s s

1 Arm circling maintains suppleness of the shoulders

2 Forward bending stretches the muscles of the shoulders, trunk and legs

3 Side bending stretches the muscles of the sides and helps keep the spine flexible

4 Ankle reaching stretches the lower back and the backs of thighs

5 Leg swinging keeps the hips mobile and stretches the thigh muscles

S t r e n g t h

1 Arm exercises strengthen the upper arms, shoulders and chest

A Curl-ups strengthen the abdominal muscles

B Chest raisers strengthen the muscles in the back

C Leg lifts strengthen the hips and back

2 Abdomen, back and hips

3 Leg exercises tone up and strengthen the thighs, calves and bottom

Stamina

The best activities for stamina are fairly energetic, make people slightly out of breath, and keep them moving for 20 minutes or more. This type of exercise is often called 'aerobic' exercise because enough oxygen has to be breathed in to supply the working muscles.

What are the benefits of sports training?

Training is necessary to become skilful at any sport, and has the following effects:

- it increases the size and power of the muscles by enlargement of the individual muscle fibres
- it makes deep breathing easier, so more oxygen is obtained
- it improves blood supply by opening up the blood vessels in muscles, so increasing the oxygen supply to muscles
- it reduces the amount of lactic acid produced and thus reduces muscle ache and cramp
- it reduces the number of heart beats per minute required to do the same amount of work, so the heart increases its output more easily when the muscles require more oxygen
- it improves coordination, for example between hand and eye, to obtain a more skilful and smooth muscle action.

53 Give six effects of sports training.

10.10 Stress and relaxation

What is stress?

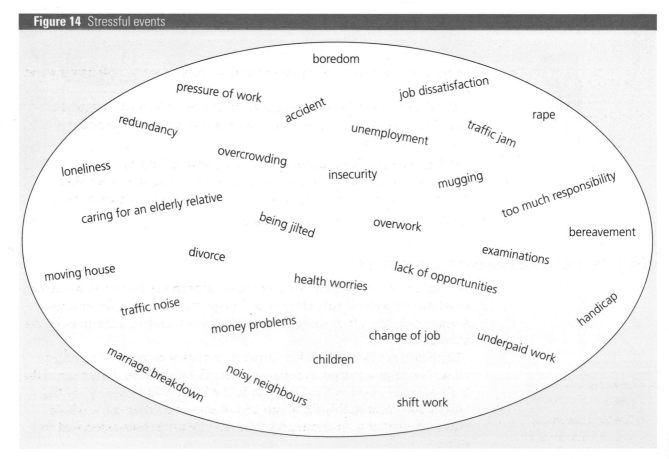

Figure 14 Stressful events

boredom

pressure of work   job dissatisfaction

accident   rape

redundancy   unemployment   traffic jam

overcrowding

loneliness   insecurity   mugging

too much responsibility

caring for an elderly relative   being jilted   overwork   bereavement

divorce   examinations

moving house   lack of opportunities

health worries

traffic noise   handicap

money problems   change of job   underpaid work

children

marriage breakdown   noisy neighbours   shift work

54 a What is the difference between stress and tension?

b When does stress become harmful?

c List three factors that affect a person's reaction to stress.

d Which six situations in Figure 14 would you find most stressful?

e Suggest how you might deal with them.

Stress, meaning mental stress, is psychological pressure caused by situations or people. **Tension** is a person's response to stress, and may include the 'fight or flight' response (see page 140) and feelings of agitation. Occasional minor stress is normal and can be stimulating and necessary.

Stress becomes harmful when it is continuous, difficult to cope with, and disrupts normal life and relationships. Whether or not a stressful situation is harmful depends on:

• the individual's ability to cope with the situation
• the total amount of stress involved – everyone has a breaking point
• how long stress lasts.

Events that can be unduly stressful often involve major change or are beyond our control (see Figure 14).

Can stress cause illness?

Harmful stress produces feelings of fear and anger and can cause symptoms such as:

• diarrhoea
• headache
• breathlessness
• chest pains
• abdominal pain
• skin rash
• insomnia.

55 a What feelings does harmful stress produce?

b What symptoms can be caused by stress?

Long-term stress can make other disorders worse, for example asthma and migraine.

The death of a close relative, a good friend or a loved animal can be stressful and may cause depression. Bereavement can also produce unexpected feelings:

• relief when the death follows months or years of illness
• guilt at not having done more for the person while they were alive
• anger that other people did not do more to keep the person alive.

All these feelings are normal responses.

Why is relaxation important?

Relaxation occurs when there is a calm state of mind. Factors that can lead to relaxation include rest, sleep or a change of occupation, for example doing a hobby, craft or sport. In some forms of relaxation, the muscles are also at rest.

The body needs to relax after physical or mental activity. Being able to relax also helps a person to cope with stressful situations. Relaxation is the basis of some kinds of therapy, such as meditation and massage. Sitting quietly and comfortably for about 15 minutes and relaxing the whole body, one part at a time, can prevent or reduce symptoms associated with stress.

56 a When does relaxation occur?

b Give some examples of ways in which people relax.

Why do we need sleep?

Sleep is a form of unconsciousness from which it is possible to be wakened fairly easily. The body needs sleep to allow the nervous system to function efficiently. Lack of sleep makes people irritable, unable to concentrate and clumsy. When people are deprived of sleep for several days they may suffer from hallucinations.

The amount of sleep needed varies enormously from person to person. It also varies with age: babies need about 16 hours of sleep a day, whereas old people need only about 5 hours a day. Good, sound sleep can be encouraged by:

- physical exercise that tires the body
- a warm, comfortable bed in a quiet, darkened room
- the ability to put worries aside.

57 a How can sound sleep be encouraged?

b From the photo caption, list seven changes that occur during sleep.

During sleep, even in less than perfect conditions, the heart rate slows down, blood pressure falls, breathing becomes slower and more regular, temperature drops, less urine is produced, the nervous system and sense organs are less active, and dreaming may occur.

What are bio-rhythms?

58 Give three examples of bio-rhythms.

Bio-rhythms are patterns of biological activity. Hormone levels rise and fall during a 24-hour period, for example the adrenal hormone cortisol is highest at between 8 a.m. and 9 a.m. and lowest at midnight. Similarly, all individuals have their own sleeping–waking patterns, and become exhausted if these are disturbed, for example by shift work or by 'jet lag'. Menstrual cycles occur about every 28 days.

10.11 Communication

Why do humans communicate?

Humans are social animals, that is, they live in groups or societies. They communicate with each other mainly by speech. This enables a vast range of ideas, feelings and information to be passed from one person to another.

59 a What is the main way in which humans communicate with each other?

b What does speech enable humans to do?

c What effect does the lack of communication often have on people?

Speech is used to:
- sort out problems
- make rules
- plan for the future
- benefit from history and the experiences of others
- develop complex ideas.

Lack of communication between people often leaves them feeling isolated and depressed. The inability to communicate may be due to deafness, a stroke or personality.

How do children learn to talk?

Speech involves putting a series of sounds together in a meaningful way that is understandable to people who have the same language. Speech is the result of the combined action of:

- the speech area in the brain
- the ears; children learn to speak by copying the speech sounds they hear
- the larynx, which produces the sound
- the throat, mouth, tongue, teeth and lips; the shape and position of these parts alters the sounds that come from the larynx.

Although young babies are unable to talk, they have other ways of making people understand what they want or feel by making different sounds (crying, laughing), using the hands (grabbing, pushing), and the expression on the face (smiling, frowning).

Young children start to use words from the age of about 1 year. They learn to talk by listening to adults and older children and copying the sounds they hear. Toddlers often find it easier to use actions rather than words to make people understand them. As speech becomes easier, fewer actions are used, but non-verbal communication remains important throughout life.

60 a Name eight parts of the body involved in speech.

b How do young babies communicate?

c How do children learn to talk?

What is the larynx?

Humans are unique among animals in the range and complexity of sounds they can make. The sounds come from the larynx, which is at the top of the trachea at the front of the neck. The larynx is lined with mucous membrane and is made rigid by cartilages, which are held together by muscles and ligaments. Two vocal cords within the larynx stretch across the opening from front to back.

Most of the time the vocal cords are kept apart and air flows freely through the V-shaped opening between them. When the cords are brought closer together, they vibrate as air from the lungs is forced through the much smaller gap between them. This produces sound. The sound can be varied in pitch and volume. The tighter the vocal cords and the closer they are together, the higher the pitch; the greater the amount of air forced out, the louder the sound.

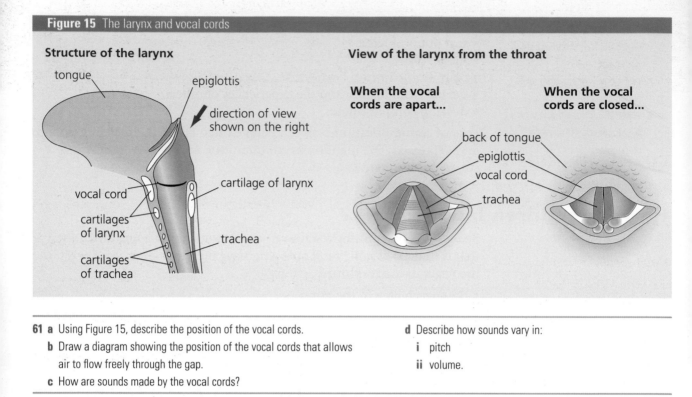

Figure 15 The larynx and vocal cords

Structure of the larynx

tongue

epiglottis

direction of view shown on the right

cartilage of larynx

vocal cord

cartilages of larynx

trachea

cartilages of trachea

View of the larynx from the throat

When the vocal cords are apart...

When the vocal cords are closed...

back of tongue

epiglottis

vocal cord

trachea

---

61 a Using Figure 15, describe the position of the vocal cords.

  b Draw a diagram showing the position of the vocal cords that allows air to flow freely through the gap.

  c How are sounds made by the vocal cords?

  d Describe how sounds vary in:

    i pitch

    ii volume.

Why are some people unable to speak?

62 a Why are deaf children unable to speak?

  b Why might older people lose the ability to speak?

  c What is the purpose of speech therapy?

  d Who is speech therapy given to?

The usual reason that some children are unable to speak is because they are deaf. They do not know how to make the right sounds because they have not heard the sounds to copy. Nor can they hear the noises they make. In older people, loss of speech may be due to brain damage caused by a stroke.

If deafness is discovered early, speech therapy can help some deaf children to learn to speak. Speech therapy is also given to children with speech impediments and to adults whose speech has been affected by surgery of the larynx, or by a stroke.

Summary of posture, exercise, stress and communication

- Posture is the position in which the body is held. A good posture protects the muscles and joints against strain. Back pain is often caused by poor posture.

- During exercise, the rate of respiration rises and muscles start to respire anaerobically as well as aerobically. Anaerobic respiration produces lactic acid which must be removed after the exercise by using extra oxygen. The extra oxygen needed is called the oxygen debt.

- Stress is psychological pressure caused by people or situations. Tension is the body's response to stress.

- The amount of sleep needed varies from person to person and from time to time. Sleep patterns are examples of bio-rhythms.

- Human beings communicate mainly through speech. Children learn to speak by listening to adults and older children and copying them.

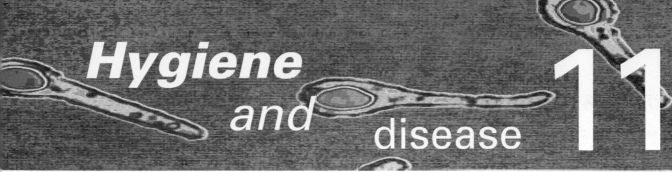

Hygiene and disease 11

Learning objectives

By the end of this chapter you should be able to:

- **define** the term hygiene
- **describe** the main causes of food poisoning and its treatment
- **review** the methods of food preservation and the use of food additives
- **describe** the safe handling of food
- **define** the terms parasite and host
- **review** the main parasites affecting human beings
- **list** the main health care activities for feet and teeth
- **describe** the causes and symptoms of some major infectious diseases including some sexually transmitted infections

- **describe** the spread and control of some major infectious diseases
- **describe** the response of the immune system to infection and vaccination
- **describe** the problems affecting transplant surgery
- **outline** the cause, symptoms and control of AIDS
- **describe** bacteria and the conditions that affect bacterial growth
- **describe** viruses and how they reproduce
- **describe** prions and diseases they cause.

11.1 Hygiene

What is hygiene?

1 a What is hygiene?
  b What does the study of hygiene include?

Hygiene is the science of maintaining health. It includes:

- provision of food free from disease-causing microbes
- the avoidance of parasites
- care of feet and teeth
- environmental cleanliness, for example the supply of clean water and the disposal of sewage (see pages 240 to 244).

Good hygiene standards are necessary in commercial food preparation and in the home.

11.2 Hygiene and food

What is food hygiene?

Food hygiene means keeping food sufficiently clean to prevent gastro-enteritis. **Gastro-enteritis** is inflammation of the lining of the stomach (gastritis) and intestine (enteritis). The symptoms of this very common complaint vary from **nausea** (feeling sick) and slight looseness of the bowels, to a severe fever with abdominal pain, vomiting, diarrhoea and thirst. The two main causes of gastro-enteritis are:

- food poisoning; this term describes
  - infection with bacteria such as *Salmonella* or *Campylobacter*, and certain viruses
  - the effect of bacterial toxins such as those produced by *Staphylococcus* and *Clostridium*
- diseases such as typhoid, cholera, and dysentery in which the gastro-enteritis is severe – these diseases occur most commonly in countries without a clean water supply or efficient sewerage system.

2 a What is gastro-enteritis?
b Give the symptoms of gastro-enteritis.
c What are the two main causes of gastro-enteritis?

Why does food poisoning happen?

Food poisoning caused by bacteria is the most common cause of gastro-enteritis in Britain. Bacteria thrive in warm, moist foods, particularly those containing protein, for example meat and poultry, milk and cream. Bacteria multiply by dividing into two, and when conditions are right this can happen every 20 minutes. In only a few hours, very large numbers of bacteria can build up in food. The essential rules to prevent bacterial food poisoning are:

- keep food clean
- keep food cold
- wash your hands and scrub under the nails before handling food
- cook food thoroughly to kill any bacteria.

3 a In what conditions do bacteria thrive?
b In the right conditions, how often can bacteria divide?
c Give four rules to prevent bacterial food poisoning.

What is the treatment for food poisoning?

For adults and older children the best treatment is to rest the stomach and intestines by drinking only water or weak orange or lemon squash. Sufferers usually recover within a day or two. No harm comes from not eating during this time provided the person drinks plenty of fluid to keep the kidneys functioning normally.

Young children need more care. They can easily lose too much water from the body and therefore become dehydrated and seriously ill very quickly. A mixture of dissolved salt and sugar aids recovery: 5 grams or 1 teaspoon of salt and 40 grams or 8 teaspoons of sugar in 1 litre (1 dm^3) of water. This replaces the water and sodium lost by diarrhoea, and the sugar provides simple nutrition.

Babies with gastro-enteritis need urgent medical attention. With older children and adults, it depends on how ill they are.

4 a Describe the treatment for food poisoning in:
  i adults
  ii young children.
b What action should be taken for babies with food poisoning?

How do bacteria cause food poisoning?

Salmonella infection

Salmonella bacteria are found in the intestines of animals such as cattle and poultry, and in human carriers. They get into food when it is contaminated by infected faeces of animals or humans, or by water that has been polluted by infected sewage. Once inside human intestines, they grow and multiply. Symptoms of gastro-enteritis occur about 12 hours after eating the bacteria. The severity of the illness depends on:

- the number of bacteria eaten
- the ability of the individual to resist infection: young children and old people have least resistance
- the particular species of *Salmonella* involved.

If food is thoroughly cooked, the bacteria are killed and cannot cause illness (see Figure 1).

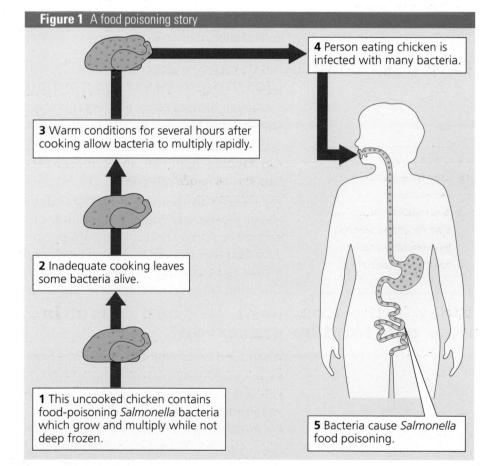

Figure 1 A food poisoning story

4 Person eating chicken is infected with many bacteria.

3 Warm conditions for several hours after cooking allow bacteria to multiply rapidly.

2 Inadequate cooking leaves some bacteria alive.

1 This uncooked chicken contains food-poisoning *Salmonella* bacteria which grow and multiply while not deep frozen.

5 Bacteria cause *Salmonella* food poisoning.

5 a Use Figure 1 to describe how *Salmonella* can cause food poisoning.
  b What are the sources of *Campylobacter* infection?
  c What is the main symptom of *Campylobacter* infection?

Campylobacter infection

Sources of *Campylobacter* include milk and undercooked poultry. The main symptom of this common form of food poisoning is diarrhoea containing blood.

Escherichia coli

Escherichia coli is commonly known as *E. coli*. It lives in the intestines of humans and other animals and is usually harmless. However, some strains, for example *E. coli* 0157, cause food poisoning when they contaminate food or drinking water.

Holiday-makers may have a short, sharp attack of diarrhoea, and sometimes vomiting, especially hot countries. This is usually due to a local strain of *E. coli* that is harmless to the local population but is new to the traveller's body.

Staphylococcus toxin food poisoning

Staphylococcus species are found in many places including the nose, throat, boils, and pus from infected wounds. In warm moist food, the bacteria grow, multiply and produce a **toxin**, a poison. Cooking kills the bacteria quickly, but the toxin is not destroyed. It is the toxin that causes food poisoning, which usually occurs within 2 to 4 hours, but can occur almost immediately if a large dose of toxin is eaten.

Clostridium toxin food poisoning

Clostridium species can grow only in the absence of oxygen, as in the large intestine, but they can survive in air. They produce spores that survive for a long time in dust and soil. So, food can be contaminated in two ways:

- by bacteria in human and animal faeces
- by spores in dust and dirt.

The bacteria are destroyed by cooking, but the spores can survive normal cooking processes. When in warm moist food, they will turn into active bacteria again and multiply rapidly, producing toxin.

Different species of *Clostridium* produce different illnesses. *Clostridium difficile* causes food poisoning, but *Clostridium botulinum* causes botulism, a rare and very serious form of food poisoning.

6 a What is *E. coli*?

b When can *E. coli* 0157 cause food poisoning?

c What happens when *Staphylococcus* species get into warm moist food?

d How does *Clostridium* get into the human body?

How can food be preserved?

When food is stored for use later, it is important to prevent damage by:

- microorganisms such as bacteria and fungi
- insects such as flies, weevils, and maggots
- mammals such as mice and rats
- natural chemical changes due to enzymes in the food.

Correct storage conditions can partly prevent damage. For example, cool, dry, dark conditions are good for keeping for fruit and vegetables. However, many foods can be **preserved** by being given special treatments, and can then be kept for a long time. Treatments to preserve food fall into three categories: killing microbes and their spores (**sterilisation**), preventing microbe activity, and delaying microbe activity.

7 In what ways can stored food be damaged?

Preservation methods allow both organic and non-organic foods to be kept for longer than when they are fresh.

Sterilisation

- **Canning**
  Canned food is heated to a sufficiently high temperature to destroy both the microorganisms and their spores. Almost any food can be canned. While the food remains in a sealed can, it cannot be contaminated.

- **Irradiation**
  Pre-packed fresh vegetables or meat, can be given small doses of gamma rays to destroy microorganisms and their spores. New microbes cannot get in until the pack is opened. No radiation remains in the food.

Preventing microbe activity

- **Drying**
  Most of the water is removed from foods such as vegetables, fruit and milk. Microbes are not active without water.

- **Curing**
  Salt or smoke are used to remove water from meat and fish.

- **Pickling**
  Vinegar (ethanoic acid) is too acidic for microbe activity. It is used to preserve many vegetables.

- **Jam-making**
  The high sugar content of jam prevents growth of bacteria, but not fungi. This is a common method of preserving fruit.

Delaying microbe activity

- **Refrigeration**
  Low temperatures reduce microbe activity, but do not stop it altogether. Refrigeration is therefore a short-term method of preservation.

- **Freezing**
  Temperatures below −18 °C can stop bacterial growth, but do not kill the bacteria. When the temperature rises, the bacteria become active and multiply. Food that is then re-frozen contains an increased number of bacteria.

- **Pasteurisation**
  This heat treatment is applied to milk. Fresh milk is pasteurised by keeping it at a temperature of not less than 72 °C for at least 15 seconds. This is high enough to kill bacteria and make the milk safe to drink. However, given time and a suitable temperature, any bacterial spores present in the milk will grow and multiply and 'turn the milk bad'.

8 a Describe two ways of sterilising food and give an example of each.

b Describe four methods of preventing microbe activity in food and give an example of each.

c Explain the difference between refrigeration and freezing.

d What is pasteurisation?

Why are food additives used?

Food additives are chemicals that are added to food. Additives such as salt, sugar, and vinegar have always been used to preserve food, but nowadays more than 3000 substances are used as additives. Many of these are for purposes other than preservation, for example:

- to make food look more attractive
- to give an appetising smell
- to change the taste or texture
- to disguise the ingredients
- to make processing easier and cheaper
- to increase shelf-life.

9 Give six reasons why additives are used.

Can additives cause ill-health?

Any additive that is known to cause widespread ill-health is withdrawn from the list of chemicals permitted to be added to food. However, some individuals seem to be sensitive to certain colourings, flavourings or preservatives. For example:

- tartrazine, a yellow dye that was commonly used in fizzy drinks, convenience foods and medicines; it may cause rashes or purple patches on the skin, hay fever, asthma and blurred vision, and might be linked with hyperactivity in some children
- sunset yellow, which was widely used to colour convenience foods; it may produce skin rashes.

Carotenes are yellow or orange pigments that come from plants and are now often used in place of tartrazine and sunset yellow. In the body, β-carotene can be converted to vitamin A.

10 a To which types of additive are some individuals sensitive?
b Give two examples of additives that have been linked with ill-health.

11.3 Hygiene and parasites

What are parasites?

A **parasite** is an organism that lives on or in another living creature and benefits by obtaining food. The organism carrying the parasite is called the **host**. Most parasites injure the health of the host to some extent, and some cause serious illness. Parasites that live in or on humans include bacteria, viruses, fungi, insects and worms.

The parasites discussed in this section pass easily from person to person in the right conditions (see Table 1). They usually do not do much harm, apart from causing irritation, but they are unpleasant.

11 a What is a parasite?
b Does a parasite harm its host?
c Describe a flea and say where it lives, what it feeds on, what symptoms it causes, where the eggs are laid, how fleas spread, and how they can be controlled.

d Repeat for the other parasites in Table 1.

e What causes scabies and where does the rash most commonly occur?

f Why does the number of threadworms in the large intestine depend on the number of eggs that are eaten?

g Why should dogs and cats not be allowed to defecate in areas where children play?

Table 1 Parasites that live on or in humans

Parasites	Where they live	Symptoms they cause	Where eggs are laid	How they spread	Control
fleas are small wingless insects that jump; they have long legs and mouth parts that pierce skin and suck blood	in crevices in buildings and furniture	small itchy red spots on skin	in crevices in buildings and furniture	jump from one person to another	keep clothes, bedding, furniture, and buildings clean
lice (singular: louse) are tiny wingless insects that can crawl; they have claws for hanging onto hairs, and mouth parts that pierce skin and suck blood					
head lice	among hairs on the head	itchy scalp	**nits** (eggs) attached to hairs	crawl from head to head	a special lotion is applied to the hair of the whole family
pubic lice	in pubic hair	small itchy red bite marks	on pubic hairs	sexually transmitted	a special lotion is applied to pubic hair
itch mites are very small and feed on skin; they have four pairs of legs for crawling and burrowing (mites are not insects)	in burrows in the epidermis of the skin	**scabies**: an irritating rash often between the fingers, at the wrists, elbows, buttocks and armpits	in the burrows	crawl from one person to another	a special lotion is applied to the skin of everyone in the family
bed bugs are small wingless insects that crawl and have a most unpleasant smell; at night they suck blood from sleeping people	in bedding and crevices in the room	intense irritation of the skin at night	in bedding and crevices in the room	in bedding and clothing	insecticide spray
threadworms are tiny worms that feed on the contents of the large intestine	eggs that are eaten hatch into worms that live in the large intestine	irritation around the anus in the evenings	about 10 000 eggs are laid around the anus in the evenings	eggs stick to fingernails and clothing	medicine and general cleanliness
Toxocara **worms** are the common roundworms of dogs and cats	eggs that are eaten hatch into worms in the gut and may get into the liver and lungs	fever, cough, and rash in young children; possible eye damage later	in the gut of dogs and cats	contact with faeces of dogs and cats	preventing dogs and cats from defecating in areas where children play; de-worming dogs and cats regularly

11.4 Hygiene and the feet and teeth

How can feet be kept healthy?

Feet carry the weight of the body and move it efficiently when walking and running. Foot care and well-fitting shoes will prevent feet from becoming painful and deformed, which would result in loss of mobility and poor posture.

Some people have feet that produce more sweat than is usual and their feet may give off a strong smell. Sweat itself has little smell. It is the action of bacteria that live in the moist conditions inside shoes that produce the strong odours. The smell is difficult to prevent, but the following actions can help to reduce the problem:

* wash feet daily, dry thoroughly and apply foot powder
* wear clean socks every day and avoid nylon socks
* wear sandals when possible
* wear shoes with uppers made of leather or fabric so that moisture from the feet can evaporate
* have two pairs of shoes and wear them alternately so that those not in use can dry out.

12 a Why do feet need care?

b Why do sweaty feet produce a strong smell?

c What actions can help to reduce the smell?

What are athlete's foot and ringworm?

Athlete's foot is a fungus infection of the feet. The same fungus causes **ringworm** if it infects other parts of the body. The fungus grows outwards from the point of infection and, when it infects the scalp, a circular patch of hair is lost.

Athlete's foot develops quickly in the warm, damp conditions encouraged by shoes and socks, especially between the toes. It makes the skin crack, turn white and peel off. The infected areas sometimes itch, and the cracks can be painful. If a nail becomes infected it becomes thickened and irregular. The fungus is spread by towels and bath mats that have been in contact with the infection. Athlete's foot can be treated by an anti-fungal cream or powder applied to the infected area, or by a course of medicine.

13 a What is the connection between athlete's foot and ringworm?

b What happens to the skin when athlete's foot develops?

c How does athlete's foot spread?

d How can athlete's foot be treated?

What is a verruca?

14 What is a verruca?

A **verruca** is a wart on the sole of the foot. Warts are caused by a virus infection. Because a verruca is pressed inwards during walking, it can be very painful. Sufferers should go to a chiropodist for treatment, or use a preparation from a pharmacist.

What problems can ill-fitting footwear cause?

Wearing high heels puts most of the weight of the body on the ball of the foot. This shortens the stride and makes walking awkward. Continued wearing of high heels may cause the calf muscles to shorten. These muscles will then ache when flat shoes are worn.

A **corn** is an area of thickened skin that develops in response to continued rubbing or pressure. Pain can be relieved by wearing shoes that fit well.

A **hammer toe** is bent so that the end points downwards. This 'pushed-up' position is due to wearing shoes that are wrongly shaped or too small. If wearing wider shoes does not relieve the pain, surgery may be necessary.

An **ingrown toenail** occurs when the flesh is continuously pressed against a rough edge of the nail. Expert advice is required, and it may be necessary to remove the nail by surgery.

A **bunion** is a painful swelling near the joint at the base of the big toe. It is caused by long-term pressure on the joint. Wide-fitting shoes, cushioning pads and, in extreme cases, surgery, can help.

Chiropodists are trained in foot care. They provide a foot care service for people who are unable to look after their own feet, for example, some elderly people. Chiropodists identify and advise on common foot problems.

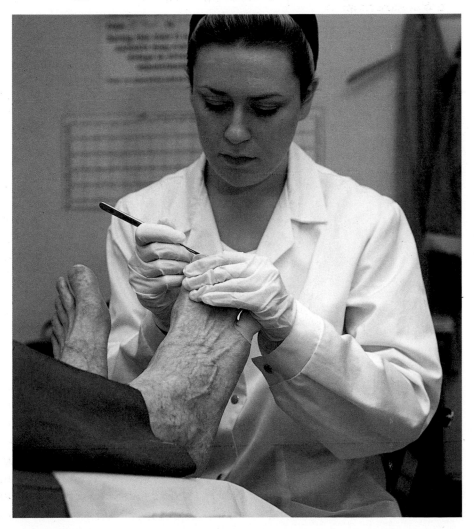

15 a Describe how ill-fitting shoes can cause:
   i a corn
   ii a hammer toe.
b What is a bunion?
c What can encourage the formation of a bunion?
d What is an ingrown toenail?
e Why do people visit a chiropodist?

How can teeth be kept healthy?

There are a number of actions that help to prevent tooth decay:

- eat any sweets, chocolates, sugary drinks or foods all at one go, and then clean the teeth to remove sugar from the mouth
- eat a healthy diet with plenty of foods that require chewing to keep the gums in good condition
- brush the teeth twice a day to prevent the build-up of bacteria and remove plaque (see page 87)
- use a fluoride toothpaste to help strengthen tooth enamel
- floss teeth at least once a day to remove plaque from between the teeth and from the crevices; dental floss is a strong thread that is pulled to and fro between the teeth to remove plaque near the gum where a toothbrush cannot reach
- visit the dental hygienist regularly so that teeth are scaled and polished to remove tartar, which is a hard deposit that forms on the teeth
- go for regular dental check-ups so that any decay can be treated at an early stage.

16 a What helps to prevent decay after eating sugary foods?

b Describe how the following contribute to healthy teeth:

i fluoride

ii diet

iii brushing

iv flossing

v regular dental check-ups.

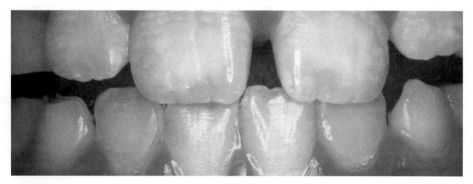

A minute amount of fluoride in drinking water helps to produce strong teeth, but too much fluoride discolours the teeth of children.

Summary of hygiene

- Hygiene is the study of the principles governing health. It includes clean food and general care of the feet and teeth, and environmental cleanliness (sewage and clean water supplies).
- Food hygiene ensures food is free from dangerous microorganisms. Food poisoning occurs when food hygiene is not carried out. Food poisoning includes a range of conditions caused by different contaminating organisms.
- Fleas, lice, mites and bed bugs live on or in the skin of human beings.
- Threadworms are parasites that live in the large intestine.
- *Toxocara* worms live in the gut and may get into the liver and lungs.

- Foot care depends on regular washing and careful drying of the feet, wearing clean socks, and wearing sandals or shoes that allow moisture from the feet to evaporate.
- Athlete's foot is a fungus infection that can affect the skin between the toes. On other parts of the body, the same fungus is called ringworm.
- A verruca is a wart on the sole of the foot; warts are caused by a virus infection.
- Ill-fitting footwear can cause a range of problems.
- Good dental hygiene requires a diet with food that needs to be chewed, regular brushing and flossing, and regular dental check-ups.

11.5 Infectious diseases

What are infectious diseases?

Infectious diseases are diseases that spread from one person to another. After starvation, they are the commonest causes of ill-health worldwide. Diseases of this type are caused by microorganisms, which are everywhere. Some live naturally on the skin or in the mouth, vagina or colon, and can be useful. Only a relatively small number of microorganisms cause disease in humans, and these are called **pathogens** (or '**germs**'). Pathogens are mainly bacteria and viruses but also include some fungi. Prions are recently discovered abnormal proteins that are **pathogenic** (have the ability to cause disease). Prions are discussed on page 282.

Infectious disease is present when pathogens enter the body and prevent the tissues in which they are living from functioning normally. Some pathogens also produce **toxins** (poisons) that travel in the bloodstream to other parts of the body where they cause harm.

Infectious disease is more likely when the pathogens are very active, or when a large number of pathogens is present, or when the body's resistance is low. Low resistance may be due to:

- a low level of antibodies
- poor nutrition
- an unhealthy environment
- age (the very young and very old have lower resistance to infection).

---

17 a Describe what is meant by:

    i an infectious disease

    ii a pathogen

    iii a toxin.

  b When is a person more likely to catch an infectious disease?

The body has a number of ways of preventing pathogens from entering the tissues:

- skin forms a barrier
- tears and saliva contain **lysozyme**, which is an antibacterial enzyme
- wax in the outer ears traps pathogens and removes them when it falls out
- mucus in the lungs traps pathogens, which are then coughed out
- low pH (acid conditions) in the stomach, vagina and urethra kills pathogens
- blood clots seal wounds.

Pathogens that succeed in entering the tissues are attacked by:

- white cells
- antibodies.

---

18 a In what ways is the body protected against the entry of pathogens?

  b What are pathogens attacked by if they enter the tissues?

How does an infectious disease develop?

An infectious disease usually has four stages (see Figure 2).

First, a sufficiently large number of pathogens must past the body's defences to set up an infection.

The **incubation stage** is the period of time between the entry of pathogens and the appearance of symptoms. The length of the incubation stage varies with different diseases. It is only a few days in diphtheria, but can be more than a year in leprosy.

Different infectious diseases produce different symptoms. However, the following symptoms are typical of many infections:

- fever and chills
- headache
- loss of appetite
- dehydration (hot, dry skin; furred tongue; dark yellow urine in small amounts; thirst) resulting from fever and sweating
- exhaustion or loss of strength.

During **convalescence** the symptoms disappear and the patient regains strength.

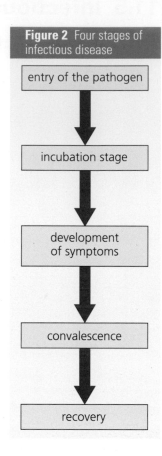

Figure 2 Four stages of infectious disease

entry of the pathogen

↓

incubation stage

↓

development of symptoms

↓

convalescence

↓

recovery

When is a person infectious?

The **infectious stage** is the time during which pathogens can spread from an infected person to other people. A person can be **infectious** (capable of spreading pathogens) during the incubation stage, during the illness itself, and, sometimes, afterwards as a carrier.

---

19 a What is the incubation stage of a disease?

   b What are the typical symptoms of many infectious diseases?

   c When can a person be infectious?

How are infectious diseases spread?

Diseases are **transmitted** (spread) from one person to another in a number of ways.

- **Contact**

   Contagious diseases are spread by contact. Many skin diseases such as ringworm, impetigo, herpes, chicken pox, and gonorrhoea are spread in this way. **Direct contact** is touching the infected person. **Indirect contact** is touching articles such as toys, handkerchiefs, or towels that have been in contact with the infected person.

- **Droplet infection**

  Minute droplets sprayed from an infected person during sneezing, coughing or talking can be inhaled by people close by. Droplets can dry rapidly and their contents can be carried some distance in air currents. Diseases of the respiratory tract, for example colds and influenza, are often spread by droplet infection. So are most of the infectious diseases of childhood, for example measles and whooping cough.

- **Contaminated food and drink**

  Food or drink contaminated by pathogens from an infected person, or by flies, dust and dirt, may cause disease. Diseases of the digestive system are often spread in this way, for example *Salmonella* food poisoning, typhoid, cholera and dysentery.

- **Vectors**

  Animals that transmit infectious disease are called **vectors**. For example, mosquitoes spread malaria; dogs and other animals spread rabies; houseflies spread pathogens that cause food poisoning.

- **Dust**

  Some types of pathogen can survive as spores for a long time in dust, dirt or soil, for example tetanus and anthrax. They can be moved long distances by wind.

- **Inadequate sterilisation**

  Pathogens can be spread from infected patients to other people by inadequate sterilisation of instruments. HIV and hepatitis B can be spread among drug addicts by the use of unsterilised shared needles.

- **Carriers**

  Some people carry infectious microbes but do not show any symptoms of disease; these people are called **carriers**. They may be unaware that they carry pathogens of, for example, typhoid, hepatitis B or HIV.

20 List seven ways in which infectious diseases are spread, giving examples for each way.

How are infectious diseases controlled?

Infectious diseases are controlled by increasing the resistance of the host, eliminating the source of the pathogens, and preventing the spread of infection.

Resistance of the host is increased by:

- a good state of health
- immunisation.

Eliminating the source of the pathogens includes the use of:

- boiling water, which kills most microorganisms, although some bacterial spores can withstand prolonged boiling
- ultraviolet light, which kills most microbes but not their spores
- **antiseptics**, which are chemicals that kill microbes, but not their spores, without damaging human cells
- **disinfectants**, which are chemicals that destroy microbes and do damage human cells
- **sterilisation** by compressed steam or gamma irradiation, which completely destroys microbes and their spores.

In hospitals, instruments are sterilised by compressed steam in an autoclave to ensure that all bacteria and their spores are killed.

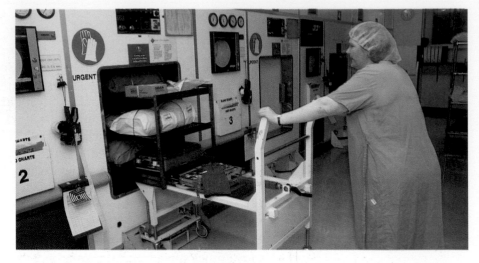

Generally, antiseptics are used on people, and disinfectants are used on things such as bed linen, equipment and drains. Any article that has been sterilised is described as **sterile** or **aseptic**.

Preventing the spread of infection involves:

- vector control, for example monitoring the movement of dogs and cats across national borders to prevent the spread of rabies, and the destruction of mosquitoes to prevent the spread of malaria
- **quarantine** (isolation) of people who have been in contact with an infection because, if they have caught the disease, they may be infectious before symptoms appear
- precautions taken by carriers to reduce the danger to other people; for example, typhoid carriers should wash their hands thoroughly and clean under their nails after visiting the toilet, and should not work in the catering industry
- medicines used to destroy the pathogens in people, for example antibiotics to kill bacterial pathogens.

21 List ways in which infectious diseases are controlled.

How do epidemics spread?

An **epidemic** occurs when a disease spreads rapidly and infects large numbers of people, then disappears until the next outbreak. An epidemic becomes **pandemic** if it spreads worldwide. Conditions favourable for epidemics include:

- little or no immunity among the population
- presence of a highly infectious strain of the disease
- pathogens that spread easily
- an unhealthy population.

An infectious disease is described as:

- **endemic** if it is always present in a particular part of the world, for example malaria in certain parts of the world
- **sporadic** if it occurs in different places at different times, with no known connection between the outbreaks.

22 a Describe what is meant by:
  i an epidemic
  ii pandemic
  iii endemic
  iv sporadic.
  b Give four conditions favourable to epidemics.

How is malaria caught?

Malaria is caused by a protozoan, a single-celled organism, called *Plasmodium*. To complete its life-cycle and survive, this parasite needs a human host and also certain species of mosquito (see Figure 3).

Figure 3 Humans, mosquitoes and malaria

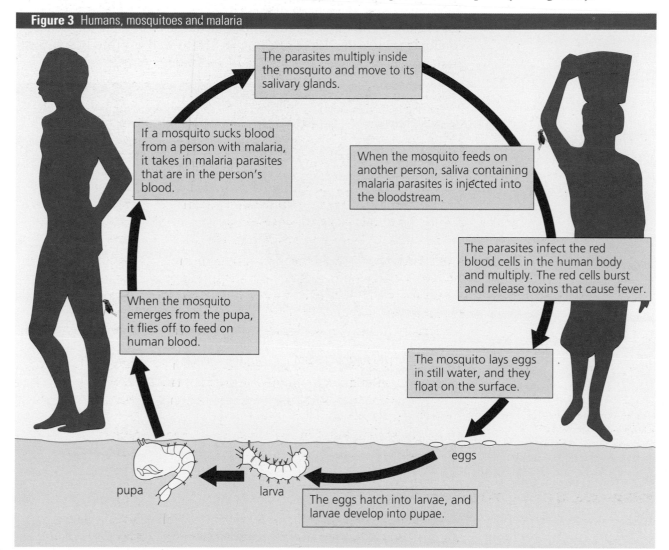

The parasites multiply inside the mosquito and move to its salivary glands.

If a mosquito sucks blood from a person with malaria, it takes in malaria parasites that are in the person's blood.

When the mosquito feeds on another person, saliva containing malaria parasites is injected into the bloodstream.

The parasites infect the red blood cells in the human body and multiply. The red cells burst and release toxins that cause fever.

When the mosquito emerges from the pupa, it flies off to feed on human blood.

The mosquito lays eggs in still water, and they float on the surface.

eggs

pupa

larva

The eggs hatch into larvae, and larvae develop into pupae.

---

23 a Name the parasite that causes malaria.

b From Figure 3, describe the life-cycle of the mosquito.

c From Figure 3, describe how malaria spreads from person to person.

d How can malaria be controlled?

d How is malaria treated?

Malaria is one of the commonest serious causes of fever in people in the tropics. Methods of controlling malaria include:

- taking anti-malarial drugs once or twice a week to prevent infection
- using mosquito nets and insect repellents to prevent mosquito bites
- using insecticides to destroy mosquitoes
- draining swamps, marshes and stagnant pools to destroy mosquito breeding grounds.

Chloroquine and other drugs destroy the malaria parasite in an infected person. Unfortunately, there are now many strains *Plasmodium* resistant to the usual drugs, especially in West Africa.

What are sexually transmitted diseases?

Various microbes can infect the sex organs (see Figure 4). Such infections are known as **sexually transmitted diseases (STDs)** because they are usually, but not always, spread from one person to another by sexual intercourse. Nowadays, most of these diseases can be treated easily and successfully at clinics for genito-urinary medicine or by a doctor. Using condoms reduces the risk of catching an STD as well as protecting against an unwanted pregnancy.

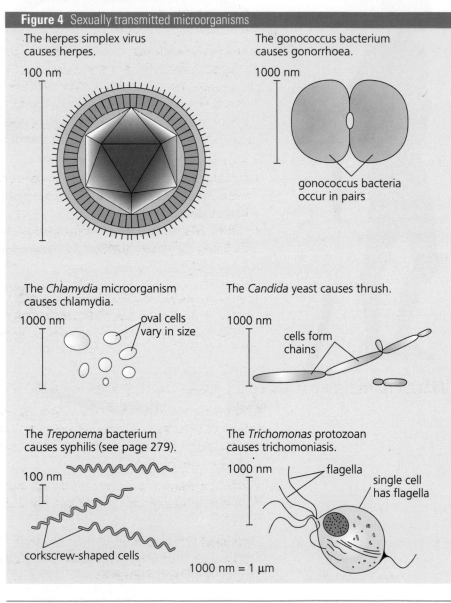

Figure 4 Sexually transmitted microorganisms

The herpes simplex virus causes herpes.

100 nm

The gonococcus bacterium causes gonorrhoea.

1000 nm

gonococcus bacteria occur in pairs

The *Chlamydia* microorganism causes chlamydia.

1000 nm

oval cells vary in size

The *Candida* yeast causes thrush.

1000 nm

cells form chains

The *Treponema* bacterium causes syphilis (see page 279).

100 nm

corkscrew-shaped cells

The *Trichomonas* protozoan causes trichomoniasis.

1000 nm

flagella

single cell has flagella

1000 nm = 1 μm

24 **a** Give the meaning of STD.

  b How are STDs spread?

  c What can reduce the risk of catching an STD?

  d Where is treatment given for these diseases?

What are the early symptoms of infection?

One or more of the following may indicate an infection of the sex organs:

- an unusual discharge from the vagina (perhaps a different colour, with a strange smell, or thicker than usual)
- a discharge from the penis
- a sore or blister near the vagina, penis or anus
- a rash or irritation around the vagina, penis or anus
- pain or burning feeling when passing urine
- passing urine more often than usual
- pain during intercourse.

If any of the symptoms listed above occur, it is important to visit a doctor or a special clinic for a check-up so that the infection can be diagnosed and correct treatment given. When necessary, sexual partners can be traced and advised to have treatment to prevent the disease from spreading.

Absence of symptoms in a sexual partner does not necessarily mean that the person has no infection. There are three reasons for this:

- an infection takes time to develop
- sometimes people do not develop symptoms; for example, many women with gonorrhoea do not get symptoms, and most men with herpes do not have sores
- sometimes symptoms clear up without treatment and people may think that they are cured; unfortunately, they may still be infected and infectious.

---

25 a Give seven early symptoms of infection by an STD.

   b Give two reasons for having the infection diagnosed.

   c Give three reasons why absence of symptoms may not mean absence of infection.

What diseases affect the sex organs?

Chlamydia is caused by *Chlamydia trachomatis*, a microorganism that infects the genitals. It is one of the most common causes of sexually transmitted disease. In some people there may be no symptoms. In others it can be the cause of:

- inflammation of the cervix and vagina (vaginitis) in women
- inflammation of the urethra in men, also called non-specific urethritis (NSU).

Untreated chlamydia in women can result in pelvic inflammatory disease (PID). This is a serious condition as it can make a woman **infertile**, that is, unable to have children.

---

26 a Draw and name the microbes in Figure 4, and say what disease each causes.

   b What organism causes chlamydia?

   c Give two effects of chlamydia in women, and one in men.

   d What can be the result of PID?

Thrush is caused by *Candida*, a yeast that normally lives harmlessly on the skin, in the mouth and in the gut. Under certain conditions, the *Candida* yeast grows and multiplies in the genital areas of both men and women, causing discomfort and an intense itch. This is more likely to happen:

- during pregnancy
- if wearing tight jeans or nylon underwear
- when taking certain antibiotics
- in those who have poorly controlled diabetes
- in those who are ill
- to women who are taking the contraceptive pill
- in people who have unprotected sex with someone who has thrush.

Trichomoniasis (TV) is caused by a small protozoan, *Trichomonas*, that infects the vagina, producing a yellow–green discharge with an unpleasant smell. It sometimes infects the urethra in men.

Genital herpes is caused by the herpes simplex virus (HSV). There are two types of HSV. Type I usually causes sores of the nose and mouth (cold sores). Type II causes sores in the genital area and can infect both men and women. The sores are highly infectious and the virus is easily passed on to others by contact.

Gonorrhoea is caused by a bacterium that is often referred to as 'gonococcus'. It can infect the warm moist areas of the genital region and is easily spread through sexual intercourse. In men, the infection is painful, with a discharge of pus. Women who are infected often have no symptoms, and so do not seek treatment. They can unknowingly re-infect their male partners who have received treatment.

Syphilis is caused by a spiral-shaped bacterium, a spirochaete. It is one of the most dangerous sexual infections. It can spread to other parts of the body and, if untreated, can eventually lead to blindness, heart disease, deafness, insanity and death. A pregnant woman with untreated syphilis can pass on the infection to her baby who may be born diseased or dead. Fortunately, syphilis is easy to treat, and is now uncommon.

---

27 a Where does *Candida* normally live?

  b What happens when *Candida* starts to multiply in the genital area?

  c When is this more likely to happen?

  d Name the organism that causes trichomoniasis.

  e What are the symptoms of trichomoniasis?

  f What type of organism causes herpes?

  g What is the difference in effect of Type 1 HSV and Type 2 HSV?

  h How does the herpes virus spread?

  i What causes gonorrhoea?

  j Why may women with gonorrhoea not go for treatment?

  k What organism causes syphilis?

  l Why is syphilis a dangerous infection?

  m What can happen to the baby when a pregnant woman has untreated syphilis?

  n Suggest a reason why syphilis is now uncommon.

11.6 Immunity

What is immunity?

28 a What is the function of the immune system?

b In what ways can the degree of immunity vary?

The immune system helps the body to resist infection. **Immunity** is the ability of the white cells and antibodies to recognise and destroy pathogens and other foreign material. The degree of immunity varies. With total immunity, pathogens entering the body are destroyed. In partial immunity, not enough pathogens are destroyed to prevent the disease, but sufficient to make it less severe. If there is no immunity, infection follows entry of pathogens.

How does a person become immune?

There are three ways of gaining immunity. Immunity is named according to the way in which it is gained.

Active immunity is obtained when the body produces its own antibodies. Antibodies are produced in response to:

- disease-causing bacteria, viruses or other pathogens
- vaccines.

This type of immunity gives long-term protection, often for many years. In the case of some diseases, such as rubella and poliomyelitis, immunity is life-long.

Passive immunity is obtained by injection of ready-made antibodies or antitoxin. This type of immunity gives only short-term protection. It is useful for treating or preventing some infectious diseases, for example tetanus and hepatitis, or preventing Rh factor damage in pregnancy (see page 42).

29 a Explain the difference between active and passive immunity.

b Which type of immunity gives long-term protection?

c When is passive immunity useful?

d How is congenital immunity obtained?

e How long does congenital immunity last?

Congenital immunity is the immunity a baby is born with. When a baby is in the uterus, antibodies cross the placenta from the mother's blood to the baby's blood. This means that a baby is born with the same protection against diseases as its mother. If breast-fed, the baby continues to receive antibodies in the milk. The antibodies survive in the baby for several months and then gradually disappear. This gives time for the baby to grow stronger and more able to withstand infection. By the age of 3 months, the baby is better able to develop its own antibodies, so this is the recommended time to begin immunisation.

What are antigens and antibodies?

An **antigen** is any substance that stimulates the production of antibodies. Antigens can be pathogens, vaccines, pollen, or even some foods. An **antibody** is a substance produced in response to an antigen. Each antigen stimulates the production of a specific antibody against itself.

Antibodies are molecules of protein. The antibody protein is an immunoglobulin (Ig), usually gamma globulin. Antibodies are made by a type of white cell called a lymphocyte. Lymphocytes are found in the blood, tissues and lymph nodes. Once the lymphocytes have 'learned' to make a particular type of antibody, this 'memory' may last for many years. The function of antibodies is to help to destroy pathogens.

30 a What is the difference between an antibody and an antigen?
  b Give some examples of antigens.
  c What is each antigen able to do?
  d What are antibodies made of?
  e Which cells make antibodies?
  f What is the function of antibodies?

How does immunisation work?

In **immunisation**, a person is given a vaccine that stimulates the immune system to produce antibodies against the antigens in the vaccine; this is called the primary immune response. After immunisation, if the person is infected with the pathogen, their immune system reacts faster and produces more antibodies than it did in the primary immune response; this is called the secondary immune response (see Figure 5).

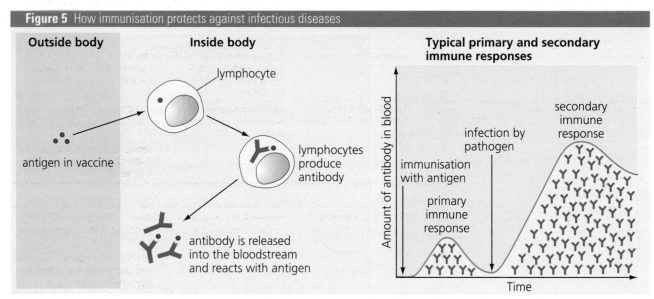

Figure 5 How immunisation protects against infectious diseases

Some vaccines are given at intervals, in two or three doses, to build up more and more antibodies on each occasion. A 'booster' dose may also be needed after a time to maintain the immunity. A vaccine can be a dose of:

- dead pathogens that have been killed by heat or chemicals; this is called a **dead vaccine** and an example is typhoid vaccine
- live pathogens that have been altered so that they can no longer cause the disease, but can grow and multiply in the body; this is called a **live attenuated vaccine** and examples are polio and measles vaccines
- **toxoid**, a harmless form of the toxin that produces the disease; an example is tetanus vaccine.

31 a Describe three types of vaccines.
  b When a person is immunised with a vaccine, what does the vaccine do?

What vaccines are available?

It is possible to protect people against a number of infectious diseases by immunisation (see Table 2).

Table 2 Infectious diseases and immunisation

Disease	Symptoms	Incubation in days	Duration of infectious stage	Other information	Immunisation
Bacterial infections					
diphtheria	a white layer, which may block the airway, forms on the throat; it produces toxin that damages the heart and nervous system	2 to 5	usually about 2 weeks after onset	uncommon, but can occur in children who have not been immunised	vaccines against diphtheria, tetanus and pertussis are often given together as triple vaccine (DTP vaccine); three injections are needed at monthly intervals from 2 months old
tetanus (lockjaw)	muscles of the neck, back and limbs tighten and the jaw may lock	4 to 21	no infectious stage, cannot be passed directly from one person to another	pathogens exist in soil and enter the body through cuts and scratches	booster doses of vaccine for diphtheria and tetanus are given pre-school and again between 13 and 18 years; further doses of tetanus vaccine may be given at 10-yearly intervals
pertussis (whooping cough)	long bouts of coughing that may end with a 'whoop', and vomiting	7 to 12	a few days before onset to 4 weeks after onset	whooping cough vaccine prevents the disease or makes it much less severe	
meningitis caused in infants by *Haemophilus influenzae* type b, (Hib)	stiff neck, confusion and drowsiness			usually occurs in first year of life, uncommon after 4 years old	three injections of Hib vaccine at monthly intervals from 2 months old
tuberculosis (TB)	usually coughing and lung damage, swollen glands in the neck	28 to 42	variable	most people infected by TB bacteria develop natural immunity to TB rather than the disease	vaccination with BCG vaccine for high risk health workers, and children 10 to 14 years old
typhoid caused by *Salmonella typhi*	fever, constipation, and a dry cough	about 14	variable, a few people become permanent carriers	can be prevented by efficient sewage disposal, a clean water supply, and clean food	two injections of vaccine with an interval between them of not less than 1 month booster dose required every 3 years in areas where typhoid is endemic
Virus infections					
poliomyelitis (polio)	headache, stiffness of neck and back, with or without paralysis	3 to 21	from 2 days after infection to 6 weeks or longer after onset	immunisation has almost eliminated this disease from the UK	three doses of polio vaccine are given by mouth at the same time as DTP vaccine booster doses are given pre-school and again before leaving school (15 to 19 years old)
measles	fever, runny nose, cough 4 to 5 days later a red rash appears on face and spreads downwards	10 to 15	from onset of symptoms to 5 days after rash appears	more serious in infancy than in older children	combined measles, mumps and rubella vaccine (MMR vaccine) is given at 1 year old
mumps	painful swellings near the jaw on one or both sides	12 to 18; usually about 18	until the swelling goes down	mumps in males over the age of 11 may affect a testis but rarely results in sterility	rubella vaccine is offered to all children who have not had rubella or MMR vaccine before leaving school
rubella (German measles)	red rash and swollen glands	10 to 21	from onset to end of rash	dangerous to the baby in the first 4 months of pregnancy (see pages 198 to 200)	
chickenpox (varicella)	small red spots that turn into blisters then scabs	10 to 21	from 2 days before the spots appear until they are dry	a mild disease in children but more severe in adults; the same virus causes shingles	
rabies	fever, delirium, convulsions, paralysis; throat muscles tighten so that it is impossible to drink	30 to 60	rabies can be caught only from the saliva of an animal with rabies after being licked, scratched or bitten.	rabies can infect all mammals but is a serious risk to people only if domestic animals are infected (this is why the UK has traditionally quarantined dogs and cats entering the country)	five injections starting immediately after possible infection (active immunity) passive immunity can be obtained by an injection of gamma globulin

32 a From Table 2, name the disease(s) that each of the following vaccines protect against:

    i DTP   **iv** polio

    ii Hib   **v** MMR.

    iii BCG

b Give a timetable for immunisation with the five vaccines listed above.

c Name the disease in Table 1 that:

    i can be caught through cuts and scratches

    ii may be caught from a carrier

    iii can cause sterility

    iv is dangerous during pregnancy

    v has no immunisation programme.

d Which virus causes shingles?

What can go wrong with the immune system?

Auto-immune diseases are caused when the body produces antibodies that destroy its own cells. It is not known why this happens. An example is diabetes: the body makes antibodies against the cells that produce insulin.

An **allergy** is a damaging immune response to an antigen to which the body has become over-sensitive. Some examples are:

- hay-fever reaction to pollen
- vomiting and diarrhoea as a reaction to fresh, uncontaminated food such as strawberries, nuts, or shell-fish
- a violent reaction with swelling of the face, tongue and mouth to bee stings.

33 a What is an auto-immune disease?

b Why does an allergy develop? Give some examples of allergy.

Why are transplants rejected?

34 a What is a transplant?

b Why can a transplant be rejected by the recipient?

c What is given to the recipient to prevent rejection, and what is the disadvantage?

A **transplant** is a living organ or tissue that is transferred from one person, called the **donor**, to another, called the **recipient**. Transplant operations may involve the transfer of heart, kidney, liver or marrow. The recipient's immune system would recognise the transplant tissue as 'foreign' and destroy it, even when the donor and recipient are well matched. To prevent this from happening, drugs are given to reduce the recipient's immune response. The disadvantage of this is that the recipient then has less resistance to infection.

What are HIV and AIDS?

HIV stands for human immunodeficiency virus (see Figure 6). **AIDS** stands for acquired immune deficiency syndrome, a disease caused by HIV. People with HIV often look and feel well for a long time, but most will eventually develop AIDS. A person has AIDS if he or she is infected with HIV and, in addition, develops certain serious infections. This happens because HIV reduces the effectiveness of the white cells and the body's resistance to infection. It is these infections, not the HIV, that eventually kill the person.

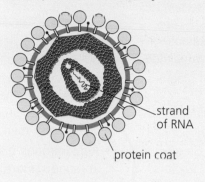

Figure 6 HIV and white cells

Human immunodeficiency virus

strand
of RNA

protein coat

This false-colour SEM shows a white cell (green) with HIV particles (red) budding away from it.

35 a What is HIV?

b What is AIDS?

c What is the effect of HIV on resistance to infection?

d What two conditions are necessary for a person to have AIDS?

How is HIV caught?

HIV is found in the blood of an infected person. It is also found in sexual fluids. For a male, this means the fluid that comes out of the penis before and during sex. For a female, it means in the fluids produced in the vagina before and during sex. The HIV virus can enter the body:

- through tiny cuts, which are quite common on the delicate tissues of the sexual organs and anus, when having sex without a condom with someone who has HIV
- by injection into the bloodstream, for example by using needles, syringes or other drug-injecting equipment that has been used by a person who has HIV
- from a woman with HIV to her baby during pregnancy, at birth, or through breast-feeding.

HIV does not survive outside the body, so it cannot be spread by:

- kissing, touching, hugging or shaking hands
- sharing crockery and cutlery
- coughing or sneezing
- contact with toilet seats
- swimming pools
- eating food prepared by someone with HIV.

36 a Where in the body can HIV be found?

b How can HIV enter the body?

c Which activities do not spread HIV?

What is an HIV test?

The HIV test looks for antibodies to HIV in a blood sample. A person is HIV positive if HIV-antibodies are found. HIV-antibodies appear in the blood 1 to 3 months after infection. Although the body makes antibodies to defend itself against infections, HIV-antibodies are not able to protect a person from developing AIDS.

37 a What does an HIV test look for and what does HIV positive mean?

b How long after infection does it take for antibodies to appear in the blood?

Summary of infectious diseases and immunity

- Infectious diseases are diseases caused by microorganisms that spread from one person to another. These disease-causing organisms are called pathogens. After starvation, infectious diseases are the main cause of death worldwide.

- An infectious disease normally has four stages: entry of pathogen, incubation stage, development of symptoms, and convalescence.

- Infectious diseases can be spread by: direct and indirect contact (contagious diseases), droplet infection, contaminated food and drink, vectors, dust, poor sterilisation, and carriers.

- Infectious diseases are controlled by increasing the resistance of the host to the pathogen through immunisation, restricting or eliminating the source of the pathogen, and using medicines to kill pathogens in the body.

- An epidemic occurs when large numbers of people suffer from the same disease at the same time. A worldwide epidemic is called pandemic.

- Malaria is caused by *Plasmodium*, a protozoan that needs both a human host and a mosquito vector.

- Chlamydia, thrush, trichomoniasis, genital herpes, gonorrhoea and syphilis are infections spread by sexual intercourse.

- Immunity is the ability of an organism to resist attack by a pathogen. Immunity depends on the action of antibodies. In active immunity, the body produces its own antibodies to fight infection. In passive immunity, the body is injected with antibodies from another source.

- An antigen is anything that stimulates the production of an antibody. Antigens include pathogens, vaccines, pollen and some foods.

- Immunisation uses a form of the antigen that produces an antibody response, the primary immune response, but does not cause the disease. If the pathogen enters the body at a later date, the secondary immune response is faster and greater than the primary immune response.

- Auto-immune diseases are disorders of the immune system and include diabetes and allergies such as hay fever.

- The immune system is also responsible for rejection of transplanted organs. Drugs are used to prevent this rejection by reducing the efficiency of the immune system, but they leave patients open to infection.

- AIDS (acquired immune deficiency syndrome) is an illness caused by HIV (human immunodeficiency virus). HIV lowers the body's resistance to other infections, which eventually kill the person.

- People infected by HIV are known as HIV positive and can live healthy lives for some years without showing symptoms of AIDS. However, they can pass on the virus during this time.

- HIV cannot survive outside the body. It is passed on only when a body fluid from an infected person passes directly into the body of another person or from mother to fetus during pregnancy.

- 1000 nanometres (nm) = 1 micrometre (μm). 1000 micrometres (μm) = 1 millimetre (mm).

11.7 Bacteria, viruses and prions

What are bacteria?

A bacterium is a single cell with a cell wall and cytoplasm (see Figure 7). There is no nuclear membrane; instead the nuclear material (DNA) is found in the cytoplasm. Substances necessary for bacterial life are absorbed through the cell wall and unwanted substances are excreted.

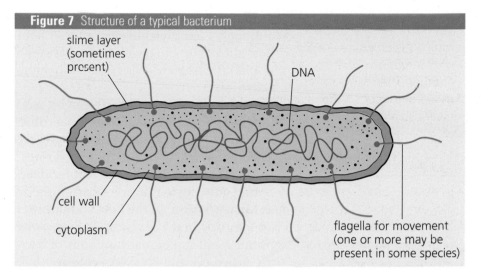

Figure 7 Structure of a typical bacterium

slime layer (sometimes present)

DNA

cell wall

cytoplasm

flagella for movement (one or more may be present in some species)

38 a Of the words 'bacteria' and 'bacterium', which is singular and which is plural?

b Draw and label a diagram of a typical bacterium.

c How are bacteria classified?

d Draw and label each of the basic bacterial shapes.

e Where can bacteria be found?

Bacteria are found almost everywhere: in air, water and food, and on both the inside and outside of plants and the bodies of animals. Bacteria range in size from 0.5 to 1.5 micrometres (μm) in diameter and can be seen only with the aid of a microscope. There are four basic bacterial shapes, which are used to classify bacteria (see Figure 8). The many different species of bacteria each has a particular shape, size, and set of conditions in which it survives and grows.

Figure 8 The four basic bacterial shapes

Cocci are spherical and occur in different groupings:
- diplococci occur in pairs, for example, the bacteria that cause gonorrhoea
- streptococci occur in chains, for example, the bacteria that cause sore throats
- staphylococci occur in clusters, for example, the bacteria that cause abscesses.

Bacilli are rod shaped, for example, the bacteria that cause tetanus.

Vibrios are curved, for example, the bacteria that cause cholera.

Spirochaetes are corkscrew-shaped, for example, the bacteria that cause syphilis.

This false-colour scanning electron micrograph shows clusters of staphylococci.

These are the curved bacteria that cause cholera.

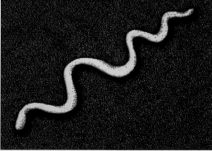

This is Treponema, *the bacterium that causes syphilis.*

What conditions affect the growth of bacteria?

Water and a suitable food supply are essential for bacterial growth. Some bacteria feed on only one type of food, whereas others are able to feed on a wide range of material.

39 a What are essential for bacterial growth?

b In what temperature range do most bacteria grow best?

c How do bacteria react to low temperatures?

d What is the difference between aerobic and anaerobic bacteria?

Most bacteria grow best in the temperature range 25 to 38 °C, although a few prefer higher or lower temperatures. Most are killed by heat above 60 °C. Low temperatures stop most bacterial activity but do not kill the bacteria. When the temperature rises, the bacteria become active again.

Aerobic bacteria require oxygen in order to grow; they respire in the same way as plants or animals. **Anaerobic bacteria** will not grow in the presence of oxygen. Anaerobic bacteria account for most of the bacterial activity that takes place in rubbish dumps and in the sludge in sewage works. These are the bacteria that produce foul-smelling gases.

After growing to full size, a bacterium divides into two, a process known as **binary fission**. In the right conditions, this can take place about every 20 minutes. In the course of 24 hours, one bacterium can multiply to produce a group of many millions of bacteria. Such a group is visible to the naked eye and is called a **colony**.

40 a How do bacteria reproduce?

b Calculate how long would it take one bacterium to produce a colony of more than one million if they divide every 20 minutes.

How can bacteria survive unfavourable conditions?

When conditions become unfavourable, bacteria that are not killed either remain inactive or, in the case of some species, produce spores. Bacterial spores can withstand drought, high temperatures and antiseptics. When conditions improve, the spores start to grow into bacteria that reproduce again (see Figure 9).

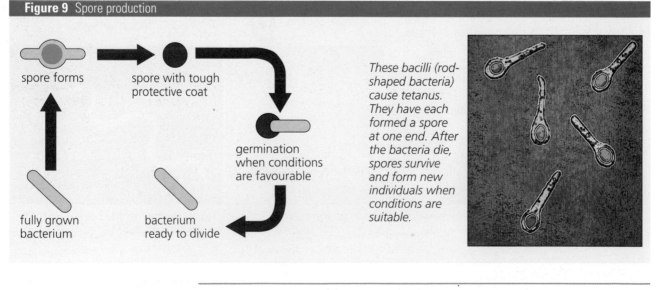

Figure 9 Spore production

spore forms

spore with tough protective coat

germination when conditions are favourable

fully grown bacterium

bacterium ready to divide

These bacilli (rod-shaped bacteria) cause tetanus. They have each formed a spore at one end. After the bacteria die, spores survive and form new individuals when conditions are suitable.

41 a What happens to bacteria when conditions become unfavourable?

b Draw labelled diagrams to describe bacterial spore production.

c List three conditions that bacterial spores can withstand.

How can bacteria be destroyed?

Antiseptics and disinfectants can kill many bacteria. Most bacteria are also killed by ultraviolet light, whether it is artificial or from sunlight. Boiling water kills nearly all bacteria, although some spores can survive even prolonged boiling. All bacteria and their spores are killed by compressed steam in an autoclave, and by gamma radiation.

An **antibiotic** is a substance that destroys or stops the growth of microorganisms. Antibiotics are widely used as medicines to treat bacterial diseases. Examples are:

- penicillins, which destroy various common and dangerous bacteria
- erythromycin, which is used to treat pneumonia.

When an antibiotic is used too freely, there is the danger that the bacteria which it is intended to destroy will develop resistance to that antibiotic. A different antibiotic will then be needed for use against the resistant bacteria.

42 a Name five ways in which bacteria can be destroyed.

b Why are autoclaves used in hospitals?

c What are antibiotics and why are they useful?

d Why should antibiotics not be used too freely?

What are viruses?

Viruses are much smaller than bacteria. They range in size from 10 to 300 nanometres (nm), and are visible only with an electron microscope. There are many types of virus (see Figure 10). Each virus particle consists of a single strand of DNA or RNA surrounded by a protein coat. A virus particle does not feed, respire, excrete, or grow. The particle becomes active and multiplies only when it is inside a living cell (see Figure 11). As the virus spreads, it damages tissues and causes disease.

Figure 10 Some different types of virus

adenovirus

pox virus

influenza virus

diagrams not to scale

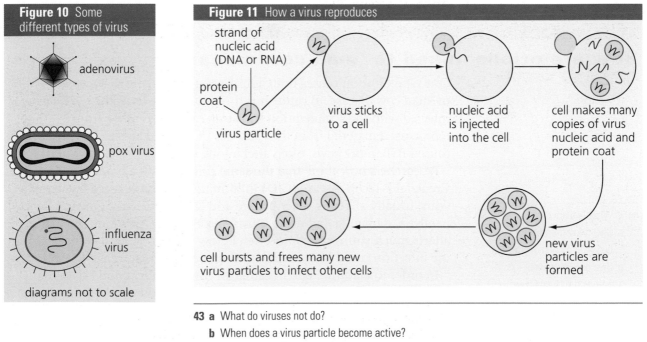

Figure 11 How a virus reproduces

strand of nucleic acid (DNA or RNA)

protein coat

virus particle

virus sticks to a cell

nucleic acid is injected into the cell

cell makes many copies of virus nucleic acid and protein coat

new virus particles are formed

cell bursts and frees many new virus particles to infect other cells

43 a What do viruses not do?

b When does a virus particle become active?

c Describe how a virus reproduces.

What is a prion?

A **prion** is a molecule of protein that can cause disease. A prion is much smaller than a virus and does not contain any nucleic acid. There are different types of prions and they are all very difficult to destroy. Disinfectants and ultraviolet light that would kill most bacteria and viruses do not damage prions. Prions spread when an animal eats another animal's tissue containing the prion. Prions are unusual because they seem to be able to infect more than one type of animal, whereas most viruses and bacteria can attack only one host.

This false-colour transmission electron micrograph shows prions (coloured orange) in tissue from the brain of a cow with BSE.

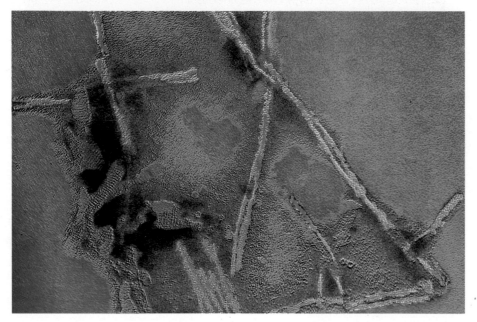

How are prions linked to 'mad cow disease'?

One type of prion causes both a disease called scrapie in sheep, and BSE or 'mad cow disease' in cattle. It is thought that cows in the UK became infected with the scrapie prion by eating cattle feed made from reprocessed material from the carcasses of infected sheep. The prion then caused BSE in the cows, often after a long delay.

Researchers now think that the same prion causes a type of Creutzfeld–Jacob disease (CJD) in humans. CJD has existed for many years, usually affecting older people and leading to loss of muscle control, paralysis, dementia and death. A new type of CJD, new variant CJD, affects much younger people, often below the age of 30. It is thought that the infection could be caused by eating meat containing the BSE prion.

In order to eradicate BSE in cattle, all cows, bullocks and calves that could be infected with BSE are destroyed. Also, because the prion tends to concentrate in the tissue of the central nervous system, the brain and spinal cord are removed from cattle intended for human consumption. These measures have been taken in the hope that they will make beef safe to eat.

44 a What is a prion?

  b Give two differences between a prion and a virus.

  c Give one difference between CJD and new variant CJD.

  d Give two ways people have tried to control the spread of BSE.

Summary of bacteria, viruses and prions

- Bacteria are single cells that contain nuclear material but have no nucleus. They are found almost everywhere. They are microscopic (0.5 to 1.5 micrometres in diameter), and are classified by shape.

- Bacteria require water and food supplies and a suitable temperature in order to grow. Aerobic bacteria also require oxygen, while anaerobic bacteria grow in the absence of oxygen.

- Bacteria reproduce by binary fission. This can occur every 20 minutes in favourable conditions, and a single bacterium can produce a colony visible to the naked eye in less than 24 hours. Many bacteria form spores that can resist unfavourable conditions. When conditions improve, the spores grow into new bacteria.

- Bacteria can be destroyed by antiseptics, disinfectants, compressed steam, gamma rays and antibiotics. Antibiotics are chemicals that act against microorganisms and are effective against many bacteria that cause disease.

- Viruses are smaller than bacteria and consist of a protein coat surrounding a molecule of either DNA or RNA. Viruses cannot grow or reproduce outside a living cell.

- Prions are smaller than viruses and consist of only a protein molecule. Prions can cause a number of diseases including BSE in cattle and new variant CJD in humans.

Assignment 1
Tanning and skin damage

What causes tanning in light-skinned people?

Ultraviolet (UV) light passes through the top layer of the skin and speeds up the chemical reaction that produces melanin. Melanin is the brown pigment normally present in the epidermis. It acts as a sunscreen by absorbing UV light and stopping it from passing deeper into the skin. A suntan is an increase in the level of melanin in the skin.

What are other effects of UV light?

Sunburn occurs when there is not enough melanin to protect the skin. The UV light then gets through to the inner layer of skin, the dermis, and damages the tissue. Several hours later, the skin feels very hot and looks pink or red. It can be very painful and may later peel. The skin gradually heals itself and returns to normal after a few days or weeks.

UV light can also affect DNA in the nucleus of growing cells. Damage here is invisible but is passed on to every cell produced by the damaged one. At some time, possibly years later, one of these damaged cells may suddenly start to multiply, grow out of control, and produce a skin cancer. Melanoma is a dangerous form of skin cancer that is becoming more common.

Where is the evidence?

In the mid-1960s the number of people going abroad for holidays increased (see Figure 1). Often these holidays were in hot countries with strong sunlight. Many people tried to get a good suntan in a very short time, and often ended up burnt. Years later, in the 1980s, rates of skin cancer began to rise (see Table 1). The cancers were appearing on parts of the skin exposed to the sun only in the summer (see Figure 2). This suggested a link between sunburn and skin cancer.

Table 1 Rate of melanoma cases per 100 000

Gender	1979	1980	1981	1982	1983	1984	1985	1986	1987	1988	1989
male	3.4	3.4	3.5	3.6	4.2	4.6	5.9	5.4	5.4	7.1	7.1
female	6.6	6.9	6.2	7.1	7.9	8.3	9.8	1.9	9.3	10.8	10.4

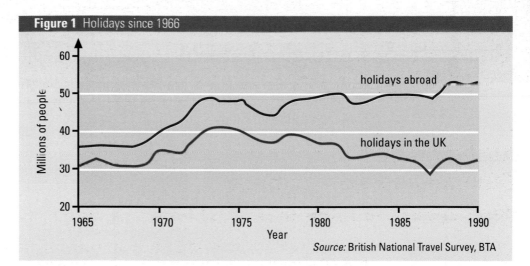

Figure 1 Holidays since 1966

holidays abroad

holidays in the UK

Source: British National Travel Survey, BTA

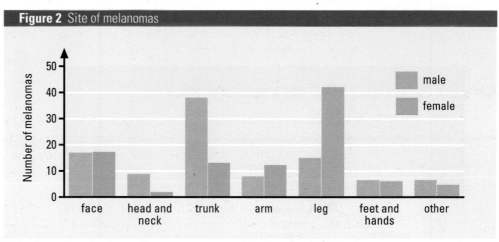

Figure 2 Site of melanomas

Skin areas that had had time to build up a protective melanin layer were less likely to suffer from cancer. Also, skin cancer seemed to be more common in people with fair skins who had lived for some years in lands near the equator. Again, this suggested that sunlight was having an effect.

1 a Which years had the highest rate of melanoma in males?
 b Which year had the lowest rate of melanoma in females?
 c Which area of the body has the highest rate of melanoma in males?
 d Which area of the body has the highest rate of melanoma in females?
 e Suggest a reason for the difference in the commonest melanoma sites in males and females.
 f How many people took a foreign holiday in 1990?
 g How many people took a holiday in the UK in 1990?
 h Draw a graph to show the change in melanoma rates from 1979 to 1989 in males.
2 Use a computer and DTP package to prepare a travel leaflet for holiday-makers. It must summarise the evidence linking sunbathing and skin cancer. Include a list of 'DOs and DON'Ts'. Make sure your leaflet is clear, but do not frighten your readers. The leaflet must include text, at least one photograph or diagram, and a set of figures.

Assignment 2
Heart attacks and cholesterol

Many people are keen to avoid cholesterol in their diet. 'A healthy diet is a low-cholesterol diet' seems to be the message from many health educators. But is cholesterol all bad? Study Figures 1 and 2, and Table 1.

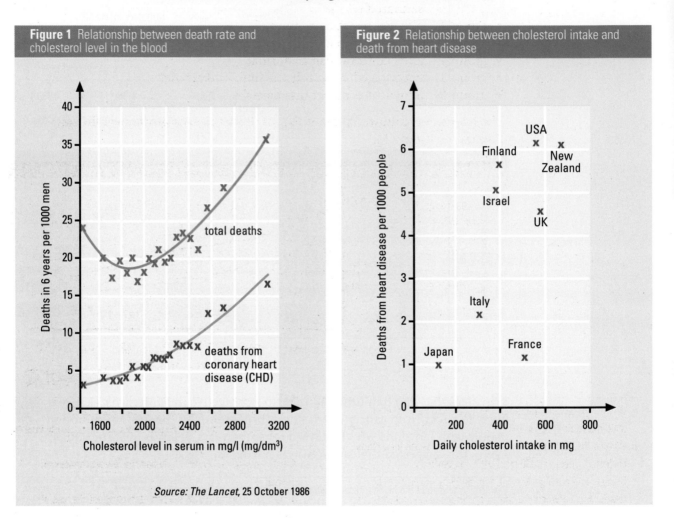

Figure 1 Relationship between death rate and cholesterol level in the blood

Source: The Lancet, 25 October 1986

Figure 2 Relationship between cholesterol intake and death from heart disease

Table 1 Cholesterol level in blood and age

Age	Total cholesterol in blood in mmol/l (mmol/dm³)	
	female	male
20–29	5.6	5.8
30–39	5.9	6.1
40–49	6.2	6.5

Table 2 Blood cholesterol levels in mmol/l (mmol/dm³)

Time	Group 1	Group 2
at the start of the trial	6.47	6.47
after 6 months	6.31	6.57
after 2 years	6.29	6.55

Preventing heart attacks

A study in south Wales used over 200 men to find out the best way to prevent heart attacks. These men had all had one heart attack. They were divided into groups and given the following advice about diet:

- group 1 encouraged to cut down the total amount of fat, particularly saturated fat
- group 2 allowed to eat fat as normal
- group 3 encouraged to eat two or three portions of fatty fish every week
- group 4 allowed to eat fish as normal
- group 5 encouraged to double the fibre in their diet
- group 6 allowed to eat fibre as normal.

The researchers followed the number of deaths in each group over the next 2 years (see Figure 3).

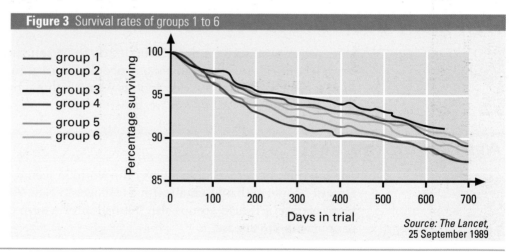

Figure 3 Survival rates of groups 1 to 6

Source: The Lancet, 25 September 1989

1 a What is the total death rate for a blood cholesterol level of 3000 mg/l (3000 mg/dm^3)?

 b What is the death rate from coronary heart disease for a blood cholesterol level of 2000 mg/l (2000 mg/dm^3)?

 c Using the data in Figure 1, write a sentence to describe the relationship between the cholesterol in the blood and coronary heart disease.

 d Draw a bar chart to show the relationship between age and blood cholesterol shown in Table 1 for both males and females.

 e Some researchers have said that cholesterol seems to prevent some kinds of cancer. Can you find any evidence in these graphs that might support this idea? What else would you need to know to be certain?

 f What is surprising about the data in Figure 2? Suggest a reason for this surprise.

2 a What does Table 2 show about cholesterol and diet?

 b How might this information be useful to someone trying to avoid a heart attack?

 c Which group in the Welsh study had the lowest chances of survival?

 d Which group in the Welsh study had the highest chances of survival?

3 Prepare a press release and a health advice leaflet for the research team.

 Press release: this should be a very quick summary of the important information from the study. It should have fewer than 200 words and no diagrams or charts. It will be used by journalists to support reports in the local paper.

 Health advice leaflet: this will be given out at supermarkets in the Cardiff area. It should include diagrams and charts to make it attractive for shoppers. Include a few simple rules for shoppers to follow if they are looking for a healthy diet.

Assignment 3
Asthma

What is asthma?

Asthma is an illness that affects people of all ages but is particularly common in children. In asthmatics, the tubes that carry air in and out of the lungs can go into spasm. This means that the muscles around the tubes contract and make them narrower. This makes breathing difficult and is called an asthma attack. An attack of asthma can have one or more of several different causes, though it is often impossible to decide exactly what caused a particular attack. Dust or pollen, stress, infections and general illnesses can all set one off. Most attacks can be managed at home, but some are so serious that the sufferers are rushed to hospital.

How many people have asthma?

Since asthma can vary so much from person to person, and from attack to attack, it can be difficult to decide how many people have asthma. People who suffer from regular and severe attacks obviously have asthma, but does a rare bout of slight breathlessness mean you are an asthmatic?

Asthma on the net?

The internet connects people all over the world. A teenager with asthma in Leicester could exchange email with a teenager in New York who also has asthma. Many asthma self-help groups also publish information on the web to support people with the disease.

Some asthma statistics

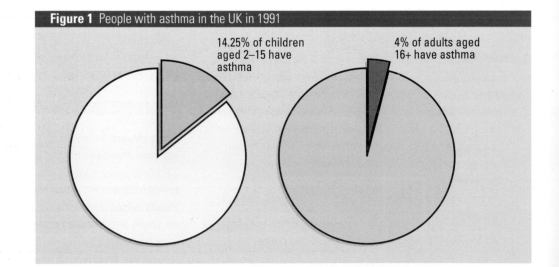

Figure 1 People with asthma in the UK in 1991

14.25% of children aged 2–15 have asthma

4% of adults aged 16+ have asthma

The UK has the highest rates in Europe for young adults reporting asthma attacks

Roughly 20% of people with asthma can be described as having a 'severe' or 'very severe' condition. This means that they might have daily symptoms, frequent trips to hospital, miss time from work or school and have a poor quality of life. Applying this to the current population (1997) gives an estimate of 640 000 people in the UK with 'severe' or 'very severe' asthma.

National Asthma Campaign Press Release August 1997

Table 1 Deaths from asthma in the UK

UK area	1995	1994	1993	1992
England and Wales	1459	1516	1701	1791
Scotland	120	119	129	115
N. Ireland	42	30	58	63

Table 2 Hospital admissions due to asthma in the UK

UK area	1994	1993	1992	1991
England	79 947	90 050	82 944	81 347
Wales	5 706	6 331	5 888	5 703
Scotland	not available	10 584	9 889	10 161
N. Ireland	3 339	3 510	2 894	3 179
Children as percentage of above	not available	50	52	53

1 a How many people were admitted to hospital in England in 1992 due to asthma?

b What proportion of people in the UK with asthma can be described as having severe or very severe asthma?

c Is asthma more common in children or adults? Give a piece of evidence to support your answer.

d Draw a graph to show the changes in the total number of people admitted to hospital in England and Wales due to asthma from 1991 to 1994.

e Describe any trends you can see in your graph.

2 Prepare a 10-minute talk about asthma. Your talk should explain what asthma is, how people can tell if they have asthma and what they should do about it if they feel they have got asthma. Your audience will be a group of young parents living in an area of Leicester where asthma is surprisingly common. Include a handout with your talk. This should be one page of A4 paper printed on both sides and summarise the points from your talk. Use words and images to get your message across and, if possible, produce the handout on a computer.

3 a List five words you could use in an internet search engine to find resources on the web that support people with asthma.

b Test your words with a search engine. Note down the websites you find. Pick the most useful ones and give a reason for your choices.

Assignment 4
Tooth decay

Tooth decay is caused by acids produced by bacteria living in plaque on the surface of the teeth. The acids dissolve the enamel and then the dentine. This exposes the nerve endings and causes pain. Once decay has started, the damaged part of the tooth is usually drilled out and replaced with a filling. Teeth do not heal, so the best way to manage decay is to stop it happening in the first place. Tooth decay can be prevented by:

• cleaning away the plaque and the bacteria
• neutralising the acids produced by the bacteria
• strengthening the enamel against the acid.

How does sugar affect teeth?

A study of tooth decay in Ghana in the 1960s followed the effects of sugary foods on dental health. The survey compared tooth decay in rich, middle-income and poor sections of the community. The higher the income, the better the access to dentists, but also the higher the tendency to eat more sugary foods.

Table 1 Percentage of different groups showing tooth decay

Test group	Rich	Middle-income	Poor
children (6 years)	70	50	33
children (12 years)	50	37	22
adults (18–65 years)	63	40	16

Data based on MacGregor A. B. 'Diet and dental disease in Ghana' *Annals of Royal College of Surgery* Vol 34 pp. 179–185

How does fluoride affect teeth?

Fluoride in drinking water seems to have two effects on teeth: it causes mottling and prevents decay. Scientists noticed that children in areas with high fluoride concentrations in the drinking water had teeth with slight discolorations. This is called **mottling** and occurred at fluoride concentrations above 2.0 mg/l (2.0 mg/dm^3). However, areas with fluoride concentrations below 1.0 mg/l (1.0 mg/dm^3) showed a much lower rate of tooth decay in children when compared with other areas. This led to the campaign for **fluoridation**, that is, to add very low levels of fluoride to drinking water.

Tooth decay has fallen in Western countries for some years, even in areas without fluoridated water. Some researchers now suggest that fluoride may not be safe and that it does not actually prevent tooth decay. They suggest that other factors are just as likely to explain the fall: better oral hygiene, better nutrition, increased cheese consumption, better standard of living.

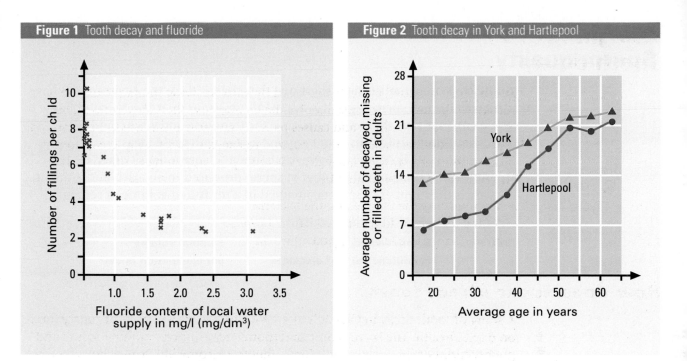

Figure 1 Tooth decay and fluoride

Figure 2 Tooth decay in York and Hartlepool

1 Why is *preventing* tooth decay better than *treating* decay once it has started?

2 a What percentage of the poor section of Ghana's adult population did not have any tooth decay?
  b How many times more common was tooth decay in the rich sector of Ghana's adult population compared with the poor sector?
  c Tooth decay seems more common for 6-year old children than 12-year olds. Suggest an explanation for this.
  d How does the evidence here support the idea that sugar and tooth decay are linked?
  e What extra evidence would you need to be certain of the link between tooth decay and sugary foods? How could you collect this evidence?

3 a What does Figure 1 show about tooth decay and fluoride?
  b What concentration of fluoride gives the best protection against tooth decay but still does not cause tooth mottling?
  c York and Hartlepool have different water supplies (see Figure 2). Which one might have fluoride? Why do you think so?
  d A water company wants to add fluoride to the water supply. It needs to convince its customers that this would be good for them. Prepare a leaflet for the company explaining the case for fluoridating water.
4 Take part in a group discussion about preventing tooth decay in young children. Your group should decide which is the most effective way to prevent tooth decay in children.

Assignment 5
Sperm quality

Some environmentalists have suggested that chemicals in the environment have damaged human sperm. They say that adult males produce less sperm capable of fertilising eggs now than ever and that if the trend continues we could see a significant rise in infertility. Not everyone agrees with these ideas.

Sperm quality is measured by sperm count and sperm density (see Table 1). Sperm counts are the total number of sperm produced in an ejaculation. Sperm density is the number of sperm contained in a measured volume of semen.

Table 1 Sperm quality in 1940 and 1990

Year	Sperm density in millions per cm³ ejaculate	Seminal volume per ejaculation in cm³
1940	113	3.40
1990	66	2.75

A group of doctors in Helsinki looked for evidence of a fall in male fertility. They studied the testes of middle-aged men who had died suddenly. They chose sudden-death males because they could carry out investigations that would not be possible on living males. Table 2 shows a comparison of the two groups, one from 1981 and the other from 1991.

Table 2 Comparison of year groups

Features compared	1981	1991
age in years	54.0	52.2
body mass index in kg m²	24.1	25.8
cause of death:		
heart disease	138	126
other disease	40	39
intoxication	23	31
violence	61	63
unknown	2	5
time from death to test in days	3.5	3.8

Table 3 Sperm-producing status of males in year groups

Sperm-producing cells present	Sperm-producing cells active	1981	1991
yes	yes	149	71
yes	some	83	128
yes	no	21	53
no	no	11	12

1 a How many men were there in each year group?

  b How many deaths in the 1981 group were due to violence?

  c How many deaths in the 1991 year group were due to unknown causes?

  d What percentage of the 1981 group died of heart disease?

  e Which year group had a larger death rate due to alcohol?

  f Do you think it is fair to compare the two groups? Give reasons for your answer.

  g Draw a bar chart of the causes of death for the 1991 group.

2 Do you think the evidence in these tables supports the idea that the quality of sperm is falling? Give reasons for your answer.

3 Prepare an article for a magazine about the fall in sperm quality. Your article must include numerical data, at least one chart, a diagram and text. If possible, produce the article on a computer using a DTP package.

Assignment 6
Genetic counselling

Genetic counselling is often offered to people who have a higher than average risk of having children with genetic problems. These people may:

- have come from a family with a history of genetic illnesses
- have had an affected baby before
- have been identified by a random testing programme
- be attempting to have children at an older age than usual.

It can be devastating to be told that your children are more likely to suffer from a genetic illness such as cystic fibrosis or Down's syndrome. If a woman is pregnant when she learns of a possible genetic problem, the choices are even more difficult. Should she continue with the pregnancy come what may? Or should she have a test to see if the fetus carries the defective gene and then decide about having an abortion? Women and their partners all over the country are facing these decisions. In the future more tests will become available and an even wider range of illnesses will be detectable.

---

1 a Prepare for a discussion about genetic screening. The discussion will raise each of these issues.
- Should genetic screening become as widespread as vaccinations and health checks for jobs?
- Who should pay for these tests?
- Who should hold the information about someone's genetic condition?
- Should people be forced to check with their doctor or genetic counsellor before they try to have children?
- Should some people be prevented from having children?
- Would you want to know if you carried an increased chance of having children with a genetic illness?
- How would you respond to news of a genetic risk?

b Hold the discussion in a small group. At the end of the discussion try to decide, as a group, whether you would like to see genetic screening used more widely. Try to produce a statement that the whole group can support.

Assignment 7
Drinking and driving

In 1998, hundreds of people were killed in road traffic accidents. One of the major causes of accidents on the roads is people drinking alcohol and then driving.

Alcohol reduces the ability to judge distances and to react quickly. At low levels of alcohol the effect is measurable but probably not dangerous. As the level rises the effects are more obvious. At some point, a drinker becomes a danger to themselves and to the people around them. But how much is too much?

What are reaction times?

In 1959, the Medical Research Council (MRC) looked at the effect of alcohol on people's reaction times. They gave people measured amounts of alcohol in a sugar and water drink and then tested the blood of these people to see how quickly the alcohol was absorbed.

The people were also tested with a driving machine that could measure how well they could drive. The machine counted how many times the drivers hit the kerb and how often their steering was bad enough to be dangerous.

Table 1 Blood alcohol levels in mg per 100 cm^3 blood after taking measured amounts of alcohol in water

Time since drink in minutes	Dose units			
	2	3	4	5
0	7	7	7	7
15	14	21	34	40
30	23	36	57	70
45	21	39	61	78
60	18	37	58	76
75	15	32	52	71
90	11	27	49	67
105	9	20	40	60
120				

Table 2 Kerb bumpings by 40 drivers given different amounts of alcohol

Driving period (minutes since drinking)	Dose units				
	0	2	3	4	5
0–20	68	64	97	59	86
21–40	32	68	79	75	112
41–60	51	58	87	58	93
61–80	58	65	87	68	68

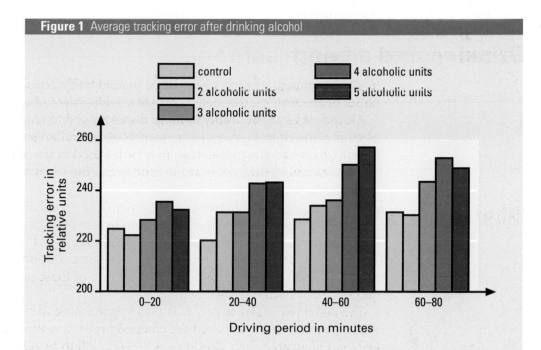

Figure 1 Average tracking error after drinking alcohol

Table 3 Measures of drinks containing 1 unit of alcohol

Beer, cider, lager	Table wine	Port, sherry	Spirits (rum, whisky, brandy, gin or vodka)
half pint	glass	glass	single measure

1 a How long after taking a drink does it take for blood alcohol levels to reach a maximum value?

 b What is the maximum blood alcohol level for a person who has drunk:

  i 2 units

  ii 4 units?

 c How many units of alcohol are in:

  i one pint of beer

  ii a double whisky

  iii three glasses of sherry

  iv two pints of lager?

 d Predict the blood alcohol level for someone, 1 hour after they have drunk a pint of beer.

 e Use Table 1 to draw a graph showing blood alcohol levels for people who have drunk different amounts of alcohol. Use one set of axes and label the trace for each dose.

 f Estimate the blood alcohol level after 2 hours for someone who has drunk 3 units of alcohol.

2 The legal limit for alcohol is 80 mg/100 ml (80 mg/100 cm³) of blood. None of the people in this test had a blood alcohol level this high. What evidence can you find that their driving skills were reduced? Prepare a letter to the local paper suggesting the current limit is too high.

3 Prepare a talk for a group of college students about the dangers of drinking and driving. Most of the people in your audience have recently passed their driving tests

Assignment 8
What makes a beach safe?

One of the dangers at the seaside does not depend on how good a swimmer you are, it depends on the local sewage works. Holiday resorts often have small winter populations and a large summer one. These holiday-makers can overload a sewage works built for the smaller permanent population. Partially treated sewage, or even untreated sewage, may be released to the sea. The tides carry most of it away safely. However, in some conditions, the sewage can be swept back towards the beaches.

Every fortnight, the Environment Agency (EA) on behalf of the European Union (EU) checks samples of water from beaches designated as 'bathing water beaches' for a range of microorganisms including:

- **coliforms** – coliform bacteria
- **faecal coliforms** – coliform bacteria that are normally found in the human gut and are passed out in faeces; if they are present in seawater, it suggests that the water has been contaminated with sewage
- **faecal streptococci** – another type of bacterium normally found in the human gut.

The number of 'bathing water beaches' has risen since the scheme began as people campaign to get the water at their local beaches checked and protected. It is unlikely that any water will be completely free of any coliform bacteria. The figures used by the two award schemes are thought to be so low that there is no significant risk of infection to swimmers.

Seaside Award
- At least 95% of the samples (19 or more out of 20) must have fewer than 10 000 total coliforms per 100 cm^3 of water.
- At least 95% of the samples must have fewer than 2000 faecal coliforms per 100 cm^3 of water.

Blue Flag Award
- At least 80% of the samples (16 or more out of 20) must have fewer than 500 total coliforms and fewer than 100 faecal coliforms per 100 cm^3 of water.
- At least 90% of the samples (18 or more out of 20) must meet the standard of not more than 100 faecal streptococci per 100 cm^3 of water.

1 Use the data in the Table 1 to answer these questions.
 a What was the highest value for total coliforms in 1997?
 b What was the highest value for faecal coliforms in 1997?
 c How many times did the beach exceed the Blue Flag limit for total coliforms?
 d Did the site pass the Blue Flag environmental standards?
 e Did the site pass the Seaside Awards environmental standards?

Table 1 The Towans beach test results for May to September 1997

Date	Total coliforms per 100 cm³	Faecal coliforms per 100 cm³	Faecal streptococci per 100 cm³
08/05/1997	10	10	10
16/05/1997	20	10	10
24/05/1997	30	20	10
29/05/1997	10	10	10
04/06/1997	77	30	10
15/06/1997	10	10	30
24/06/1997	270	160	10
30/06/1997	40	10	10
05/07/1997	40	20	10
13/07/1997	10	10	10
22/07/1997	30	10	10
28/07/1997	30	10	10
06/08/1997	320	30	20
15/08/1997	320	252	10
23/08/1997	60	30	30
29/08/1997	990	200	10
02/09/1997	20	10	10
09/09/1997	10	10	10
15/09/1997	220	190	30
24/09/1997	50	30	10

Table 2 Bathing beaches and compliance in England and Wales for 1979 to 1997

Year	Number of bathing beaches	Bathing beaches meeting EU standard
1979	27	?
1980	27	19
1981	27	20
1982	27	21
1983	27	21
1984	27	21
1985	27	21
1986	27	23
1987	360	251
1988	364	241
1989	401	303
1990	407	318
1991	414	312
1992	416	28
1993	419	332
1994	419	345
1995	425	379
1996	433	386
1997	448	396

Original data: Environment Agency

2 a Work out the percentage of tested bathing beaches reaching EU environmental standards in the UK between 1979 and 1997.

b Draw a graph to show the change in the proportion of bathing beaches in England and Wales reaching EU standards between 1979 and 1997.

c Use your graph to decide whether the situation is getting better or worse.

3 a Prepare a leaflet for holiday-makers about the Blue Flag award. Your leaflet must reassure them that beaches with Blue Flag status are safe or swimmers. Include a chart and an image in your leaflet. Make the leaflet attractive so that people will pick it up from a rack in a Tourist Advice Centre.

b Prepare a technical report for the EA about The Towans beach. You should use the data here to decide which environmental awards the beach should get. Include enough data in your report to convince your manager at the EA.

4 a Many environmental groups publish information about their local areas on the internet. List five words you could use in an internet search engine to look for up to date information about an area where you have been for a holiday.

b Use an internet search engine to collect information about pollution in an area where you have been for a holiday. Prepare a summary of the information you locate and a list of the websites where you collected the data.

Index